AN END TO ALL DISEASE:

Towards A Universal Theory of Disease, Rejuvenation & Immortality

&

THE DA VINCI CODE REVELATIONS:

A Roadmap to Health and Enlightenment

Two works by

Lt. Lawrence F. Frego, USNR (ret.) HKt.B.

authorHOUSE®

AuthorHouse™
1663 Liberty Drive, Suite 200
Bloomington, IN 47403
www.authorhouse.com
Phone: 1-800-839-8640

First published by AuthorHouse 5/7/2009

ISBN: 978-1-4259-1349-6 (sc)

Printed in the United States of America
Bloomington, Indiana

This book is printed on acid-free paper.

TABLE OF CONTENTS

Book Two

INTRODUCTION

We are at the crossroads of world health. On the one hand we face the possibility of a world-wide pandemic, the likes of which has never been seen before. We are, likewise, on the threshold of discovering natural cures for nearly every disease. As choosing wisely may mean the difference between life and death, this book is designed to help the reader choose alternative options that are seldom if ever in the news.

Jared Diamond, in his groundbreaking work, Collapse: How Societies Choose to Fail or Succeed, addresses the fact that only civilizations that recognize the threats against their existence, and deal with the threat effectively survive. Civilizations with their heads in the sand become extinct or are conquered by more vigorous nations.

The robber barons of the last century were able to create a monopoly for oil and the automobile by ruthlessly and systematically destroying all competition. They tore up cable car lines and public transportation so the public would have no other alternative except their oil. Today, the drug monopolies, owned by the descendants of these same robber barons, are nearly complete in their plot to eradicate all natural, low cost remedies for disease prevention and treatment. In the state of Florida, naturopathic physicians were de-licensed unless they also had a conventional medical license. The "powers that be" want to create a drug-induced society at an enormous financial and emotional cost to the public at large. They are even trying to outlaw vitamins via European health treaties and side step the American constitution and the public. The ever escalating cost of medical care created by lack of natural alternative options can only lead to the eventual total collapse of the entire medical system.

It is exceedingly difficult finding the truth about alternative medicine as "the system" has a vested interest in making profits and keeping the truth from you. A few thousand deaths is an "acceptable loss" if a few billion dollars can be made. And it will be a cold day in hell before a drug company puts itself out of business by telling you about a low cost natural cure that their product can manage.

The guardians of public health know which side their toast is buttered on also. The career politicians and beltway bandits at the FDA know where the money is and they don't get it from you or providers of natural cures. The drug monopolies pay the big bucks. There have been no checks and balances. Corruption has become so pronounced that the US House of Representatives is seeking to pass the **Consumers' Access to Health Information Act (H.R. 2352)** to ensure that accurate health claims ARE NOT SUPPRESSED. Consumers would be given TRUTHFUL AND COMPLETE information about the curative, mitigation, treatment, and prevention effects of foods and dietary supplements on disease or health-related conditions. The time to exercise your God given right to the health care of your choice is now. (www.lef.org)

America has the finest emergency health care in the world. Bar none. However that is not the nature of the coming threat. American baby boomers will soon be retiring in the tens of millions. Their health care needs will be staggering and costly. However 92% of American health care providers are trained in emergency medicine and only 8% in long term preventative medicine. As it takes a minimum of 6-7 years to obtain a medical degree, America is unprepared for a crisis that is inevitable.

Elderly baby boomers aren't the only ones at risk. Epidemics such as the Asian bird flu strike the young and middle aged as well. In a worst case scenario, as many as 250 million deaths could result world wide should the bird flu go airborne. In an emergency only 1% of the American population could be inoculated at best. What happens to the rest of us?

Late one night I was again watching Jared Diamond's Guns, Germs and Steel TV show on PBS (http://www.pbs.org). Jared stated that germs have always been one of the great factors in history, but frequently their importance is totally overlooked. As western society seems to be concentrating on producing the greatest number of game show contestants, instead of the greatest thinkers, I suspect the lessons of history will be repeated. Man made diseases or "genetically enhanced ones", like AIDS, Ebola, SARS, Lyme disease, West Nile fever, mad cow disease, super black plague virus, just keep rolling off the biological warfare assembly line. Now stand by for the bird flu! It seems to me that we are already on the receiving end of the Book of Revelations and this is just the warm-up game. The Super Bowl game of world domination can't be far away, unless humanity suddenly sees the big picture and calls the game off.

The great influenza epidemic of 1918 killed between 20-40 million people. Hospitals ran out of beds and undertakers ran out of coffins. This event may soon be repeated if the Avian or bird flu H5N1 mutates and becomes more actively infectious. That is what happened in 1918 and is more likely to occur with greater severity due to changes in agriculture, population density, and air travel. China has 15 billion chickens and each one is a virus test tube, unless protected from wild fowl in a secure barn. Senate majority leader, Dr. Bill Frist, has estimated a possible 500,000 deaths in the USA should a mutation occur. Worst case scenarios project upwards of 250 million deaths worldwide. I question whether even 250 million deaths is an accurate assessment. America doesn't have a vaccine and only 104,000 ventilators to handle tens of millions. I wonder if the world "experts" have factored in the possible results when the bird flu collides with the 100 million people in Africa infected with AIDS and the bird flu has a chance to mutate at will in immune compromised people? The bird flu has already infected tens of thousands of fowl in Nigeria. Impoverished Nigerian farmers have been trying to dump their sick and dead birds on the market before the government catches up with them. I have the same concerns for immune compromised animals with mad cow disease, including American and Canadian deer, elk, and moose. The more people and animals the bird flu has to mutate in, the more severe it could possibly become. I believe the potential for a pandemic of Biblical proportions is far greater than we are led to believe. The economic destruction that could be created by a world wide pandemic is incalculable. Tourism alone accounts for 10% of the world's revenues and it would be totally destroyed for years. Half of the world's workers could be affected and trade and industry would grind to a halt. The West would be a sitting duck to anyone seeking conquest. With millions of feathered stealth bombers dropping their "payload" of deadly viruses all over the Western world, the "Glorious Revolution" envisioned by Chinese Communists would be easier to achieve. Viruses can achieve what the greatest armies can't. That is why they were created.

The bird flu is already in 26 provinces of Eastern Turkey. There have been several human deaths, mostly in young children. I have spent a great deal of time in Turkey and in Istanbul in particular. Istanbul is a major crossroads of the world. The bird flu, as of this writing, has made it to Ankara, which is only 218 miles away. Once the bird flu gets to Istanbul, it's all over. Those who know Turkish economics know that one of Turkey's greatest exports is illegal and undocumented workers. Although Germany is their most frequent destination, they are all over Europe and to a lesser extent the USA. Conversely, millions of Germans, Russians, and other Europeans flock to the southern Mediterranean beaches. The bottom line is that if the bird flu breaks out in Turkey, it will be all over Europe in a matter of weeks. No one is prepared for this possibility. To see how the bird flu has spread and the migration patterns of wild fowl check out the excellent coverage on the BBC. (http://www.news.bbc.co.uk)

An Israeli company, Razei Bar Industries (1996) Ltd., has developed a medical preparation called SAMBUCOL. Testing at the University of London and clinical trials at the Hebrew University of Jerusalem, found that Sambucol was at least 99% effective at reducing the replication of the bird flu virus. The question now remains as to whether this product can be manufactured and mobilized in sufficient time and quantity to meet the threat of a world wide pandemic.

Miraculous discoveries sometimes occur in the most unusual ways and places. In 2000 a BBC TV crew was filming a science documentary on saltwater crocodiles in northern Australia. The documentary producer, Jill Fullerton-Smith, observed that "despite the horrendous injuries the crocs inflict on each other, their wounds rarely get infected." Crocodiles have been around for 20 million years and appear to have developed some special method of immunity that enables them to thrive in hostile and disease ridden environments. After discussing this observation with a young crocodile expert, Ms. Fullerton – Smith thought that, "it would be interesting to try to find out why." Blood samples were collected and sent to scientists at the New Jersey Medical School. The blood samples were split into their component parts and then tested on common bacteria. One peptide, a naturally occurring chemical made of amino acids, was found to destroy bacteria. This natural antibiotic has been dubbed "crocodillin".

Crocodillin offers the widest range of healing power against all known deadly viruses and bacteria. Millions of dollars have been spent so far researching this discovery. It is being tested for applications against AIDS, cancer, SARS, and the bird flu. And let's not forget the pesky common cold. Clinical trials on patients with a broad range of diseases have noted improvement or remission. What really surprised me was the diversity of diseases treated, such as cancer, AIDS, diabetes, arthritis, panic attacks, and even high cholesterol. It would appear that there is bacterial and viral involvement in more diseases than we would expect.

The manufacturers of Crocodillon are currently marketing the product as "The Antidote" at: (www.biologicalmiracle.net) They claim it is particularly useful in treating infectious diseases that are resistant or immune to current drugs and vaccines. As an alternative for certain vaccines, it is recommended to take it annually. More serious conditions, such as AIDS and cancer, require the antidote be taken every 3 months. The product is deemed safe for children and adults, and can be ordered without a prescription or medical consultation. The cost is a modest $60. I'll be testing it myself. If you try this product please inform me of your results. This product would appear to have great potential in combating the spread of the bird flu. I wonder if it's possible to make a "gatorcillin?" Lots of alligators and crocodiles here in Florida. It sounds like crocodile ranches and crocodile wranglers will be quite common in the future. I certainly hope so.

America also has another epidemic, an epidemic of obesity that is spreading throughout society at a record rate. Leah D. Whigham, lead researcher at the University of Wisconsin at Madison, has discovered that human adenoviruses play a role in obesity. He has identified AD 36 in up to 30% of obese people. The work is just beginning on this form of research. It would be interesting to test "crocodillon" on obese individuals and see if it kills the appropriate viruses. Also several of the anti-viral remedies in this book are worthy of consideration against obesity viruses. This should open up a whole new era in the "battle of the bulge".

Waiting for a pandemic to strike or until 30-40 million Americans become retired is not the time to take a critical look at the health care challenges of the future. Doing nothing is like waiting for a train wreck to happen. The time to examine the weaknesses of the world wide health care system and our basic food supplies is now. If we continue to recklessly poison our food supplies we will travel the same path to decline, sterility, and insanity as did the Roman Empire.

However with knowledge and determination we can begin to correct the problems of our senior citizens RIGHT NOW. The senior citizens currently coming to retirement age would have had a bleak future ahead of them. They could have counted on plenty of diseases, heart failures, and lots of unnecessary surgery and expensive and dangerous prescription drugs. We could have predicted nearly a million deaths a year from heart disease alone, if Dr. Bruce West hadn't found a natural cure for it. Thirty years ago Dr. West discovered that 95% of heart disease cases were misdiagnosed. **He found that heart disease is actually caused by a vitamin B complex deficiency**. Once this deficiency is corrected, heart disease can vanish in about 90 days of vitamin B and niacin therapy. Medical science had thought that severe B complex deficiencies, named Beriberi, were a thing of the past. Dr. West has treated over 62,000 patients and has proven the medical community dead wrong. Why haven't you heard about it? Because heart disease is a multi-billion dollar "industry", that's why.

Dr. West was so elated about his discoveries concerning heart disease that he began to look at nutritional deficiencies in other diseases, such as high blood pressure, arthritis, diabetes, gall bladder, prostate problems, glaucoma, cancer, dementia, memory loss, and a host of other diseases. He found that phytonutrients treatments were a viable, low cost, and painless solution for dozens of diseases. These plant-derived nutrients can begin the healing process in a matter of minutes. He is the author of 33 special reports comprising: "The Encyclopedia of Phytonutrient Treatments" I especially like "Bad Drugs and & Big Lies: Big Pharma's Secret Assault on Your Health". You may order these reports from Dr. West's Health Alert at: (www. healthalert.com) or by calling 1 (800) 944-6465. Please note that most vitamins on the market are synthetic spin-offs of natural whole food vitamins. Consumption of synthetic vitamins may cause more harm than good and actually corrode your arteries. I have reserved the following website to help educate the public as per the benefits of whole food vitamins and chelated minerals: (http://www.dontforgett otakeyourvitamins.com/frego13358). Proceeds from the sale of these vitamins will help defray our research, development, and publication costs. Please consult a knowledgeable medical professional before beginning any nutritional regimen or exercise program.

Fortunately, there are natural cures for nearly every disease. Some methods are very ancient and some are modern, but the immune system can be increased 1,000-1,500%. I.Q can be increased 20 points, and emotional and mental disturbances can be alleviated. The mineral deficiencies of our soils can be corrected and the missing 70-100 vital minerals can be replenished. As Benjamin Franklin used to say, "An ounce of prevention is worth a pound of cure".

In this small volume we'll be examining healing systems as old as yoga and the healing systems Jesus used to the most modern findings of Nobel Prize winners and orthomolecular doctors. Over 100 web links are provided to take you directly to hundreds of natural cures and techniques and the doctors and specialists familiar in their use. In a hard hitting, no holds barred narrative, we'll look where others have feared to tread.

We'll even show you where to find formerly TOP SECRET Russian military cures for anthrax, the flu, and other diseases. And loads of hidden cures right now at: (www.isecureonline.com/reports/HSI/W6HSG156/home.cfm) Learn what is happening in the medical underground. See Dr. Gary Null's 700 page, THE COMPLETE ENCYCLOPEDIA OF NATURAL HEALING at: (www.bottomlinesecrets.com) or order it directly from Amazon.

com. If you are concerned about cancer and are in a rush, you can download the top 12 world cancer cures in a report entitled "ULTIMATE CANCER BREAKTHROUGHS" by Marco Wutzer at: (www.cancer-secrets.info) The cost is $100.00. Again and again, you'll see that there is no such thing as an incurable disease. Prepare yourself for a healing and spiritual adventure of your own making. You are nature's greatest healer. Welcome to the winning side!

To your health,
Lawrence Frego

PART 1

The great library at Alexandria, Egypt was said to have 700,000 volumes. These priceless works were destroyed to heat the public baths. While this may have been the worlds' greatest ancient collection of books, the library in Carthage had nearly 500,000. The Romans burned it. The library of Pergamos in Asia Minor had 200,000 volumes. The destruction of accumulated knowledge has continued through the centuries from ancient times, through the Great Inquisition, up to Hitler and Chairman Mao. China has burned thousands of monasteries and killed a million Tibetans in the latest attempt to destroy and control knowledge. What is it exactly that the forces of darkness want to conceal so badly? [1], [2]

It is said that knowledge is power! Whoever controls knowledge can control economies and thence control over the masses. The control and subversion of knowledge runs deeper than questions such as, "Who built the pyramids and when?" (www.crystalinks. com/emerald.html) "Or what is the riddle of the sphinx?" [3] **The more fundamental questions as to who we are, where do we come from, what is the true potential of our species, and what is our true destiny have all been shrouded in a dark veil of secrecy**. If there were no secrets, there would be no opportunity for a ruling elite. Since we have entered the End Times as foretold by the Biblical prophets, the time for secrecy is at an end.

Plato said that the key to all knowledge was to **"Know Thyself"**. This at first glance sounds like a vast understatement. However when we understand that we are made of the same "stuff" as God and the universe Plato's words take on a new meaning. There are no greater secrets than the origins and inner workings of the human body. Therefore my goal is to draw an outline of a Universal Theory of Disease and Rejuvenation and explain how true immortality is indeed possible. I will speak plainly and simply so as many as possible may understand my meaning.

The Biblical Genesis states that in the beginning there was **"THE WORD"**. All of creation or destruction is created by thought. Man began as little more than an amoeba shaped blob millions of years ago. Man has, according to Mayan, Aztec, and Tibetan tradition, survived 4 previous epochs. Civilizations have come and gone and man has been genetically modified and restructured several times. Man however was NOT the first creature to inhabit the Earth. Reptilian creatures have that dubious honor and a part of our genetic makeup is reptilian in nature. We still have remnants of gills and a tail. And worst of all, the center of our brains is still very much a function of this primitive reptilian consciousness. Planned (and unplanned) inbreeding with other species from other parts of this universe and beyond hasn't overridden some of our most basic flaws. Author Zechariah Sitchin (www.sitchin.com) uncovered ancient Babylonian records that told of one of the first races of man being created as a beast of burden. Apparently other species in the universe find planet Earth a treasure house of minerals, particularly gold. Therefore a Human proto-type was created to work the African mines about 300,000 or more years ago. Nature took its course and things immediately got out of hand. The bible speaks of the ancient times in **Genesis 6:4** when "the sons of (the) God (s) saw the daughters of men and took them as wives". The first "batches" of humans weren't particularly successful except in their ability to conduct warfare and cause trouble. Some were obliterated in the past due to atomic warfare. Sections of the Indus Valley and Saudi Arabia are still radioactive to this day. The Biblical flood got most of the rest. A new batch of humans was needed to work the fields and the mines. In present day Iraq in the land of E.Din, between the Tigris and Euphrates rivers a new "Adama" (the golem from Orion) was cloned from alien and human stock. [4] The hybrid nature of man is "allegorically portrayed in the Bible by Abel, Cain, and Seth, as the 3 sons of Adam and Eve, who had no daughters. The killing of Abel by Cain represents atrocities committed by later races upon the original human race or the first born." Man has 3 separate consciousnesses from 3 different planets. One group is humanity, one is referred to as "the grays" and the other is the Dracos or reptilians. If you have the inclination and time to open up the reptilian "can of worms", see (www.greatdreams.com/reptlan/reps.htm) or read anything by David Icke. (www.davidicke.com) The Anunnaki or Nefilim, meaning "Those who came down from heaven", then created a ruling class to keep their new creation in line. This is the origin of the divine right of kings. As there are now so many humans on the planet, the ruling elite keeps them all in check by creating covert slavery, wars, and diseases to keep the population down. And if we don't "get it" soon, the Gardeners that made us [5] may decide to scratch this current experiment and start over again as they have in the past. The only viable alternative is to raise the consciousness of the human race to their true potential. A gigantic and difficult task to be sure, but one must start with a small step.

The pre-Adamic humanity was created as a link between the 2nd and 3rd densities of reality. The Adamic race has the capacity for higher spiritual evolvement. At this point in time both races are thoroughly mixed. The pre-Adamic race is essentially more anthropoid in nature and does not currently have the capacity to spiritually evolve. Jesus referred to them as **human Tares** or the "**Bad seed**". The Tares are characterized by their lack of compassion, lack of empathy, deceitfulness, cunning, lies, and a general robotic mechanical nature. (Sound like any politicians you know?) They are merely **Organic Portals**, soulless beings, who mimic real life, but have none of their own. Since they have no souls of their own, the only way they can mimic life is by stealing energy from a souled being. Tares don't consciously do evil; rather they do it because they are unconscious of what they are and how they function in the world. They are unaware of where and from whom their thoughts originate. Their main function in life is to destroy life and stop the spiritual progress of souled individuals. Like vampires, they feed off

3

the energy of souled beings. In psychological terms they are garden variety psychopaths and they think they're normal. Only the more destructive ones who step over the line and commit heinous acts are caught. All the rest are "stealth psychopaths" who feed off society like parasites and are considered "the norm" of the material world. I mention this because some of society's most outwardly successful (in terms of wealth) businessmen, lawyers, scientists, and doctors are nothing but Tares in disguise. THEY will tell you that many of the techniques in this book concerning healing and higher consciousness are not real. And for THEM that is true, because they don't have the capacity to achieve higher consciousness. Jesus implied in his good seed parables that Tares may make up half of the Earth's population. So, we're talking about 3 billion Tares, or every other person you know. They are the counter balance to the world's progress and make victory harder to achieve. This balance is shown in the Tree of Life. However, the greater the struggle, the sweeter the victory.

A souled individual who IS awakened spiritually has the ability to "see" the Tares of this world. However, while you are spiritually "asleep", you may be running along with the crowd of Tares and consider it perfectly normal. If you are not connected to a higher source, then you will be nothing more than a puppet for hyper-dimensional thought forms that choose to play with your mind. And there are some nasty ones out there. The main theme of this book is spiritual evolution and preparing for ascension. You can not progress spiritually and reach a critical mass escape velocity if you allow the Tares to steal all your energy. Before you can heal completely, you must develop the discernment to see both good and evil. Then you must choose which side you're on by every thought, word, and deed. Discernment or the ability to "see" is essential for ascension and for progress on any level. In hindsight now I look upon Zen Buddhism as an antidote for the Tares of this world. Nothing annoys a Tare more than your refusal to play the game of "drama" with them. As Laura Knight-Jadczyk writes, "You need that energy to advance. It is yours, and it is your right to claim and retain it. But to do so, you must stop this "dance of death" with the Organic Portals in your life". (http://www.cassiopaea.org/cass/organic_portals.htm) (Part 2, page

22) My advice is to cultivate a pure heart and live the Noble truths. And let the Tares do as they may.

The origins and true history of the human species are shrouded in mystery, controversy, and perhaps outright lies. Trying to grapple with whom and what we really are isn't easy. And how does the body actually work? It would be nice if those who created us had left behind the blueprints! I suspect a few blueprints still survive in the vicinity of the Dead Sea, but until these are discovered we will have to start with the basics and work our way up to an understanding of the human body.

The easiest way to conceive of the human form is to say that it is composed of pure energy from the creator as **golden spheres of light**. Everything in the universe is made of golden spheres of light and organized into an energy matrix or blueprint corresponding to its function. Rocks, humans, trees etc. are all made of the same "stuff": **PURE ENERGY**! The major difference is that humans have further "instructions" imbedded in their blueprints as DNA that allow for more complex living structure to come into being. Thinking conscious souled beings also have the ability to interface with the creator and to maintain a harmonious existence. Failure on our part to get in touch with our source of creation, love, and light creates what we call "dis-ease". Kevin Trudeau tells the story of an individual with multiple personality disorder who when in one personality, was disease free, but within minutes of shifting into another personality tested positive for diabetes. [(6)] We create disease when we cut ourselves off from our source and ignore the laws of the universe. Therefore the greatest cause of disease is ignorance. Arrogance is a close second. Once a basic understanding of the human form is gained and how it works, then we can take steps to regain our harmonious balance and true health.

The human blueprint is an energy grid! When the grid is fully charged the aura is lit up like a Christmas tree. Many spiritual traditions depict saints as those who have halos of energy over their heads and wings on their shoulders. For those who have the ability to see auras this is actually what they look like. An aura is just a corona of energy surrounding the body. That's all it is. Those who are "super-charged" may have a radiant white aura so large that it extends up to 40 feet. Conversely, those who are ill, disabled, or otherwise undercharged may experience the equivalent of an energy "brownout". A diseased person has a murkier aura with patches of red and brown in it. A sludged up aura eventually leads to a premature death. To see a graphic illustration of this consult Barbara Brennan's superb book **Hands of Light** at: (www.barbarabrennan.com)

A normally functioning souled person draws in energy through the 7 main chakras. The body is recharged during sleep as energy enters the solar plexus. Depending on the tradition there are as many as 144 minor chakras. The chakras are described as resembling the petals of a flower or lotus in Eastern tradition. We absorb energy constantly from the ground, radiation, air, water, food, sunlight, and even sound or music. We are awash in a sea of energy! And our thoughts constantly generate energy patterns and broadcast them all over the universe.

Not all energy is beneficial energy however. Any energy system can be polluted, inharmonious, or downright deadly depending on its interaction with the human body. And every action has a reaction. An overabundance of adverse energy can eventually overwhelm and break down the defense systems of the body and create what we call disease. Any type of energy blockage can create a problem. Edgar Cayce (www.edgarcayce.org) used to say that all problems are created by either too little energy or too much of it. Not only is there no blueprint to the human body, but also no one is born with an owners' manual either. Therefore I will attempt to provide some helpful insights into the care and feeding of the human body.

The most fundamental spiritual insight is that the human body functions much like a walking, talking battery. We run on electro-magnetic energy. And as the body is frequently treated haphazardly or even maliciously it is inevitable that more energy is lost from the system than is gained. The secret of health and long life is to gain as much energy as you can and to lose as little as possible. It sounds easy, but few have mastered the procedure. Energy sources need to be maximized and energy leaks need to be plugged or minimized. Remember those pesky Tares!

Chakras themselves can become torn, damaged, closed, polluted, or even reversed! To get the energy grid functioning properly all 7 chakras and all 144 minor chakras must be functioning properly. This is sometimes a major spiritual challenge in Western "civilized" society. The benefits of civilization are well known to many, but the hazards are less well known and numerous. Pollution, toxins, poisons, stress, noise, and electromagnetic radiations all take their toll. In order to live a more healthful existence within the context of civilized society we must understand the hazards. And we must come to realize the true function and potential of the human body. It is easier to achieve results when the goal is clearly fixed in the mind.

The body has a built-in capacity that is at least 10 fold of what is commonly utilized. And at least 90% or more of our brainpower remains dormant. The power is there but the switch is turned off. Our electrical circuitry could compute 10,000 times faster if we developed our true potential. And why shouldn't we live for hundreds of years?

As the cell is the basic unit of the body let's begin here. As stated previously the body is an energy matrix, and behaves much like a battery. A vibrantly healthy supercharged cell looks like a 72 pointed (or more) crystal star. As the energetic and spiritual capacity of the cell expands, it unfolds into its true dynamic crystalline structure.

Several religious traditions speak of the "perfection" of the saints. A true saint has this perfect cellular structure where the cells have unfolded into the 72-pointed crystalline star structure. The chakras unfold as the petals of the lotus flower. Their cells are so perfect that they exhibit many extraordinary powers, such as healing, clairvoyance, clairaudience, great feats of strength and endurance. Sometimes they choose to live to a great age. Due to this perfect crystalline structure upon death, the physical body of a saint may remain intact for hundreds of years. Paramahansa Yogananda's autopsy stated that, "Weeks after his departure his unchanged face shone with the divine luster of incorruptibility" [7]. According to Jasmuheen at the Cosmic Internet Academy (www.selfempowermentacademy.com.au), the energy of a true saint or avatar can cancel out the negativity of up to 700 million people.

In contrast the cellular structure of a diseased person lacks electromagnetic structure. Disease begins when electromagnetic structure begins to collapse and the energy-carrying capacity of the cells is compromised. The proper crystalline structure transmits energy correctly. Imperfect cells transmit energy imperfectly. Cells communicate with each other via laser bursts of light. As the shape and structure of the cell is diminished, the carrying capacity also diminishes. Compare the difference between a perfect crystal and a round drop of murky water. This is basically what happens. The diseased cell rounds out, looses its structure, collapses, and becomes surrounded by a film of toxins and a crust resembling soap scum. As the cell is now full of impurities, is cloudy, and has lost its normal electrical capacity, it transmits its functions incorrectly. Diseased cells replicate wildly and are out of control of the energy matrix. The guidance system has collapsed. Understanding how this occurs is the key to reversing the process and restoring health!

Once cellular structure begins to escape the control of the energy matrix the disease cycle begins in earnest. Instructions to the cells are abnormal, diseased cell replication runs rampant, and eventually the immune system can be overcome. This is especially true if the immune system is already compromised and functioning improperly. Cancer cells and cells from other diseases may be permanently present in the body. Several researchers believe a cancer microbe is ALWAYS present in the body, but only replicates when conditions are optimal and immune defenses are down allowing it to escape.

Dr. Serafina Corsello, M. D., founder of the **Corsello Centers for Nutritional Complementary Medicine** in Huntington, N.Y., states that no single factor creates disease. She operates on a **loading theory of disease** that states that it is in fact the "**compounded layers of toxicity, malnutrition, and dysfunction**" that create the opportunity for disease to occur. (www.corsello.com) Dr. Corsello had her medical license revoked for 2 years for the crime of "too much testing". Since when are licenses revoked for being too professional and helping one's patients? I wonder what the bad guys were afraid she'd find.

Dr. Gabriel Cousins has stated that this loaded state of being puts undue stress on the liver and gallbladder. The liver has 600 jobs to do already, with its primary task being to filter out all the environmental toxins and carcinogens in our food, water, and air. When the liver is overburdened it's ability to maintain healthy cholesterol levels decreases. This can lead to heart attacks and strokes. Eating harmful oils and an overloading of toxins may be the principal cause of heart attacks and strokes. It is my opinion that toxins and their role in disease don't receive enough press coverage. (www.treeoflife. nu/spalivercolon.html) I believe the medical community has been blaming the patient and this process needs much more study. If Dr. Cousins is on the right track, as I think he is, then the public is being sold a false bill of goods.

Disease, like a fungus, likes a low energy, dark, acidic, low oxygen cesspool type of environment. The stomach becomes something like a beer brewery of parasites where disease ferments and grows rapidly. The stomach often becomes caked like a hard crust on a pipe, and loses its ability to transfer energy from food to the cells. On the cellular level the cells are all gummed up with toxins and a soap scum type of crust forms around them carrying benzene and other industrial toxic byproducts. If the process continues unabated the body dies (www.rrrs.com). Click on NATURAL CANCER FIGHTING SUPPLEMENTS (www.cancer-prevention.net) for 80 free pages of information.

In the Navy and Coast Guard I attended fire fighting school over a dozen times. In fire fighting school we learned about the fire triangle. It takes fire, heat, and fuel for a fire to continue. If one item of the fire triangle is removed then the fire dies. If all the items of the fire triangle are removed the fire can never start up again. The same is true of disease. If we remove one or better yet several aspects that allow disease to function, then the disease will be stopped permanently. We can manipulate the body environment to regain a balance. The immune system will bounce back and do its job.

The body environment is generally called "**the terrain**". This consists of many vital factors such as the ph (http://www.naturalhealthschool.com/acid-alkaline.html), whether the environment is too acid or too alkaline, oxygen levels, parasitic conditions, hormones, vitamins, minerals, and a long shopping list of various fluids and secretions (www.hidden-cancer-cures.com/measure-your-terrain.htm).   All this data can be acquired by laboratory testing and once gathered a plan to adjust the terrain to an optimal level can be formulated. There are computer programs of TERRAIN MODELING SOFTWARE to track your progress towards regaining cellular balance. A more through work-up on your "terrain" can be achieved with more extensive testing done by a trained orthomolecular specialist. To get an idea of what a bio-terrain chart looks like see: (www.brl-labor.com/html/bioterrain.html). Once the body is severely out of balance, multiple abnormalities may exist. Like so many dominoes, several components of your terrain can be unbalanced. Professionals seeking more info on the subject of biological terrain may consult the Institute of Bio-Terrain Sciences (www.terrainmed.com).

The field of BioElectromagnetic Response Technology began in Europe 20 years ago and is now employed by thousands of physicians in the USA and Europe. The Bio-Tracker is one such device that enables the electromagnetic fields of the body to be accurately measured and assessed (www.biotracker.com). "The Bio-Tracker produces graphic profiles showing clearly where there is need for adjustment to bring imbalances back to ideal readings. The technology further embodies vast libraries of remedies to assist the return of maximum health for the patient visiting your medical facility." "**Every health problem is firstly an energetic phenomenon**. The Bio-Tracker can therefore possibly help detect biochemical changes before they develop into full-blown problems. Electro-magnetic profile evaluations can then also be confirmed by laboratory tests once the analysis has been made. The Bio-Tracker has the unique advantage of possible detection of systemic stress caused by past exposures to chemicals, diseases, micro-organisms or radiation of one kind or another that may contribute to a patient's underlying health problem." John Lubecki, D.C, the author of **The End of Cancer** has stated that "This is undoubtedly the method of the future. When it becomes widely used most health problems will cease." I believe the Bio-Tracker is an assessment tool no medical clinic or research center should be without.

THE TRUTH ABOUT CANCER

"You are never told the truth about the incidence of cancer. It is growing by leaps and bounds (www.ghchealth.com) (and go to the learning center). In 1960 1 out of 4 people had cancer. Today it is 1 out of 3. Soon it will be 1 out of 2. In just the last 30 years the incidence of cancer has gone up a shocking 40%." It is now America's #1 killer.

If your financial situation requires a more cost effective approach then Dr. Hulda Clark has formulated a regimen that you can use quite effectively at home. In her books THE CURE FOR HIV AND AIDS, THE CURE FOR ALL CANCERS, AND THE CURE FOR ALL DISEASES, she outlines simple but highly effective procedures to reverse the disease process at low cost. According to Dr. Clark two of the most important essential aspects of disease reversal are 1) KILL PARASITES THAT PERPETUATE THE DISEASE PROCESS and 2) ELIMINATE TOXINS, SUCH AS BENZENE, FOUND IN ORDINARY HOUSEHOLD PRODUCTS LIKE SOAP, COSMETICS, ADDITIVES and CHEMICALS. Benzene from soaps and industrial solvents is particularly harmful as it dissolves the cell membranes. You can make your own bug zapper and find out how to eliminate deadly chemicals from your daily life. Dr. Clark says that common ingredients such as cloves and wormwood capsules will eliminate most parasites. Using old-fashioned lye soap and avoiding chemicals and pesticides will put many of you on the road to recovery. All instructions and ordering addresses are included in her books. I would recommend following her regimen under the care of a naturopathic physician. Dr. Clark's books and

80 other alternative titles can be ordered from **The Cure Zone** at: (www.curezone.com). Just click on "Dr. Clark" and follow the links for the information of most interest to you. Dr. Clark's work is controversial and she is under constant legal attacks as a medical fraud. However I feel that her work on toxins alone would be reason enough to read her books. I haven't noticed any challenges to what she says about toxins. Without knowledge of toxins it is difficult to get rid of them.

It will take a lot of work to get all the toxins out of your life. It may be necessary to replace virtually every product you currently have in your home and refrigerator. Dr. Clark's books cover sources for many toxin-free products. The Edgar Cayce remedies and formulas also have many toxin-free products and herbal remedies. The Baar Company (www.baar.com) is the sole authorized distributor of the Edgar Cayce products and remedies and has a great selection of safe "old fashioned" products plus the latest products on the market. Regardless of who your favorite author is: get the lead out!!

I strongly feel that indeed pesticides, toxins, pollutants, and energy depletion are leading causes of disease. Read "REVOLT AGAINST THE EMPIRE- THE BOYCOTT AGAINST PESTICIDE COMPANIES at (www.ghchealth.com) for the whole scoop on this. If natural remedies such as Dr. Clark's are inadequate for the job, additional low cost remedies to remove toxins are available. If toxins are removed the cells will begin to repair their structure and energy carrying capacity.

Acute observers of nature have discovered many of the most effective purifying formulas. Harry Hoxsey's grandfather observed his horse eating red clover and other herbs when the horse had a cancerous tumor on its leg. The secret formula was passed down to Harry and he opened 17 cancer clinics using the famous Hoxsey formula. As Harry believed in the common man, he refused to sell his formula to the director of the AMA and consequently was arrested over 100 times for practicing medicine without a license. Even worse, Harry always treated the poor for free (www.herbalinformation.com/hoxseyarticle.html). There is an excellent documentary movie entitled: **"HOXSEY: How Healing Becomes a Crime."** Search on (www.wellmedia.com). Harry Hoxsey's clinics marked the beginning of the civil war between "organized medical monopolies" and alternative medicine. Hoxsey's Dallas clinic treated 12,000 patients. His chief nurse Mildred Nelson took the clinic to Tijuana in 1963 and the Tijuana clinic treated another 30,000 patients. Harry Hoxsey believed that overall his treatments were about 80% successful on average patients, and 25% successful on terminal cases (http://curezone.com/art/read.asp?ID=91&db=5&CO=779).

There are a number of natural medicines that reverse cancer and AIDS. There is the Canadian native formula called Essiac Tea. Sir Jason Winters developed his tea of red clover, chaparral, and spices to reverse his own inoperable brain tumor. In clinical trials aloe vera juice was found to be helpful in the reversal of over 130 diseases. It also scored a 50% reversal rate for AIDS. It was found to be particularly beneficial in reducing tumors. Gravizon, from The Amazon Herb Company, may be 10,000 times stronger in killing colon cancer than Adriamycin, a commonly used chemotherapeutic drug, but research has not begun on humans (www.essentialplanet. com/Amazon/gravizon.html). This is a product that needs to be tested ASAP!

Swiss botanical Km is a formula of bitter herbs and as the name implies is high in potassium and magnesium. As it both removes toxins and provides magnesium it has effected improvement in many conditions. Clinical studies on Km's effectiveness show that it increases cellular activity by 100%. Cellular activity is a gauge we can use to measure other herbal formulas (www.kmstories.com/ Km.html). (Go to clinical studies). The first time I ever detoxified myself was with Km. After about 3 months I could rip phone books in half. It was amazing. I felt like Popeye with a can of spinach! Whenever I feel sluggish- I detoxify again.

As we've seen in Dr. Hulda Clark's work, removing toxins is an essential part of any natural treatment regimen. This is why the various herbal formulas and food supplements are effective in providing improvement in many diseased conditions. **Toxin** removal systems such as EDTA chelation reduce the mortality rate of patients by 90% [8] (www.detoxamin.com) (go to home, and then page 3 to download this clinical study). This would seem to confirm that indeed the toxin factor is essential to understand and to deal with in the treatment of all disease. If you let toxins "stockpile", then you have to pay the price in disease later. Fortunately, Dr. Rita Ellithorpe, MD has developed an effective CA-EDTA suppository that works while you sleep. There are no needles involved, no driving and waiting at the doctors office for hours and best of all it's only 30% of the cost normally associated for chelation. Detoximin CA-EDTA Chelation suppositories are clinically proven on 15,000 patients to remove heavy metals such as mercury, cadmium, lead, and aluminum. Detoximin is safe and effective and can be ordered without a prescription. An initial order includes one container of Detoximin, a heavy metal toxicity analysis, and a copy of Dr. Sherry Rogers' book, **Detoxify or Die**. Each container of Detoximin is equal to approximately 10 conventional IV EDTA chelation treatments. A free video and medical support is available at the above website or call: (877) 656-4553.

There are perhaps hundreds of plant-derived or herbal remedies available. There appears to be an herbal remedy for every disease. You can find them on Kevin Trudeau's website on the next page. The problem is, therefore, how to select the correct remedy for the condition you have. For instance if you have cancer, it would cost approximately $800.00 to buy the top 12 herbal remedies and some of them could conflict with your current treatments or worse. To solve this problem, Paul Winter established the Alternative Cancer Treatments Comparison and Testing Home Page (http://alternativecancer.us/index.htm). By purchasing a test kit with samples of the top 12 remedies, you can test yourself to see which treatments are right for you. This is done using the process of Behavioral Kinesiology. You can use this process to test any remedy for any condition once you've mastered it. As Dr. John Diamond says, "**Your Body Doesn't Lie.**"

Later in this book, we'll reveal how and why herbal remedies work. We'll take a look at health's "missing link," and why disease

is so rampant in today's industrialized societies.

The world drug and medical cartel has a vested interest in keeping all such cures off the market. It is deeply embedded into the military-Industrial-financial complex and has massive profits to protect. Cancer alone is a $110 billion industry in just the USA. In the USA alone over $ 1 trillion was raked in from 1970-1990 on cancer. Dr. Patrick Rattigan, ND, has written an excellent summary of "**THE CANCER BUSINESS**" (www.truthcampaign.ukf.net/articles/health/cancerbusiness.html). The bottom line is that these forces of darkness, addicted to the God of Mammon, would rather kill a patient for $100,000 than cure one for $29.95. **As the FDA receives approximately 55% of their money directly from the drug manufacturers, there is no question whom they serve**. It is not a coincidence that former FDA directors get multi-million dollar drug company jobs after they deliver the lives of thousands and billions in extra profits to the drug companies. They are well paid (off) to conduct witch-hunts on alternative medical practitioners. The battle between institutional medicine and alternative medicine is a classic battle between good and evil (www.ghchealth.com). (Also see **HOLOCAUST AMERICAN STYLE** and other fine books at Global Healing Center).

Therefore, there has been little research into natural remedies to provide low cost treatments for the common man. Which toxins do Hoxsey, Essiac, Km, Flor-Essence, kochumba mushrooms, and others remove? Which formulas are best for which diseases? Is Graviola truly 10,000 times more effective than chemotherapy drugs? How do they work? I don't believe anyone can answer these questions because the medical establishment doesn't want anyone to know. The truth is that drug manufacturers have done their best to make synthetic patentable substitutes for natural herbal remedies whenever possible. The problem with this procedure is that the synthetic versions lack the protective buffers in the natural remedies that protect the patient from adverse side effects. [9] Kevin Trudeau has written one of the most informative books on the subject of the repression of natural cures. His book entitled **Natural Cures THEY Don't' Want You to Know About** states that there IS a natural remedy for nearly every disease. His website lists these remedies and provides links for 122,000 medical practitioners who are familiar in the use of them (www. naturalcures.com). This is a paid private members only website so that the truth can be told. I highly recommend this book and website as one of the best in the field of alternative health. You may also wish to consider Jane Heimlich's classic expose, **WHAT YOUR DOCTOR WON'T TELL YOU** . One of the things your doctor won't tell you is that 95% of conventional treatments are unproven.

Conspiracy to keep low cost, home-made medicines off the market to keep obscene profits flowing to the pharmaceutical companies and Uranium mine owners would be bad enough. A very strong case can be presented for the suppression of all alternative treatments NOT owned by the health "establishment." However it doesn't stop there. On the contrary it is clear that tax monies that were designated for the war on cancer were used to create a new cancer: AIDS. The US Military and the CIA used their $20 billion in research money to study cancer, so they could replicate the process and create new designer biological weapons to target specific racial and lifestyle groups. According to Dr. Robert Strecher, the aids virus is a genetically spliced combination of bovine leukemia and sheep visna virus. [10] The bottom line is that THE WAR ON CANCER WAS FOUGHT WITH BLANKS!

I mention this because the weapons of choice for **World War III** will be biological weapons. They are the cheapest and easiest weapons to make and it is difficult to trace who made them or where they come from. And unlike bombs they leave property intact, an important consideration to those who would take over the world. The Russians have super black plague virus, the Chinese have tanker loads of Ebola virus, one of the deadliest diseases known to man. Ebola is one of the fastest acting usually resulting in death in a day. Smallpox and anthrax are also popular weapons in the biological warfare stockpile. I wrote about this threat in my first article, **Got Gold?** (www.gold-eagle.com/editorials_02/frego100102pv.html).

Unless more critical core research is done on disease, with the intent of stopping it, then we can expect as many as 4-5 billion people to die during the course of WW3. A grapefruit sized batch of viruses could wipe out all of lower Manhattan in a short period of time. And there is no security system in the world that can detect something of this nature.

Biological warfare is nothing new. It's just reached a new level. Mongol invaders used catapults to toss dead bodies with the plague over castle walls at their enemies. Spanish conquistadors and English traders gave blankets with smallpox to unsuspecting Indians to make conquest easier. Biological warfare goes on everyday almost everywhere. It is so subtle and covert it goes unnoticed. Cancer is continuously on the rise despite all of our so-called modern medicines. It is a key indicator of what is wrong with modern medicine worldwide. Millions of dollars go into cancer research on a daily basis. We can't help but ask why isn't there a cure? Apparently there have been effective treatments around for several thousand years, but like an elephant in one's pajamas, doctors don't seem to be able to find them!

To answer that question we must take a look at history. Until the early part of the 1900s cancer was an uncommon and virtually unknown disease. And this wasn't because no one lived to be 100 years of age either. So what happened in the early 1900s that changed the future? The chemical agriculture business emerged! That's what happened. Chemical pesticides, chemical fertilizers, and chemical soaps and solvents in the food preparation industry. Using toxic chemicals to kill bugs and force plants to grow was the beginning of our current health plague.

One of the most basic reasons why there are no cures for cancer is that the owners of the chemical industry and pharmaceutical industry are the same guys!! So what we have is a chemical and toxin industry that makes you sick and then a medical industry that pretends to make you better and everyone runs to the bank with your money, laughing all the way. What a deal!! **"It is estimated that over 95% of all food purchased has as many as 300 chemicals added to each product that are NOT listed on the label."** [11] Well-placed bribes have seen to that. Whatever may be in your food is a total mystery even to those who sell it.

The big bankers (banksters) also control all the major research institutions and universities. This is to insure that no one "accidentally" blows the lid off, points any fingers, or lets any low cost cures OUT. That is how the system works. Billions of dollars flow into the banker's hands. And whether you live or die, $100,000 a head is raked in. My favorite quote is, "Hospitals are kind of like whore houses, no one makes any money unless all the beds are filled."

What about the term "acceptable limits." You see this all the time on chemicals, pesticides, and electrical products. Well, the limits are acceptable to the bankers as they make money both ways. They aren't the ones dying and they plan to kill everyone in the next war anyway, so it's great for them. Not so great for you and me. The air quality is just fine in the South of France, but not so great in Lackawanna, NY or LA. But THEY don't live there. Do you think THEY eat what you do? When was the last time you had a $60,000 lunch?

The banksters have no incentive to make you well as they make money on both ends for making you ill. And a sick population is easier to control and conquer than a well robust population. If you're too busy working to make ends meet, due to your $500 monthly insurance premiums, then you'll be too busy to ask any pesky questions to anyone in authority.

So let's speak plainly. The forces of darkness control worldwide banking, the world economy, the pharmaceutical industry, the chemical industry, medicine, mining, and damned near everything else. The state of medicine today is but the tip of the iceberg of the coming of the Fourth Reich. Once you understand this, you'll understand many things. (12)

How do we dig ourselves out of this hole we find ourselves in? The first step is to admit that we put ourselves there by giving our power away. We made doctors, insurance companies, bankers and scientists gods they are not. In fact doctors misdiagnose patients 2 times out of 3. It happened to me when Navy doctors sent me back to die, but I was one of the lucky ones. Thank God I made it. A hospital is one of the most dangerous places you can be in due to infections. It's a proven fact that when doctors go on strike, the mortality rate goes down. Doctors are great at emergency medicine. Don't get me wrong. They're great at that. But preventive medicine is in its infancy. Is there another way? Is there a better way? I believe there is!

Before we can approach an alternative path, we must first understand the most basic concepts of disease that have been hidden for centuries.

PART 2

Doctors and scientists are allowed to search for answers only where their superiors tell them to look. Too much "creativity" can result in the loss of tenure and paycheck. Our researchers are like the lovelorn, they're looking for love in all the wrong places. The pieces of the puzzle are all there, but few have ever bothered to put them together into a cohesive whole. To do so requires thinking "outside the box". There is no forum to bring all the parts together. Therefore the time has come to look at the other half of the puzzle. We must break the code and look at possibilities and potentials we have heretofore barely imagined. We must explore a Universal Theory of Disease, because this is an idea whose time has come. It is time for miracles to become commonplace and to realize all of our problems are caused by the wrong adjustment to life. Only a radical departure from the present can deliver us from darkness. The turning point in history will soon be at hand and we must choose the correct path to progress materially and spiritually. As history moves in cycles, the key to our future is in the past. So, let's proceed boldly where few have dared to tread before. The failure to cure all diseases known to man is a failure of politics, not human invention. God provided the inspiration, but the forces of darkness have kept it from us.

Royal Raymond Rife (1888-1971) (www.rt66.com/~rifetech/) was every inch the genius as his contemporaries Nichola Tessla, Thomas Edison and Guglielmo Marconi. He achieved something no one had ever conceived of before in modern history: a method to cure and prevent all disease. He found the biggest pieces of the puzzle anyone ever found. For this crime he was severely punished.

His accomplishments have ended up in the scrap heap of history. His patrons were murdered or coerced. His associates all denied knowing him. His inventions have been deposited in that big government warehouse next to Indiana Jones's Lost Ark, where no one can find them.

Royal Rife was an unlikely hero. He arrived in San Diego, CA. in 1906 and obtained a job as a chauffeur. His employer, industrialist Henry Timken, noticed Rife's fascination with microscopes and sent him to Germany to study. Rife studied and worked at the Zeiss Works for 6 years under its leading technician Hans Luckel. Rife then spent years to create a Universal Microscope (www.rife.org) that could see living cells. His creation of a 200 pound behemoth microscope with over 5,000 parts may still be the most powerful microscope ever devised. It allowed Rife to view living cells in their natural state. He then brilliantly "stained" them with different light frequencies to make them luminescent. [13] Rife would sit at his microscope for periods of over 24 hours. He studied bacteriology for over 40 years.

The first of Rife's amazing discoveries was that **"viruses are released from bacteria just as a chicken lays an egg."** Rife was able to isolate all the major pathogenic organisms of the day such as polio, tetanus, typhoid, tb, sarcoma, carcinoma, bubonic plague, anthrax, influenza and 40 additional virus strains never before isolated. He then discovered "coordinative resonance" and that all microorganisms lived in a certain frequency range. Using the principle of "coordinative resonance" he developed a machine to make frequencies exactly equal and opposite to the target microorganisms. With his Rife Frequency Generator, he calculated by trial and error, the specific frequencies or mortal oscillatory rates (MOR) of the various diseases. When he bombarded microorganisms and cancer tumors with these correct frequencies they "exploded" and became "deactivated". The organisms would become "deactivated" and began to "jam up like logs".

Rife then discovered that virus forms could be altered with chemicals. He could create disease by simple chemical manipulations and then destroy them using the Rife frequencies. Rife obtained financial backing to conduct a trial on 16 terminally ill patients in 1934. Using Rife technology, all 16 recovered. Did Royal Rife receive a prize? No! "The results were squashed, records and equipment disappeared, and the entire project was swept under the carpet." It wasn't until 1971 that the Nobel Foundation honored Rife.

Rife was the first to isolate a cancer virus (in 1931). By 1933 he had isolated over 40 more viruses. But little of his frequency research remains. The problem was his frequencies could be borne by a carrier wave for over 12 miles. If a general "healing frequency" were thus broadcast, everyone within range would remain in a state of health. And there is the rub! There is no money in health that can be dispensed for free, but a fortune to be made in disease!!

Rife's major supporter, Dr. Johnson, died under mysterious circumstances (possibly murder) before he could testify in court for Royal Rife. Bad things started to happen to Royal Rife after he refused to sell his technology to Morris Fishbein of the AMA. Records and machines disappeared. Doctors were jailed who used his technology and his main research facility burned down. Rife had discovered several of the keys to the elimination of all diseases and therefore he had to be stopped at all costs.

The work of Royal Rife was stopped dead in its tracks, but knowledge has a way of coming to the surface like a telltale ghost from an unspeakable crime. The death of knowledge always comes back to haunt the perpetrator. And even the dead refuse to remain silent. See (www.rifeenergymedicine.com/bibliob2.html) for more articles about Royal Rife and a bibliography of some of the best alternative medicine books. While some of Royal Rife's research is indeed lost, researchers around the world have labored to recreate it and to continue to experiment. Lists of Rife frequencies, normalizing frequencies, and Dr. Hulda Clark's frequencies can be found at: (www.electroherbalism.com). See the Consolidated Annotated Frequency List (CAFL) as compiled by Brian McInturff.

Frequencies of disease, rejuvenation and immortality

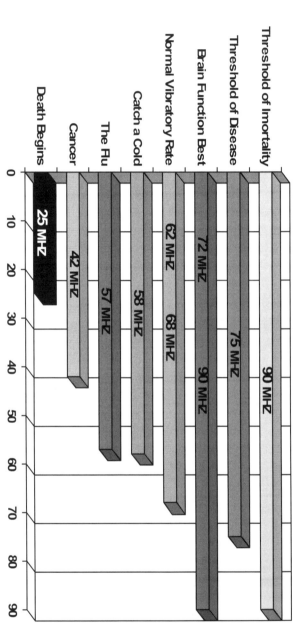

Threshold of Imortality — 90 MHZ

Threshold of Disease — 75 MHZ

Brain Function Best — 72 MHZ / 90 MHZ

Normal Vibratory Rate — 62 MHZ / 68 MHZ

Catch a Cold — 58 MHZ

The Flu — 57 MHZ

Cancer — 42 MHZ

Death Begins — 25 MHZ

24

It may be easiest to perceive of Rife frequencies as healing codes or something akin to homeopathic vibrations to counteract specific diseases. This however doesn't answer the basic question as to what the actual frequencies of the body vibrations are. This type of material is exceptionally hard to find. However an anonymous author at Bridger House Publishing has published a partial list of body frequencies in the **Handbook for the New Paradigm**. [14] These are particularly useful to this discussion as we can now build an energy grid chart for evaluation and experimentation upon A Universal Theory of Disease. And we can further interpolate where frequencies for the threshold of disease and immortality may lie. Without an actual human immortal body to measure, these later frequency positions are simply a shot in the dark. They may be considerably higher or lower. However knowing what to look for will spur later researchers to find the correct values and plug them in as soon as they are found. The frequencies are as follows:

90	MHz	THRESHOLD OF IMMORTALITY THEORETICAL
90	MHz	Optimal Brain function, upper
75	MHz	THRESHOLD OF DISEASE THEORETICAL
72	MHz	Optimal Brain function, lower
68	MHz	Normal Vibratory rate, upper
62	MHz	Normal Vibratory rate, lower
58	MHz	Colds
57	MHz	Flu
55	MHz	Candida
52	MHz	Epstein Barr
42	MHz	Cancer
25	MHz	Death begins
00	MHz	Dead and buried

The Handbook also makes note of 2 frequencies of immense importance. Above 68 MHz one begins to gain the ability to "**walk through walls.**" And most importantly for our discussion, a level of **90 MHz** or above must be achieved to **"tune in" one's mind to "the universal flow and receive the keys to the mysteries of galactic intentional focus."** [15] This is the realm of co-creation with God and the beginning of immortality. I've placed the threshold of immortality at 90 MHz solely for my own convenience to round out the graph. It could be higher or lower. I'll let you know when I get there.

Lastly, French microbiologist **Gaston Naessens** invented a dark field microscope in the 1940s that could be used to examine living tissue like Rife's microscope. During the course of his work, Naessens discovered dense particles he named somatids. Tracking the abnormal cycles of somatids in the blood allowed him to diagnose and monitor the disease processes. His system is in effect an **"early warning system"** of impending disease, which may alert the patient of disease factors by as much as **2 years in advance of the onset of a disease**. He observed that cancer cells created a nitrogen sink and that by supplying nitrogen it would stop their toxic secretions. He named the nitrogen solution 714X and it is composed of camphor and ammonium salts. Lastly, he was able to identify a cocancerogenic K (CKF) factor which paralyzes the immune system. 714x neutralized this factor. For his contributions to medicine and saving lives, Gaston Naessens has been charged with illegal practice of medicine both in France and Canada, and one count of contributing to the death of a patient. However, Gaston Naessens has endured and his 714X is available in Canada, Mexico, and Western Europe. He currently resides in Quebec, Canada. (www.sumeria.net/tech/naessens.html)

Prevailing theories of disease may be nothing more than historical relics masquerading as truth (www.euroamericanhealth.com). You may judge for yourself.

PART 3

Although much of Rife's accomplishments have been deliberately suppressed, he has left us a basic framework to conquer all disease. He proved that all diseases "live" at specific frequency ranges. For example carcinoma is 2128, sarcoma is 2008, typhoid is 862, and tuberculosis is 803 for its rod form. In fact, "an amazing number of pathogens seem to respond in the low range from 20 Hz to 900 Hz. [16] Therefore most diseases live in the LOWER frequency ranges. A threshold of all disease may exist at or above 75 MHz. **The expanded energy carrying capacity of a perfected crystalline cellular structure may indeed have the capacity to cross the threshold of all disease!! The trick is: How do we get there?**

We are awash in a sea of energy. Energy comes to us from the sun, stars, moon, planets, air, water, food, sound, and the Earth. Our minds continuously broadcast energy back into the universe where it remains forever. In order to maximize our energy gathering potential and achieve a more nearly perfect crystalline structure, we must first understand the true nature of the energy sources. And conversely, we must stop energy leaks, and avoid energy "pollutants" and hazards. Once we understand how it all works, perfect health is easier to achieve.

THE SUN Our sun is the primary source of energy and life on this planet. We receive solar energy and all the constituent parts such as x-rays and gamma rays. We also receive energy from the stars, planets, moon, and cosmic energy from the entire solar system. The action of the sun and moon generate winds, tides and the rhythm of life on Earth.

Sunlight is actually best classified as a "group" of energy waves or frequencies. If we separate white light with a prism, we can divide the light spectrum into the colors of the rainbow. **Each color has a specific frequency range and corresponds to the same 7 color frequencies of our chakras**. Each chakra corresponds to a different band of light starting with red at the base chakra and ascending in order up to the crown chakra, which is violet in nature. Each chakra also corresponds to the energy of a different planet and a different mineral. Balancing the influx of energies is a key ingredient to health.

The ancient Egyptians used to worship the sun as the giver of life. The biblical Essenes, of whom the Master Jesus was one, harnessed the power of sunlight in their meditative techniques. The Essenes and the ancient solar cults learned a way to gaze safely into the sun the entire day and thereby increased their energy structure and fortified their neurological systems. Modern explorer Gene Savoy claims to have found a manuscript in Tibet written by one of the Disciples of Christ. Using this document he founded the International Community of Christ and teaches these techniques. His discoveries are outlined in his book: **Project X and the Search for Immortality**. [17] Its fascinating reading. Don't try this technique yourself without proper training, as permanent blindness will result. See: (www. genesavoy.org) and (www.solarhealing.com).

THE AIR The most well known source of additional energy is found in the air we breathe. Air has not only oxygen, but also electrical particles called ions. These particles can be charged either positively or negatively. Negative ions are associated with well-being and elation, while too many positive ions are blamed for mood swings, and temporary insanity. The ancients called the energy in air "prana" and developed many sorts of breathing exercises to utilize and capture this energy. There apparently is enough electrical energy in air to live on without any food source. Practitioners of this art are called Breathairians. This method of energy gathering can be gained using certain yogic techniques. [18] There are yoga masters proficient in this technique who can live on prana alone and forego breathing entirely for hours or even days. This level of deep meditative state is the mark of a true prophet. NASA scientists discovered during the space race that without the electrical components of air death results within a matter of minutes. Breathing exercises taking in fresh ionized air full of oxygen is a vital component of health.

Oxygen levels may have fallen by 3-4 percent since ancient times. Deforestation and pollution have taken a toll on oxygen levels. Trees both manufacture oxygen and absorb pollutants and CO2. They also generate negative ions.

Oxygen is very beneficial in killing germs, viruses, and bacteria. If you don't have enough from your environment you can take Ozone therapy or consume powdered oxygen formulas. This form of therapy can potentially reverse many degenerative conditions. One of the leading proponents of Ozone therapy, Ed McCabe, was jailed for his efforts in combating aids and cancer with ozone. This was in clear violation of his rights to freedom of speech, but he was jailed anyway by the medical monopoly.

Ozone therapy has been around for over 100 years. In fact Nicola Tesla operated the "Tesla Ozone Company." HIV positive infected blood can be rendered negative in 16 seconds in the test tube. Peer reviewed medical journals have rated it between 97-100% effective for killing AIDS. However in the USA all attempts at ozone research are treated with S.W.A.T. TEAMS (www.trunkerton.fsnet.co.uk/ozone cure for aids.htm) and jail sentences. Wonder why? **It appears that 33 major diseases are reversed by ozone**. To view the list of diseases affected see page one bottom on the link above. That is why researchers get their homes burned down, sent to prison, or murdered. Dr. James Boyce turned 254 HIV positive patients to HIV negative. He got 5 years in prison for it and his medical license revoked. This is a fairly common event for alternative practitioners and researchers if you take a look at its history of suppression (www.thefinchleyclinic. co.uk/nojavascript/therapies/ozone/supression.htm). There are big bucks at stake and millions to be killed. Even worse for the bad guys, oxygen also appears to be an aid to ascension, which we will talk more about later. Ozone is legal in 11 states. If you don't happen to live in any of them, there is possibly stabilized oxygen as used in colon cleansers such as Oxy-Powder (www.oxypowder.com). This powder cleans the colon, kills off a lot of unfriendly bacteria, and has Germanium 132, which may suppress some forms of cancer. I have tried stabilized nascent oxygen from Ascension Alchemy in the form of Aquascension (www.asc-alchemy.com/asc.html). It really did the job and I had a Kundalini rising, which I'll also talk more about later. Also visit: (www.oxygenamerica.com).

Air, ions, and oxygen are all essentials of good health and the foundation of many systems of immortality. Ancient systems such as Yoga, Tai Chi and Qi Gong employ this wisdom. And there is the rub. Oxygen is free!

The ancient arts of Feng Shui and Vedic architecture deal with the proper construction of buildings and homes for harmonious energy and air levels. The West has been slow to adopt this knowledge and many "sick buildings" have been built. The occupant suffers endless health complains due to improper construction. This can be avoided by the use of natural log cabins as they breathe, they don't allow harmful electrical charges. to build up, and are naturally heated and cooled.

WATER Water is perhaps one of the most overlooked sources of energy. As our bodies are composed mostly of water, the quality of the water we consume has a tremendous bearing upon our health. Not all water is the same! It is a fundamental agent in the formation of a super-charged crystalline cellular structure.

DR. PATRICK FLANNIGAN

For over a decade America's most distinguished scientist, Patrick Flannigan attempted to discover the secrets of the Hunzas people in Pakistan. The Hunzas all seem to live beyond 100 years of age, with some as old as 150. Patrick Flannigan eventually discovered that the milky white glacial water from the mountains was their secret. Their water was full of small micro-particles of minerals and this allowed a greater accumulation of electricity to gather around them. [19] Later he was able to reproduce these micro-clusters of energy or colloids in the lab. Eventually he created **"CRYSTAL ENERGY"** (www.wetterwater.net/why_take_crystalenergy.html) or Flannigan colloids. Dr. Flannigan found that the higher the electrical potential or Zeta potential, as he called it, the more beneficial the water was to health. Colloids form long electrically charged chains, holding as much as 40,000 volts. They form in series like little batteries and the electrical charge helps the water remove toxins from the body. The result of this high electrical charge in the water is a 500% improvement in vitamin absorption and a greatly increased life span. Crystal Energy also "pulls your body's pH in the right direction. More alkaline if you need it, more acid if you need it." "And daily use of Crystal Energy acts as a natural 'chelator' pulling out heavy metals and other toxins."

Dr. Flannigan has continued his research on the healing waters of the world for over 3 decades. His work has focused primarily on what mechanisms are involved in hydrating the cells of the body. He found that negatively charged hydrogen ions are responsible for delivering water to the cells. It is the combination of oxygen AND hydrogen (in an electrically charged structure) that is needed for the body's energy and fuel. Hydrogen restructures the blood, separating the cells so that they can efficiently remove toxins and free radicals that destroy cellular DNA. As free radicals and oxidants are the cause of cellular deterioration and aging, the effects of rehydrating the cells is dramatic. Hydrogen is the key to life, death, and aging.

Normally we get our hydrogen from water, fruits and vegetables. Due to all the hazards of "civilized" life, chemical agriculture, food processing, stress, etc., we don't get enough hydrogen in our diets to maintain a healthy balance of our cellular structure. Our cells become oxidized and full of free radicals. We wear out our cells like an old rusty pipe. The addition of silica hydride in the form of MegaHydrate reverses the process, and rehydrates our cells and rebuilds their energy carrying capacity (Zeta Potential). "One daily dose of Megahydrate has more antioxidant power than hundreds of glasses of fresh vegetable and fruit juices, broccoli, brussel sprouts, leafy greens, and other foods rich in antioxidants to prevent free radical damage." In short, MegaHydrate can be considered an anti-aging pill. It also "**provides natural pain relief from headaches, sore muscles, and inflammation of the joints**." Normally it takes about a month to rehydrate the cells using Megahydrate. For additional information on this product click on the link: (www.megahydrate.net/hydration/hydrated-copper-ii-sulfate.html). Dr. Flanagan publishes a free **Health Secrets Newsletter** at: (www.megahydrate.com).

As I like to practice what I preach, I ordered a bottle of Megahydrate for myself. I took the first 2 capsules and had a restful nights sleep. In the morning I had energy again. I could feel it working all day and it didn't fade out in the middle of the afternoon due to my stressful schedule. My body feels stronger, the arms especially. It is obvious that the toxins are leaving and my stomach is working better. My mind feels clearer. All this happened in the first 1-2 days. After 2 weeks I began to feel younger. Can't wait to see what will happen after the normal 30 day period of detoxification! I'll report more on my findings in a future newsletter. For now I want to assure my readers it really works fast!

PERFECT SCIENCE WATER

A miracle happened in the late 1980s, but only a few people ever heard about it outside of the FBI, CIA and other high government agencies. Officials in Russia and eight other countries immediately began to investigate this new discovery. The Turkish government built a new $48 million dollar plant to produce 100,000 gallons a day of what is called "Perfect Science Water". This super ionized water with 3 extra electrons on its outer orb it is like no other water on Earth. Due to its molecular structure it is alive and (www.macedonia.co.uk/mcic/soulandspirit/healingandtouristresorts/water.asp) has "God-Consciousness". It has the uncanny ability to turn toxic substances into proteins and amino acids. It works on chemical dumps, polluted rivers and bays, and even possibly nuclear waste. It can clean up a polluted river or lake in as little as 3-4 days! Just a couple of gallons of Perfect Science water cleaned up Izmit Bay near Istanbul. It went crystal clear. Tests were done on a swimming pool full of sewage. In less than a few hours it was clear! (www.perfectscience.com). You may also order Perfect Science Waters from: (http://www.perfectwaters. net/ise.html).

Perfect Science Water can be used to clean up toxic sites, mining wastes and polluted agricultural land. It even puts out forest fires and chemical fires in a very rapid fashion.

Perfect Science Water may be the best toxin cleaner ever developed. We'll see as time goes on. Its potential for use in the human body is immense. There are already anecdotal evidence of its usefulness in fighting degenerative diseases such as cancer, heart disease, AIDS, and diabetes. An aids clinic is planned for Haiti to test its effectiveness. Much more testing and clinical studies need to be done.

Scientists at the **University of Georgia** discovered that **"every cell in our body that is diseased, or that is harmed in one way or another is surrounded by UNSTRUCTURED WATER."** Unstructured water is missing electrons in the outer orbit. Therefore providing these missing electrons returns the cells to a "structured" state and hence eliminates the foundation of disease!

The use of clustered water "appears to be a definite step forward in allowing consciousness inside the human body to emerge faster!"

Under the microscope clustered water looks like tiny snow flakes with structured hexagonal patterns. You can think of clustered water as "liquid electrons." And the more you have, the better. Every function in the body is either pushed or pulled by electromagnetic action, like tiny magnets moving stuff on a conveyor belt. Without this electrical activity cellular functions slow down and the body gets sludged up. And that is the primary cause of all our problems.

Only clean running water has the minerals, energy and "life" in it to keep your body healthy. Tap water is DEAD. It can be full of sewage, toilet paper and chlorine. If it is pure, then all the minerals and electrical energy are also removed (the reverse osmosis method). Dr. Patrick Flanigan calls drinking tap water a slow form of suicide. Today's tap water is yesterday's toilet. Dr. Flanigan has discovered everything in tap water from cesium 6, made famous in the film Erin Brokovich, to rocket fuel. Your body is made mostly of water and if you need to regain your health you need to first rebuild your cellular system with structured super-ionized water. Prana or energy and water combined are the structure of our DNA.

JOHN ELLIS & THE LIVING WATER MACHINE

Finding a source of pure clean water is an extremely difficult task in today's environment. Bottled spring water and even distilled water aren't totally clean in many respects. Ever wonder why bottled water has an expiration date? It's because algae will start growing in it in a few weeks. Engineer John Ellis set out to solve this problem by duplicating the same process that nature uses to purify water. He found that in nature, it is the very rapid heating and cooling of water, 3 times a minute, and passing through an air gap that totally purifies water. This breaks the hydrogen bond angle and reforms it at an impressive 114%. Tap water is dead at only 101%. The result is electrified purified water that kills the bad bacteria and leaves the friendly ones untouched. Free radicals are also removed. It appears that **normal water retains the disease markers and disease memories,** even if it has been recycled as rain for millions of years. The disease "signature" is still there. Purification in such a manner apparently removes them and the results are said to be very impressive. The **Living Water Machine** creates water that will pass through cell membranes allowing relief from several diseases. The LWM creates about 1 gallon of purified water in 1.5 hours. Mr. Ellis states that several major cancer centers use his machines and that over 100,000 of them have been sold. He also states that blood samples taken of cancer patients show remarkable changes in a matter of hours. To read more see: (www.johnellis.com). The price for the LWM is comparable to a water distiller at $1,700. This machine should produce enough household water for all one's normal needs. Use in a hot tub would be ideal for skin absorption and no chemicals are needed. Some clients reported a return of their hair and hair color; therefore there may be some anti-aging effects of the water as well. I am looking forward to testing it myself.

DR. DAVID WHEELER & M-WATER

A clinical study of the effects of M-Water and Core Water was conducted by Fenestra Research, Las Vegas, Nevada, from January through June 2005. They tested the patent pending M-Power Aqua Technology created by Dr. David Wheeler. Improvement was noted in several critical areas as measured by an Optimal Wellness Test. Test subjects showed a 29.2% improvement. **Stored intracellular toxins decreased by 46%.** Neutral pH improved 26%. The improvements appear to increase with the duration of the living water intake, with the most notable results occurring after 4 months. Overall most test subjects noted less anxiety and less depression. They felt much happier. Dr. Wheeler is the author of **WATER EMPOWERMENT FOR LIFE** and is currently working on a sequel to be completed this winter. Sample chapters can be downloaded from his website (www.0disease.com). The website has some incredible information on the discovery of the Aquaporin Channel (winner of the 2003 Nobel Prize in chemistry), aura photos of test subjects using M-water and computer generated H2O models showing the expanded structure of water molecules. One of the best sites on water I've found.

THE EARTH The Earth is a living conscious entity not just a ball of rock spinning through space. It also has polarity, energy fields and underground currents of energy. Every spot on the planet is slightly different and has its own magnetic signature. Some places are exceptionally healthy and vibrant due to the additional energy focus they possess. The ancients paid particular attention to the magnetic lines of force that run above and below the Earth's surface. They altered the landscape with standing stones to adjust the frequency of these ley lines for agricultural, health, and other spiritual purposes. The goal was a harmonious environment or as the Chinese called it "Feng Shui" (www.wofs.com).

Mountainous areas due to their considerable mass and shapes focus energy in a unique way. Bell shaped mountains are viewed as particularly beneficial to health. Eastern tradition views all mountains as sacred mountains, while particular mountains such as Mt. Kalais and Mt. Everest are revered as abodes of God. Pilgrimages to sacred mountains are frequent events in the East, but little known in the West. In the USA Mt. McKinley, Mt. Shasta, and the Sedona Arizona mountains are noted for their high energy. As Sedona has 4 mountains with different energy frequencies it is a popular healing destination with several clinics in the area. The energy is so strong you can feel it in town a few miles away. Dick Sutphen and others lead healing and past life seminars in the area. See Dick Sutphens' Sedona Psychic Energy Vortexes at: (www.dicksutphen.com), Reiki classes and other healing modalities are also held at The Infinite Light Healing Study Center in Sedona (www.reikiclasses.com).

The Sacred Mountain of Endwebu is located in South Africa in a remote part of the Zulu Nation called KwaZulu-Natal. According to Gary Smith (www.authorsden.com/garysmith) founder of Sacred Merkaba Techniques, Endwebu is where the human body and the human spirit originated. Therefore it is sacred to all humanity. It has been and continues to be the site of "whole body" ascensions. A healing and training center for treating AIDS orphans is currently being built upon the mountain (www.merkaba.org/aids_babies.htm) thanks to the generous gift of the site by the Prince of the Zulu Nation.

THE KILLING FIELDS

It is often jokingly said that "we treat our soil like dirt!" The soil is however a living, breathing, spiritual entity full of living microorganisms, enzymes, and minerals all bonded together in a dynamic biosphere. This all takes place in, and is influenced by, a local and cosmic electromagnetic environment.

Agribusiness has turned this sacred ground into killing fields solely for the sake of profit. There are over 2,300 cancer causing chemicals sprayed upon our food, some of which are so lethal that one drop absorbed through the skin causes death. The chemicals designed to kill insects kill the soil as well. Farmers are going bankrupt in record numbers because their reliance upon expensive poisonous sprays and synthetic fertilizers simply doesn't work in the long run.

THE NEW GARDENERS

There are other ways. Organic gardening has been popularized in this country by Robert Rodale. Biodynamic gardening (www.biodynamics.com), originated by Rudolf Steiner in Austria in 1924, has developed a highly effective approach to gardening. Spiritual gardeners such as Peter Caddy from Findhorn, Scotland, [www.findhorn.org] and Michelle Small Wright of Perelandra Farms in Jeffersonville, Va. (www.perelandra-ltd.com), have reintroduced gardening in its original form. These later approaches take into account the sacredness of all life and work with respect for and cooperation with the elemental forces of nature.

Foods grown in the sacred manner are vibrantly alive: full of energy. They are highly structurally organized on a cellular electromagnetic level. When eaten raw, the maximum amount of food energy is released into the body through a process called "subtle organizing energy fields" (SOEFs) (www.treeoflife.nu/gabrielshanti.html). These energy fields are "coded" like a computer disk and help direct the food energy to its proper location and purpose through a process of electromagnetic attraction. Unenlightened growing practices result in weak, inferior, and often toxic food. (And ultimately a weak, inferior, toxic population) Cooking practices further destroy its vitality as heat destroys the electromagnetic bonds of the SOEFs. Doctors at the Shanghai College of Traditional Chinese Medicine have discovered that foods cooked in glass or ceramics were the most effective in inhibiting cancer growth. As they say in computer programming, "garbage in- garbage out". Incorrect thinking, growing, and eating habits result in a loss of energy throughout the body. This in turn creates a "brown out effect" where vital bodily functions are taken "off the circuit" in an attempt to save the most vital functions and life. Imbalances of energy within the body are the unguarded gates through which disease invades the body. Correct dietary, mental, and healing practices can "super charge" the body and make it extremely resistant, if not totally immune from all diseases.

Organic gardening techniques provide the proper nutritional "structure" in an electromagnetic environment that allows nutrients to be fully utilized by the body. Compost is a natural chelating agent that promotes absorption of essential elements, trace elements, and minerals. Using "rock dust", such as Azomite (www.azomite.com) can add 70 different minerals and trace elements for absorption. A technique called "sonic bloom" enhances mineral and trace element absorption by as much as 700%. Protein content can be improved, even doubled. As Christopher Bird has so eloquently pointed out in his **SECRETS OF THE SOIL, there were virtually no degenerative diseases in this country until the advent of chemical agriculture at the turn of the century! Degenerative disease accounted for only 1% of all deaths in 1902, but accounted for 60% by 1948**. As early as 1936 US Senate hearings were being conducted as per the poor state of America's soils. With the exception of a few enlightened organic gardeners, the downward trend continues with disastrous results to the public health.

According to a Seattle Times article (www.rense.com/health/toxicchem.htm) radioactive and toxic chemicals are frequently sold as farm fertilizer. In the USA, there are no regulations set on toxic and radioactive waste in farm fertilizers. Steel mills, pulp mills, smelters, and even medical and municipal waste companies find "recycling" their waste as fertilizer saves them money. "Use of industrial waste as a fertilizer ingredient is a growing national phenomenon, The Times reported". Can there be any doubt why humans and animals aren't as healthy as they were 100 years ago? You can safely and easily find out whether you have been affected by this trend by sending in a sample of your hair for analysis to this address: (www.herbalhealer.com/hairanalysis.html). The cost is approximately $170.00. And throw your toothpaste away while you're at it. It's full of toxic waste also!

Dr. Joel Wallach, N.D. has contributed significantly to our knowledge of mineral deficiency as a major cause of death. He is the author of the best selling **DEAD DOCTORS DON'T LIE** and **RARE EARTHS - FORBIDDEN CURSES**. He was nominated for a Nobel Prize in 1991 for his stunning discoveries in the use of trace minerals to prevent catastrophic diseases in the newborn. You can obtain his books on minerals, audio tapes, and vitamin and mineral line at: (www.wallachonline.com). Consumption of the 90 different minerals you need brings very noticeable improvement to your overall health.

Perhaps the most critically missing ingredient in commercial chemically produced food is nitrogen. It would appear that chemical techniques do not make nitrogen available in a usable form for use by the body. Organic techniques such as crop rotation and lightening both affix nitrogen to the soil where it can be absorbed by the foods grown in it. According to Gaston Naessens, cancerous cells crave nitrogen and when it is supplied in sufficient quantities they dissolve! This may explain why Chinese, Egyptian, Mayan, and Inca agriculturists went to such great pains to add more electromagnetic energy to their soils, to improve soil fertility, and to promote human and animal vitality and longevity (www.subtleenergies.com/ormus/tw/paramag.htm).

The most basic problem with chemical agriculture is that it is incompatible with the true nature of the Earth. It ignores all the true rules of physics and of the universe to make a quick buck. Like many other systems purveyed by hucksters and bankers, chemical agriculture is a scam. It's a Ponzi scheme to trick the Earth and farmers into producing more for less money. In actuality it produces less for more money and creates a tidal wave of death and disease in its wake. It would cost an average family of 4 over $1,000 a month in vitamin and mineral supplements just to replenish half of what is missing in our foods. The problem is the consumers don't know what they're missing. And many will never realize it until they have a life threatening disease. What they are missing is best classified as super conductors of energy. These superconductors are known as **monatomic metallic elements**. Regardless of how many vitamins and minerals you have, you can't live without M-state elements in your diet. M-state products haven't made it into use in agriculture yet except on an experimental basis. You can judge the results yourself of Barry Carter's experiments with Walnut trees at: (www.subtleenergies. com/ormus/tw/walnuts.htm). Zero Point Technologies has stated that, "There is a super health and wellness revolution on the horizon" and I totally agree (www.zptech.com).

RECREATING THE GARDEN OF EDEN

The Biblical Garden of Eden is believed to have been the delta area where the rivers Tigris and Euphrates meet in modern Iraq. We must ask ourselves, what is so special about river deltas that would make agriculture in such an area a veritable Paradise on Earth?" In other words, what creates a perfect soil for agriculture? Previously, we discussed how the white milky glacial melt water in the Hunzas lands brought down a wealth of colloidal minerals in a highly charged electrical matrix. Obviously, the richer the minerals in the area, the better the resulting soil will be. High volcanic mountain ranges, rich in gold, silver, platinum, and copper or other minerals **ALSO** have their M-state or Ormus isotopes of these same elements. Delta areas made of high concentrations of M-state minerals are the richest soils in the world, both for agriculture and for healing. One such area is located 40 miles south of Lima, Peru. M-state minerals from the Andes bless the area with a healing mud that is extremely popular with the local inhabitants. As minerals are absorbed through the skin, the inhabitants cover themselves in mud daily for about 30 days. This method is very popular as a low cost method of treating skin conditions. As each stream in the area has different minerals, some streams work better on certain diseases and ailments than others. Any river system carrying M-state and glacial melt from high volcanic mountains is a candidate for healthful agriculture and healing. Volcanic hot springs in the Andes, such as the ones in Calca, (near Cuzco) may be the source of these minerals and are highly beneficial. Many islands in the world are volcanic in origin and are a great place to look for hot springs. The Hawaiian chain is the best place in the USA to look for mineral-bearing hot springs. The volcanic island nation of Iceland holds the record for having the longest lived people.

We can naturally recreate these Edenic conditions using M-state bearing sands, M-state sprays, bio-dynamic gardening, rock dust (Azomite), and placement of large crystalline stones of certain vibrations. We've seen how walnuts the size of tennis balls can be achieved with M-state sprays (C-11 from Ocean Alchemy). This seems to hold true for other plant species as well. View an M-state grown pepper plant 10 times the size of its control in the gardening section and "minerals for soil enhancement" of (www.purganic.com) . The list of minerals and trace elements in Pureganic Mineral Powder will open your eyes to all the minerals you've been missing. (See the frequently asked questions section, page 2.) The time has come to plant entire farms using m-state sprays and soils. I believe the results will be dramatically superior to anything chemical agriculture ever produced. Personally, I believe M-state minerals are the missing link in human health. M-state minerals are what can help humanity reach its true God- given potential. Dr. Patrick Flannigan has already proven that the simple addition of colloids can increase vitamin absorption by 500%. Imagine what would happen if everything we ate was full of the proper amount M-state and colloids!! One farmer reported growing ears of corn 22 inches long using water from a Living Water Machine. The use of living water and ormus products opens a whole new dimension in agriculture.

For starters, I believe the obesity rate would decline dramatically.

I believe that part of the overeating scenario is the body's quest for sufficient energy and hydration. These are terribly lacking in today's foods. In 1965, Dr. Nilo Cairo and A. Brinckmann came to the same conclusion as I did that colloidal gold was the one remedy against obesity (www.visionminerals.com/gold.htm).

Foods rich in M-state, such as grapes, deserve a larger role in the common diet. Grape plants have roots that can extend down 40 feet and gather more m-state minerals than nearly any other plant. This explains the "French Paradox", as to why the French have long life spans despite their very rich, fatty diets. **Concord grapes in particular have enough of the antioxidant resveratrol to inhibit the reproduction of the flu virus by 90%. If we could get a better picture of the M-state ingredients of grapes, it may be possible to create an effective countermeasure for the avian flu virus**. I believe that a doubling of human lifespan is possible solely through a complete understanding of the health benefits of M-state minerals. The Hunzas can do it, why can't we?

The bottom line on natural foods and herbs is that there is indeed an herbal or whole food remedy for nearly every disease or condition under the sun. Many have been used for thousands of years with no ill effects. I've provided a number of additional books in the bibliography section to assist the reader in this regard. You've all seen the impressive Madison Avenue ad campaigns for drugs on TV. Some guy comes on offering wonderful news that you can reduce your cholesterol level by over 30% just by taking their magic drug for $100 in cash. What they don't tell you is that you could do the same thing by eating an onion! Yeah an onion! Or garlic. The same story goes for just about every other miracle drug out there. There is a natural alternative that works as well without the side effects. Stressed out? Don't take a dangerous mind altering drug: eat an apple and detoxify. See your naturopathic physician. He can help you sort it all out. And finally, I believe that once more knowledge is gained about the daily requirements of Ormus metallic elements there will indeed be a revolution in growing practices and dietary consumption. A new dawn of "super foods" is about to rise and our medicine cabinet will look a whole lot different when they do. I'm talking about foods and medicines WITHOUT toxins that actually help, not kill, the patient. Haven't convinced you yet? Then men consider this: toxins and plastics can mimic estrogen and make your penis smaller. And you can get what my thirteen year old daughter calls, "man boobs". Plus you get fat of course. Are you convinced yet? I hope so.

THE PHILOSOPHERS STONE

Monatomic or Ormus (High Orbital spin rate) metallic elements may be nature's most bizarre, unusual, and ultimately most useful materials on the face of the Earth. While you may never have heard of Ormus (also spelled Ormes) materials or as it was called "The Philosophers Stone" by the ancients, without them you'd probably cease to exist. It has also been known as "manna from heaven", "the universal cure", and "the holy grail" to name a few. While gold is a perfect conductor of electricity, Ormus gold is a "super-conductor" of the highest magnitude. The super conducting ability of monatomic elements has any number of radical and fascinating applications.

The high orbital invisible "stealth elements "of gold and platinum group metals can do amazing things including a disappearing act into other dimensions. Just a partial list of discoveries will give an indication of future developments in metals refining and agriculture.

First of all, our very brain tissue itself is by dry weight, composed of 5% monatomic iridium and rhodium. The implications for creating a few geniuses or treating brain dysfunctions are immense. **Ormus iridium affects the pituitary gland in a way that reactivates the body's junk DNA and underused parts of the brain.** Feeling stupid today? Take a little iridium and rhodium and call me in the morning. Colloidal gold has been proven to raise I.Q. as much as 20 points in 30 days. Certainly the thing to have for finals week. White powdered gold (M-state) can be used to connect the "GOLDEN TRIANGLE" of the upper chakras and open THE CRYSTAL CAVE" of latent brain power and alleged "junk" DNA with incredible results (www.asc-alchemy.com).

Bristol Meyers Squibb found that when single ruthenium atoms are placed at each end of a short strand of DNA it becomes **10,000 times more conductive**! It becomes in effect a superconductor. The use of platinum, iridium and ruthenium atoms in the treatment of cancer, corrects the deformed cancer cells. **Monatomic gold and platinum group metals dismantle incorrect DNA and rebuilds the DNA again, correctly.** They activate the endocrine system and pineal gland in a way that heightens awareness and aptitude to extraordinary levels.

Increased melatonin from the pineal gland affects the immune system and heightens energy, stamina, physical tolerance levels, and sleep patterns". All of these bodily enhancements lead to heightened self-awareness, inner vision, psychic phenomena, and intuitive vision.

Ormus products have been used successfully to treat leukemia, AIDS and cancer. They've been used on MS, Lou Gehrig's Disease, MD, and even arthritis. They even get rid of KS (Karposi Sarcomas) **Ormus materials are so potent that a mere 2 mg injection raises white cell count from 2,500 to 6,500 in 2 hours. Stage 4 cancer patients who have taken Ormus materials orally were totally cancer free in 45 days.** The mass production of Ormus products would seem to have the potential to totally eliminate the current corrupt cancer industry. Which may explain why you haven't heard of them?

Although understanding why Ormus does what it does is a matter for conjecture among nuclear particle physicists and alchemists, the lower level formulas are not hard or expensive to make. In fact the wet methods can produce Ormus from rather ordinary sea water, well water, or even tap water for under $45.00. The Purganic website, (www.purganic.com) has Mr. Hudson's British and Australian patents, transcripts, interviews, thousands of pages of text and instruction on manufacture. Follow the links at The Alchemy Website (www.

levity.com/alchemy/texts.html) and you can download complete 12th century texts or order modern ones. **An "Ormus evaluation" of 140 products** can be found at: (www.pleiadian.org/products/allresult.php).

Alchemy means "higher science" and is the forerunner of the word chemistry. Alchemy is the missing key to the mystical experiences of Western religions and Western science. The "stone the builders rejected" is the foundation of Egyptian, Greek, Gnostic, Christian, Hebrew, and Islamic religions. In the East, manna or the Philosophers Stone is the means for creating the SOMA: THE ELIXIR OF IMMORTALITY. The Soma are actually hormonal secretions from the roof of one's mouth created by the activations of various latent glandular functions. To view an interview with a key player in the alchemy field enter the white gold website through the links at Purganic.com above. Then scroll down to the library and look for the interview.

The Egyptian Pharaohs were the first to use white gold powders for health and longevity. Then came the Greek philosophers in Alexandria, Egypt, with its great library, was a hot- bed of alchemists and learning. Adepts from all over the world traveled to Alexandria to learn its secrets.

One such group that knew the secrets of practical alchemy was the Essenes. Their monastery was located on the Dead Sea, which is a tremendous source of minerals and Ormus materials. The Dead Sea salts produce one of the highest concentrations of M-state gold. The precipitate contains approximately 70% gold and can be ordered from Ocean Manna (www.oceanmanna.com). The most well known Essene was of course Jesus the Nazarene. Jesus was a "Master of the Craft," not a master craftsman or carpenter. This I believe was a deliberate misconception, not a clerical error. A "Master of the Craft" is one who has mastered the art and science of alchemy and metallurgy. Jesus used (and possibly made) the ancient Egyptian white gold powder formulas as used by the pharaohs (www.thetruejesus.org). Jesus was a guardian of the ancient knowledge and therefore the scientific knowledge Jesus possessed was immense.

45

Mary Magdalene, the high priestess, and wife of Jesus was also an accomplished alchemist and apparently one of the first women to write a book on alchemy. She was known in France simply as Mary the Jewess. She was also an inventor, creating such things as the hot ash box, the dung box, and the double boiler still in use today (pg 70 Hendaye). After a long life of prayer and meditation in the caves south of Marseille, France she was interred in the chapel at Ile de Mary, France. (Gardener cites St. Maximus Monastery.)

Moslems throughout the world worship the ancient meteorite encased in the Kaaba at Mecca, Saudi Arabia. This sacred black stone is a piece of purplish red tektite. Meteorites and asteroids have a high concentration of nickel and iridium. It has been at the Kaaba since before the time of Abraham. However only a small portion of it remains embedded in the wall of the cube. Apparently the rest "went missing" after each rebuilding of the cube. I suspect it was refined into the various gold and platinum group metal powders and consumed and hence began the mystical traditions of Al-chemy that eventually became Islam via Mohammed.

Jesus was crucified and around 70 AD the Romans drove the Jews out of Jerusalem. The fledgling Christian sect moved primarily to France where it evolved into Gnostic and Cathar sects. The established Christian church persecuted them for over 1,200 years, killed untold numbers during the crusades, and then started the Inquisition. The mystical tradition of the family of the prophet Mohammed didn't fare much better and all except one of his descendents were murdered. Islam split into various factions, with the greatest secrets going completely underground. The most logical explanation for the persecution of both early Christians and Moslems was to contain and destroy the knowledge of how **"the way"** (ascension) is attained by spiritual and alchemical means.

Knowledge is the antidote to enslavement and therefore a threat to all authoritarian governments. What we commonly think of as names for the people in the bible are in actuality spiritual titles. "A Mary", "A Joseph", and "A Christ" are all titles given to individuals who have gained proficiency and knowledge of a certain degree.

These titles were also used to keep their true identities secret and therefore safe from persecution. What therefore is most relevant is how do we begin these studies? Without knowing where to begin it is difficult or impossible to attain "the Christ within" or **The Second Coming of Christ**. [23] It is this "Second Birth" that is truly important. That is why so much effort has been exerted to keep this knowledge under wraps.

Ironically, while the Christian Crusades were primarily a vehicle to destroy knowledge, exactly the opposite happened. The Knights Templar recovered not only the Ark of the Covenant, but the knowledge associated with it in regards to the manufacture of Ormus materials and metallurgy. Sir Laurence Gardener covers this extensively in his book: **LOST SECRETS OF THE SACRED ARK: REVELATIONS OF THE INCREDIBLE POWER OF GOLD** (www.graal.co.uk/lostsecrets.html) (This site also has a link for the major ormus manufacturers.) The Arabic conquerors of Spain also preserved for the West the ancient knowledge of Al-chemy and the knowledge of the Greeks. These same Arabic scholars were willing to share their knowledge and men of learning from all over Europe gravitated to Moslem Spain. The reintroduction of knowledge thus preserved led to the Gothic Revival of alchemy and eventually to the renaissance. Again, the "higher science" is emerging in the form of scientists seeking the many benefits of Ormus materials. As this knowledge emerges, it will transform our current civilization into a new Golden Age. All religious thought is based upon the same essential core truths as Universal law is the same for all. As the rains fall equally upon the just and the unjust so Universal law governs all.

Sufficient amounts of ancient knowledge and practices have survived in the East and in the West. The problem is, despite improved communications media, the left hand rarely knows of what the right hand is doing. As much of the ancient knowledge remains secret, there is a HUGE information gap between East and West.

The potential to eradicate disease totally is immense. Likewise the potential to create a new world economy, without booms and busts is also apparent. What currently prevents this is that "knowledge" is too compartmentalized and specialized and not in the public domain and awareness. Historically, whenever any new form of technological or philosophical outbreak is turned loose, society as a whole is transformed. The industrial revolution immediately comes to mind as it changed the entire world, as indeed every new major invention or concept does. That is why the "powers that be", try to keep all knowledge under wraps, so it doesn't break free from their control. No power can keep knowledge under wraps indefinitely. It will always seek to escape despite all the book burning and authoritarian governments of this world.

HEALTH'S MISSING LINK

I began my own investigations into AIDS and cancer treatments by studying aloe vera juice and acemannan. This product is currently marketed by **R-Pur Aloe 18X** and is made with the cold extract method to preserve the active ingredients. **Dr. Terry Pulse** of Grand Prairie, TX had conducted a clinical trial on AIDS patients and had achieved a 50% reversal rate. 81% showed immediate improvement. (www.aloe-info.nl/aids.htm) The first question that came to mind was, "Why only 50%?" And the second question was, "How does it work?" It took me a decade to find the answers to these simple questions. Dr. David Wheeler provided the answer to why it works. Aloe Vera has 2 active ingredients called mannose and galactose. These molecules enable immune system cells to communicate effectively. Dr. Wheeler created dry powdered forms of aloe vera called MPS GOLD 3X and MPS GOLD 100. This eliminates the need for preservatives or other non-active ingredients and therefore a more concentrated product. Dr. Wheeler is one of the few accessible doctors in the world who is experienced with aloe vera and M-Water. He is available for consultation by phone. (www.0disease.com/0dietary.html)

My friends and I began searching the world for cures. I interviewed some of the biggest names in research. A buddy in Lima, Peru got me on the right track. He told me that the herbalists at the

Amazon Herbal Remedy Center in Iquitos, Peru had developed effective treatments for AIDS and cancer. He was elated about this and so was I. Oddly, he went on to tell me that only herbs gathered near the rivers worked and that the exact same herbs gathered inland didn't work at all! Curiouser and curiouser! I suspected that it was the gold (M-state) and other minerals and colloids in the flowing river that provided the active ingredients. Several years later Sir Laurence Gardener wrote to me and gave me the tip that Bristol-Meyers-Squibb was testing M-state ruthenium to cure cancer. He sent this letter a couple of years before he published the information in his book about white powdered gold.

By 1996 8 major institutions were studying the effects of M-state (Ormus) materials (http://www.subtleenergies.com/ormus/health/health.htm) (See page 8) on abnormal cells, i.e. cancer.

These institutions are as follows:

1) Roswell Park Cancer Institute
2) National Cancer Institute
3) University of Illinois
4) Rutgers University
5) Merck and Co.
6) Biotechnology Institute of Oslo
7) Wayne State University
8) University of Wisconsin

So why all the sudden interest in M-state minerals? The answer is that the actual active "ingredients" in healing foods and several well known herbal cures are M-state minerals.

Aloe vera's acemannan is 90% rhodium. Chinese mushrooms have rhodium and iridium. Flax oil, almonds, apricots, grape juice, and watercress all have M-state rhodium and iridium. Carrots have rhodium only. Formulas like Essiac Tea, with sheep sorrel and slippery elm bark work because they contain rhodium and iridium. So does Vitali tea. Tahitian Noni juice, the sacred fruit of the Hawaiians, also contains Ormus. Edgar Cayce used to say that 2 almonds per day would keep cancer away. Guess he was right. (I used almond oil from the Cayce remedies to treat my diabetic girlfriend's feet. In about a month her feet went from cracked, bleeding and hideous to pink smooth baby's feet).

Gold and iridium seem to speed up the body's metabolism by about 40%.

The discovery of the presence of M-state minerals in known herbal cures began to shed some light on their healing abilities. Consequently research began on direct application of M-state minerals in treating patients with various diseases. The testing began with 2 basic M-state formulas, M-3 and C-11. A summary of the results of one researcher were subsequently published as, "**Health Effects of the ORMUS Elements** (www.bibliotecapleyades.net/ esp_ciencia_oro11.htm). As this is such a critical report, I've listed 2 locations for it. A great deal of work and substantiation needs to take place before these remedies can enter the marketplace en masse.

M-3 is made from mine tailings and it is balanced to contain 70% rhodium, 15% iridium and 15% gold. C-11 or M-11 contains 11 m-state minerals from a sea water source (http://www. subtleenergies.com/ormus/health/another.htm).

The results were quite amazing. AIDS patients recovered, Alzheimer's patients all went home after 30 days treatment, bipolar disorders responded well, 38 of 40 patients fully recovered from cancer, diabetes treated with C-11 and vanadium-chrome were treated 100% successfully, 6 patients with heart disease recovered and high blood pressure cases responded well. Other recoveries were noted in patients with lupus, multiple sclerosis, muscular dystrophy, and osteoporosis. Hepatitis C, liver disease, kidney problems and Lou Gehrig's disease also have been treated successfully. You can order M-3 (the white dove) and Sea 11 at: (www.oceanalchemy.com).

Lastly, "**most of the effects generally associated with aging: gray hair, wrinkles, etc. have been linked to copper deficiency. Copper deficiency is what kills most of us.**" I spoke with one researcher involved in this work and he told me that it takes approximately 1 year of m-state copper intake to reverse ageing. Needless to say I'll be trying it out myself! Old age doesn't work for me.

The only "bad" (sort of) news is that M-state platinum causes strong Anabuse type reactions to alcohol. If you drink alcohol while taking it, you'll get a hell of a hangover. I can personally confirm that spiritual development and alcohol don't mix. Just one beer and you get a hangover. Not to mention that you could fall out of your chair. So, if you're on the path, you can no longer drink anything stronger than weak wine. Fortunately wine has a good deal of M-state in it already.

At the present time we don't know how much Ormus or M-state minerals the human body really needs or how much is provided in our daily foods. Not enough testing has been done. There is no "daily minimum requirement" for Ormus materials as they haven't reached the mainstream research community. As the list of diseases apparently reversed or improved by Ormus materials is quite long it would appear that we are on the threshold of a major breakthrough in fundamental health concepts.

There are many different levels of products containing gold and platinum group metals. Not all are effective and great care must be taken to insure that no impurities such as lead or mercury used in the preparation. First are plain elements in their natural or base metal state. Expensive restaurants in Japan will sprinkle gold dust on your dinner for $800.00 and more, but metals in their base metal state aren't absorbable and it's simply a waste of money and gold. You get more usable M-state gold in a glass of cheap wine. Colloidal minerals have small particles and an electrical charge, so they are more absorbable. Colloidal gold and silver products can deliver a lot of benefits for the buck. However colloidal minerals aren't M-state or Ormus materials. Ormus materials as we've discussed are an entirely different state of matter and deliver massive amounts of energy compared to other elements. These too differ greatly in strength and preparation techniques. Generally speaking Ormus materials derived from plant and liquid sources are much weaker than Ormus derived from fire methods. As all M-state formulas are very powerful, it is recommended that new users start slow with the weaker liquid and plant derived sources and then gradually work up to stronger formulas. Plant and ocean derived Ormus formulas, diluted half strength, are ideal starters for small children and small animals. Depending on the company and formulas used, a 6 to 12 step plan is used to bring the body gradually up one octave in healing at a time over a 1-2 month period with each formula. This may result in an overall improvement in immune function from 1,000-1,500%. Formulas can be custom designed in various configurations, from M-3 to M-11, as per the goals of the user. Ascension Alchemy is particularly open to custom formula designs for deeper spiritual growth and healing. As the entire process may take anywhere from 6-12 months to complete one cycle of formulas, commitment is necessary. You may also cycle through the formulas again and again, as the effect is cumulative over time.

As I like to try the formulas I write about I choose ones from Ascension Alchemy, Ocean Alchemy, and Ambrosia Technology. I found all of their products to be excellent, but will relay my experience with Ambrosia Technology as it was the most recent and I kept a diary of my experiences (www.liquid-chi.com). One of the aspects I particularly like about this website is that it gives an assay for each product so you know exactly what you're getting with each level. It does take commitment to stick with the program and cycle through the entire product line in order to get the full benefit. The formulas should also be taken in the recommended order so the user can build up gradually to higher energy levels and octaves of healing.

As I've mentioned throughout this book, disease or disease patterns reside at their own specific frequency levels. As you work your way up through the formulas, you may eventually "hit" a frequency band with a latent weakness, energy block or predisposition to disease. **(See Appendix B to calculate how many hours of healing will be required to remove these).** When you hit one, you'll know it as the healing that occurs can be quite intense and profound. I have had several weak links in my body due to accidents and injuries suffered while in the Navy. I've knocked out all 33 discs in my back in a car accident, had a nearly fatal appendicitis attack, and have had all the "required" vaccines that one must get while in the military. Although Reiki saved my life in many respects, there was and still is much work to be done on my body to get it back to 100% functioning. When I saw the "VULCAN'S TREASURE" formula on the internet, I "knew" it was the one I needed. I had a reaction to just seeing the name and immediately ordered the product. Within a few days of taking it I experienced what I can only describe as a "body wave" healing in my stomach. A wave of energy, from side to side, went from my heart down my torso. I've experienced a lot of different forms of healing before, but never anything like this. On another day it seemed like my kidneys were loading up a computer program and spinning like a hard drive. Just clicking and churning away as it was storing bits of information. I also experienced a sharp electrical current going down a meridian in my chest and then taking a hard left 90% turn into my left kidney. During the month that I took Vulcan's Treasure, there has been healing throughout my body, the lower back and stomach especially. Some were painful of course, but it is a joy the next day. When you take Ormus products every day is a new adventure in healing, as you never know what is going to be healed on a particular day. The feeling of euphoria is wonderful also. I find I laugh deep and loud now, more so than ever before. As I progressed through levels 3 and 4 a number of miraculous events happened almost unnoticed. I realized one day that my lungs were clearer and I was breathing easier. The aches and pains in the joints were strangely gone. Towards the end of level four I apparently hit a number of blocks and they were painful to remove, especially when all my teeth were healed. After loosing "the battle of the bulge" for 20 years, my stomach is flattening out and working normally. My chronic fatigue is gone as well. I'm particularly looking forward to level five as this level uses Indium to balance the hormonal levels of the body. So it should be quite exciting. Everything seems different and I feel more alive. Once finished with the Ambrosia Technology regimen I will commence the Ascension Alchemy regimen. I expect it will take an entire year to complete the whole regimen. It's pretty hard to describe, so I can only say to experience it yourself. Even in a terminal hospice setting, Ormus products will greatly enhance the quality of life. I have never experienced more healing effects from any other method. I can't guarantee that you'll rise above the threshold of disease, but it's certainly a very powerful step forward. You'll have to follow your inner guidance to travel the rest of the journey.

A number of Ormus products contain the element Indium (#49) in the higher level formulas. As I was curious I tracked down the website of the discoverer of Indium as a health supplement (http://www.marketlaunchers.com/bonadio.html). First of all Indium has been found to raise average mineral uptake between 60-694%. In clinical studies with mice, Dr. Henry Schroeder, a research toxicologist, showed 42% less cancer and malignant tumors when an Indium supplement was given. Upon researching this subject further (www.liquid-chi.com/mannatonicNE.htm). I noticed that Indium is also noted for being useful in the elimination of addictions and normalization of body fat. Indium appears to work by normalizing 31 hormones and bringing them into balance. This in turn improves approximately 40 different common health problems. Improvements were shown in libido, energy, PMS, migraines, cancer, colds, Parkinson's, hypoglycemia, hair and skin conditions, high blood pressure, stamina, sleep, memory, ageing and AIDS. Mr. George Bonadio, the patent holder for the Indium refining process, states that he tested Indium with over 1,000 volunteers. I have noticed that several Ormus manufacturers now add Indium to their formulas for it's hormonal balancing effect. I cannot state that these claims are true, but I will test it out myself and report upon the results in later articles.

Currently there are over 800 scientists and laymen in the Ormus Group working on making knowledge of Ormus materials available to the public domain (www.subtleenergies.com). I believe a dramatic increase in personnel is needed and that exploration into Ormus materials and white powder gold needs to be a #1 world priority (www.whitepowdergold.com). Nothing else holds the promise of both preventing a world plague and at the same time jump starting the world economy into a new "golden Age" renaissance of discovery and progress. Only the creation of enlightened minds can create an enlightened leadership. If wisdom doesn't trickle down to the masses of humanity, they may become extinct.

The world is once again on the brink of extinction. Like Sodom and Gomorrah, if 10 good men can't be found, whole nations shall perish in the twinkling of an eye. The combination of Western alchemical tradition, combined with Eastern Vedic tradition can not only heal and transform the world but can also bring it back from the brink of destruction.

A combination of the best systems of East and West is what is needed to revitalize a sick, morally bankrupt, stressed and impoverished world. As all of this is created solely by ignorance, the cure is applied practical knowledge. As the general public is more attuned to sporting events, let's use the training of an olympic athlete or multi-million dollar professional as a concrete example. We would spare no expense on his care and training as the more our athlete wins, the more dollars he brings in. We could combine the following systems to create a superior athlete.

1) Yoga to strengthen the body and mind
2) Use the yogoda muscle strengthening system developed by P. Yogananda.
3) A bow flex machine would be used to give every muscle a good workout.
4) Japanese Reiki is used both to heal and to strengthen the body and mind.
5) Gold powders to increase strength, aid digestion and nutrient assimilation and promote healing.
6) Biodynamic foods and Perfect Science water for nutrition, energy, and waste and toxin removal.
7) The use of western computerized energy testing and movement analysis for the particular sport.
8) And last our athlete would be housed in a natural healthy building with no energy or chemical pollution of any kind.

I am absolutely certain superior athletes can be created and trained with such a combination of the best of East and West. So why can't the same approach be used for someone with AIDS or cancer?

Are we not worthy of the same care as our sports heroes? Are we not all the same in God's eyes? I believe we are.

SOUND The sounds we hear everyday are mostly taken for granted. But like all other forms of energy, sound can either heal or destroy depending upon its wavelengths and duration. Words themselves have an impact directly on our nervous systems. And the mind "believes" whatever you tell it repeatedly and acts accordingly. There you can program a positive or negative result simply with your words. The science of nuero-linguistic programming is a fascinating way of studying what words really mean and how to effect a positive, healthy life.

Music also can alter our mood, hormonal levels and stress levels. Inspired classical music is generally healing, while loud acid rock or heavy metal will make you deaf and destroy your immune system through stress. Acid rock is an appropriate name as the stress it causes can create an acidic imbalance in your body. This in turn creates an environment for cancer and other diseases. Inharmonious music will kill plants in a day or 2 while classical music will encourage their growth and strength. Acid Rock maintains drug addictions.

Chanting and singing are ancient methods of raising the vibratory level of the body. A good deep resonant chant will add structure to your cells and is therefore one step on the path to enlightenment. Monks don't just sit around and chant because they have nothing better to do! A mantra done in ancient languages, such as Sanskrit or Hebrew is considered more powerful than modern languages, as the ancient ones are Star languages. To be most effective an affirmation or prayer must be said 70 times a day to embed it firmly into your consciousness.

Sound has vastly more power than is recognized. For instance if you simulate the sounds and wavelengths of a thunderstorm the sound alone will clean the air and purify it, just as if a natural rainstorm had occurred.

Sound apparently has "healing activation codes" that are highly beneficial to the body. You can hear for yourself by visiting "The Amazing Background on the Sacred Mountain of Endwebu" and downloading a free 7 minute recording. Or by purchasing a 70 minute CD (http://www.merkaba.org/aids_babies.htm). I found the Jesus DNA test quite healing as well.

One ancient sacred mantra that I am allowed to share with you is: BA BA NA KE VA LUM. Its literal translation is: **LOVE IS THE ANSWER TO ALL THINGS.** You can use this especially in traffic. To transform yourself into a higher vibration, your mantra must be done all day long. Deep resonant mantras reverberate in your heart and you can really feel them working and building healing energy.

PART 4

ENERGY: THE GOOD, THE BAD, AND THE UGLY

Every energy source is a potential pathway to health and eventually enlightenment if used correctly.

Up until now we've mostly talked about beneficial forces of energy for healthful living and spiritual unfoldment. Indian Vedic architecture and Chinese Feng Shui deal with increasing the positive harmonious aspect of a home or workplace and diminishing the unhealthy, inharmonious forces of nature.

In 1879 Thomas Edison invented the light bulb and shortly thereafter the first hydroelectric plants were built to electrify homes. This was hailed as a great achievement at the time. Behind the scenes however was a raging battle over the health and safety issues of electricity. Edison maintained that only D/C was safe and that A/C was extremely dangerous for the human body to be exposed to. The big money interests were behind Tessla's and Westinghouse's inventions, A/C, and the benefits of large industrial capacity electricity. In short, there was money to be made! THEY lampooned Edison in the press as an old fool, although we know now that Edison was totally correct. A/C is dangerous! The cycles of A/C too closely mimic the heart. The magnetic currents created can disrupt the activity of the aura and if left untreated can create an environment for degenerative diseases such as cancer and diabetes. As medical science doesn't often recognize energy "pollution" for what it is, the patient is sent home to die with a pain pill.

Helmut Ziehe became interested in the effects of electricity when he developed diabetes and a host of other health problems. He eventually discovered that the magnetic forces created by A/C are especially harmful during sleep, when the body defenses are down. So he put a switch on his fuse box and began to turn off the current to his bedroom during the night. He replaced his electric clock with a battery powered one. Within a few months, his diabetes and other health complications vanished. The culprit was apparently the electric clock near his head.

Helmut Ziehe became so fascinated with what he had discovered he founded the Bau-Biology Institute and developed a course of study to certify home "inspectors" who could ferret out the harmful situations in a home. (www.bau-biologieusa.com)

Billionaire developer Donald Trump has embraced the principles of Feng Shui in his buildings, but he is the exception. Many thousands of offices are now classified as "sick buildings" and have a syndrome named after them. However for most the home is the most dangerous place you can be. If you are ill, check out **The Natural House Book**, [24] Bau-biology, or Feng Shui. Natural log cabins are a perfect alternative because they "breathe" and don't build up harmful electrical charges. Hospitals in particular may be the most dangerous places on the planet. A hot springs, spa type environment with log cabin cottages would provide a more nearly ideal environment for patients to recuperate.

SCIENCE OF MIND

Our consciousness is what makes us who we are. We have the ability to join the consciousness of the creator. Our thoughts echo throughout the universe and last forever. Every thought is recorded in the Akashic record. Our subconscious remembers everything we tell it (nuero-linguistic programming). The power of our thoughts and <u>the focus of our intentions actually change the structure of matter</u>. Our very thoughts create an electromagnetic field that structures matter according to our thought patterns. This is hard to visualize, so let me direct you to the amazing work of Japanese photographer Masaru Emoto (<u>www.masaru-emoto.net</u>). Our minds can structure water into a beautiful snowflake design if we think of love and thankfulness (<u>www.hado.net</u>). Or it can structure water into a glob of sewage if we fill our minds with hate. Those who are complete masters of the Earth plane can create matter with their thoughts alone. It is the unlimited power of the mind and its ability to structure matter that accounts for spontaneous healing and miraculous remissions of disease. Russian experiments have proven that mind alone can restructure DNA. The golden spheres of light and the pure love of the creator ARE the fabric of the universe. And prayer is our voice. We are immortal souls.

HANDS OF LIGHT

The universe is in perfect harmony, but at times we are out of balance with it and hence out of balance with ourselves. At such times we need healing to regain our inherent harmonious state.

Contrary to the opinion of some, healing didn't stop occurring 2,000 years ago. It has always been present as a gift to those who serve others. ANYONE can learn to become a healer. It is only a matter of intent and dedication. And the purer a channel of love you are, the more power to heal you will receive. It takes only three weekends to learn to become a healer and receive it's blessings to you for the rest of your life.

I began with Japanese Reiki in the tradition of Dr Usui (1865-1926) (<u>www.reiki-healing.com</u>) and within the first hour of instruction I was able to heal others. When I was initiated into the second degree of Reiki by Suzanne Pletcher, it felt as a bolt of lightning hit me in the head. It felt like a spark four inches long. I was so charged up, my hands kept me awake at night. Eventually I completed level III and after daily treatment upon myself I was again able to live a normal life, instead of years of pain that I had endured previously due to several car accidents. Reiki saved my life!!

There are many amazing things about Reiki energy. It seems to have a mind of its own and heals "the weakest link". I took Reiki with the hope of healing my damaged neck and back (due to whiplash) and discs did indeed jump back into place on their own. But my hearing improved 100% within the first 15 minutes of treatment. And internal organs such as kidneys and such heated up like hot coals burning out of my body and then completely healed also. I had no idea anything else was even wrong. Having learned this lesson I spent a year working on each section of my body, sometimes for a couple of hours per day. I regained the strength in my arms and legs. And adverse energy patterns passed out of my feet like gout exiting the body. Reiki also seems to increase fertility dramatically, so be prepared.

When I treat others I see the energy patterns of illness, just like an X-ray. Sometimes I see a past life situation or a genetic memory. I was lying in bed one day doing Reiki when I felt an incredible pain go through my left thigh. I could "see" a past life lance going through my leg. In my case the lance had been a real lance, thrown by someone in the Trojan War, I felt, as I viewed the battle. I lost this battle as I was first hit with the lance in the leg and then the arrows and swords everywhere. The pain in the leg was excruciating (in the present tense) until it heated up with healing energy and passed safely out my foot. Quite an experience and the slide show of the battle was fascinating. My leg was stronger after this past life lance had been removed by Reiki healing. Depictions of past life lances are to be found in Barbara Brennan's **Hands of Light**.

Reiki can be very powerful and heal the seemingly impossible. Suzanne Pletcher told us the story of her sensei who was run over by a logging truck while driving her VW beetle. Her car was crushed flat like a pancake, her ribs and hips were broken. She was torn up quite badly and was in a coma for 3 days. Her students all came and performed a **Reiki marathon** with dozens of people treating her by the hour. In a month she was walking around with only a slight limp and no evidence of being injured.

After doing Reiki for over a decade I began training in Sacred Merkaba. We believe these teachings are the same that Christ taught 2,000 years ago. I can only say that Sacred Merkaba is incredibly powerful (www.merkaba.org). Each level feels like a 1,000 % increase in healing energy. It is so powerful I've had to rest daily for a six month period to readjust my body to the new energetic level. **It takes only a couple of weekends to learn the first two levels and heal yourself and others.**

Upon reaching each new energetic level, the process of treating and healing the entire body begins over again. After completing 2 levels of Sacred Merkaba training I was able to heal a disc in my back by simply putting 1 hand on my chest. I plan to take the 11 day intensive training course in South Africa at the healing center as soon as I can and then teach Sacred Merkaba to others. A list of instructors in various parts of the world is posted on the above site. You may also receive free "trinity healing" treatments from the world wide list of practitioners. A gift of a teddy bear for AIDS Orphans is the suggested donation.

Healing often feels like disease in reverse. Instead of disease coming in, it's going out! In Reiki we have a description of the process called "achy-Reiki". The body aches or feels pain as the adverse energy finds it way out of the body. Charging up a formerly unused meridian of energy is like a shock along a wire and it can really smart. Over time more and more circuitry of the body is opened up. The longer you do energy work, the more capacity your body has to deliver it. Once a high capacity is developed you'll have "hot hands" and be able to deliver large amounts of healing energy and feel a prickly sensation in your hands. The beauty of Reiki and Sacred Merkaba is that you always have your hands with you. On a bus, plane, or train or in an emergency, all you have to do is give yourself a healing treatment. Placing your hands on each side of your neck and shoulder creates a warm healing current going down your spine. You may look like king Tut, but the energy is very healing for your spine and it goes all the way down to heal any hemorrhoids or other localized problems as well.

As you progress into spiritual maturity many changes occur over time. Your perceptions become more acute. Hearing, sense of smell, and awareness become more acute. I can only describe it as having the awareness of a hawk. Your psychic facilities emerge including clairvoyance and clairaudience. You may eventually develop "eyes that see" and "ears that hear". You can suddenly hear even the planets spinning through space. Even the music of the spheres may play in your ears. Illnesses you didn't even know you had become healed BEFORE they manifest. The energy from healers hands are believed to create more stem cells and therefore heal the patient from the inside out. The more you practice the longer you can maintain an enlightened state. Enlightenment is simply a state of bliss where you are in balance and harmony.

How does one achieve enlightenment and a pure state of health? The answer is simple, but the path is long.

Earlier in this article we spoke of the chakra system of seven major energy portals and over 144 minor ones. If any are damaged or torn we lose energy. If they are all open and flowing correctly we experience a greater degree of health and well being. This does not mean however that they are operating to their full potential. To achieve the full potential of our chakra system all the chakras must be joined together as one unit. They must be connected and then fully charged to full energetic capacity, like batteries connected in series. Traditionally this is called **Kundalini yoga**. This technique gradually raises the energy from the base of the spine and connects each chakra one by one until all are connected. This produces a chain reaction of energy like a nuclear reaction. This is why it has to be done SLOWLY to give the body time to adjust, adapt, and build the "circuitry" of the nervous system to handle it. The Kundalini force is routinely depicted as a coiled serpent at the base of the spine. A diagram of the return path of the Kundalini energy up the "'Tree of Life" can be found on page 274 of Jay Weidner's and Vincent Bridge's masterpiece: **THE MYSTERIES OF THE GREAT CROSS**

OF HENDAYE: ALCHEMY AND THE END OF TIME. [25] Or you may order a full color chakra chart from (www.crucible.org) for only $6.95. Go to "artwork" and then to charts to order. For a more in depth personal consultation on your astrological and alchemical influences, go to consultations at the above website.

Sometimes this energy is activated accidentally in an unprepared individual and the body circuitry becomes massively overwhelmed. This is labeled Kundalini psychosis, where the individual develops a (we hope) temporary insanity, until the energy is either dissipated or redirected by a Kundalini yoga master.

I mention this because I experienced an unplanned "Kundalini rising" myself. I was reading a book one night entitled: **The Return of the Serpents of Wisdom**. [26] When I read the part about the high priests of Egypt, I had the realization that I was one of them. I saw myself under instruction at the Great Pyramid of Giza and a lightning bolt of energy struck from the base of my spine to my heart. It was like having a heart attack and it took a few hours for me to compose myself and redirect the massive amount of energy.

PART 5

The Buddhists say we live lives of illusion. We are continuously directed by forces unseen and actions unknown to us. We are influenced by entities we can not see and are playing out scripts we don't remember writing. The greatest of these unseen and un-remembered scripts is called karma.

Karma is defined as the law of cause and effect. Or as the Bible says, "you reap what you sow." No deed is forgotten by the soul, although you may have no conscious memory of it. During the process of gaining spiritual maturity you may begin to remember past life incidents and their bearing upon your current life situation. Every soul's goal on Earth is to pass through every sign of the zodiac, and you may live a life on every continent, every race, and every religion to balance your soul's energy. If in this life you have hatred for any particular race, group, or nationality you merely hate a part of yourself. Once you "know yourself" you can use your past life experiences to help you in this incarnation. When Jesus spoke of **"THE WAY,"** he was referring to the way back to God via the process known as ascension. To accomplish this return trip, all past karma must be cleared. P. Yogananda stated that if one waits for the natural evolution of the soul it would take **A MILLION YEARS** to clear out all one's negative karma. However, with preparation in Kriya yoga, it could be "cleared" in as little as three years working (meditation) full time eight hours per day. This is an ancient natural way to accomplish ascension.

In Ascension Alchemy's "Golden Seed" manuscript it was stated that it is practical to recognize 12 major chakras and that each one has 12 depths. They call it a 12X12 matrix which is related to all the other chakras and their counterparts in the brain and endocrine system. Therefore the process of clearing out all the energy blockages of the chakras, called **samskaras** in Indian Sanskrit, is a much bigger job than it would appear to be on the surface. If the minor 144 chakras have the same 12 depths, were talking about another 1,728 energy "sites" on the human hard drive to clean out. Whew! Lots of work!!

For sake of simplicity let's assume we have nearly a couple thousand energy storage sites. The next obvious question is, "What is stored there?" The answer is: "Everything you've ever experienced in your past lives and present life." Every anger, every love, good deed, bad deed, and every emotion in between strong enough to register. This can amount to a lot of "stuff" or "psychic garbage," or Karma. Whatever you want to call it, it's there. Clairvoyants have told me that there can be as many as 300,000 to 600,000 "events" recorded on that hard drive of your energy system. Except for special talents developed in previous lives, all the other garbage needs to be deleted!! The psychic garbage just clogs up your life, dampens it, and prevents you from living a fuller, freer life. That is why you see yoga masters smiling all the time: they've completed the lengthy task of removing all that karmic junk from their unconscious memories. Experiencing disease is "the hard way" of removing karma. On the other hand removing just 1 layer of a karmic or energy blockage is NOT a total cure. It may appear to be when you are in remission from something, but it isn't complete. To be complete all the levels have to be cleared. And being "cured" of cancer, only to find yourself hit by a bus a year later doesn't really do the trick either. There is no karmic "free lunch". Either you do the spiritual work and remove all the blocks or you suffer the consequences. A weekly hour in church just isn't going to cut it.

I personally have found that all the various healing tools, such as Reiki, Merkaba, and Ormus formulas bring the blockages and memories to the surface where they can be seen and dealt with effectively. It's not an easy task to give up your cherished assumptions about yourself, but knowing yourself is a lot better than waiting a million years for natural evolution to take place. When you begin to see yourself for what you truly are, then many of your current relationships will suddenly make sense. If for instance you murdered your spouse in a previous life, it becomes apparent why she is treating you like a whipped dog now! So you married an ax murdering psychopath, OK, time to heal this situation and move on. End of story there. Gaining some clairvoyance and insight adds countless benefits to your life. When you "see" what is "really" going on in the actions of yourself and others the whole world changes. And life gets better.

Use of specifically formulated M-state or Ormus powders can be very beneficial to the ascension process in synchronizing the brain waves. Ascension Alchemy (www.asc-alchemy.com/asc.html) has a product line made to assist in this process. I believe a basic problem in the West is that we are conditioned to expect everything to overwhelm us. We cultivate a culture of biggest, fastest, best, etc. and therefore have some problems dealing with more subtle energy. It just doesn't have enough of a kick to it. The addition of an appropriate amount of M-state products and mineral supplements will provide a sufficient strength that it will register in the body and mind. It will be readily apparent that healing and consciousness changing is occurring and this will encourage the beginning student to continue with the work. It has been my experience that a good gold powder will add what seems like an additional 1000% increase in healing energy and it will make it easier to get into those difficult spots you may not have been able to get into with other forms of healing. Be sure to heal the entire body at each level before going on to another level. When you feel you've reached a sort of plateau and nothing is happening, then it is time to go to the next one. Don't be in a rush as toxins have to be removed and many blockages have to be removed at each level.

We tend to think of diseases, accidents and misfortunes as terrible things. However in reality these events are either spiritual tests or karmic balancing. Once we pass our tests, we can move on. Negative thoughts about ourselves or others tend to settle in the weakest parts of our bodies. Negativity creates acidity in the body and creates a fertile environment for diseases such as cancer. Love, healing and forgiveness will reverse the condition. Remember, Love is the answer to all things. This is how "alleged" spontaneous remission occurs. If you've learned the lesson, forgiven yourself, and move on then there is no longer any need to experience "dis-ease."

Diseases are not what they appear to be at all! Another example is autism. Parents whose children have this disease are quite upset and at a loss for what to do. Most of us are firmly grounded into 3rd dimensional reality. Those with autism are not. There is no separation between their left and right brain and therefore they spend their time in the 6th dimensional angelic reality. An autistic person is in constant prayer with the angelic realms and this excess energy causes a great deal of pain to the brain. This is why autistic children bang their heads on the wall, trying to relieve the pressure. A trained trinity healer can gradually bring the child back down into 3rd dimensional reality and a more nearly normal life. Again, once the spiritual lesson is achieved, there is no longer any need for the condition. The world is not what it appears to be. We are only ignorant of its true working and natural laws. Restoring the physical and neglecting the spiritual and mental aspects of "dis-ease" only invites a return of the illness or something worse.

To appreciate fully the spiritual and emotional causes of most disease, I suggest purchasing Gary Smith's excellent books on Autism and Cancer treatments using the ancient healing secrets of Jesus. This can be found at: (www.thetruejesus.org). Scroll down to books and tapes and enter there.

In the final analysis it can be shown in the realm of particle physics that "disease" is the logical "wavelength" created by negative emotions. It is the defense mechanism by the body to protect itself from adverse conditions and thoughts. As in the case of a cancerous tumor, the body tries to protect itself by enclosing the adverse energy and trying to push it someplace else if possible. This is hard to comprehend without actually seeing the process in a graphic format. Researcher **Dan Winter** has completed some fascinating research in this regard in a work entitled, **"SACRED GEOMETRY AND COHERENT EMOTIONS."** This can be ordered on CDs from the following website: (www.soulinvitations.com/indexdw.html).

The work of Nobel Prize winner Albert Szent-Gyorgyi (1893-1986) and Dan Winter suggest that there is a mathematecics of life and death centered upon what the Greeks called **THE GOLDEN MEAN** or Pii (.618). A healthy cell is elongated and proportional to the Golden Mean, whereas a cancerous cell has a lower electrical charge and a rounded shape. The wavelength structure of the emotions called LOVE and COMPASSION emanating from the heart chakra can realign the cells back to the GOLDEN MEAN. Therefore there is both an emotional and mathematical component to health that has been lost to the public domain. Cancer is thus the mathematical opposite of the Golden Mean wave fraction. See "**Is Embedding a Mathematical Opposite to Cancer as Wave Fractionation** (www.soulinvitation.com/cancer/index.html)." Historical literature is full of accounts of Jesus, Mohammed and various saints performing acts of compassion and humility. True masters perform acts of compassion to maintain their harmonic wavelength or octave upon the golden mean of love.

Our true potential as human beings is immortality itself. If toxins are removed perfectly, and our energy is balanced perfectly, then we should be able to live forever. Few however chose this path. Nearly all get lost in an ever descending realm of denser matter, materiality and sensuality. One who did choose the path of immortality is known simply as Babaji or father. He was born in the 3rd century AD and is therefore nearly 1,700 years old. He acquired this mastery at an early age using the **18 Siddha Kriya Yoga Tradition.** [27] Babaji currently resides in the Himalayas, but his disciples are available for instruction in many locations including Quebec, Canada. (www.babaji.ca) This is a discipline you can investigate for yourself by either correspondence courses or physical initiation into kriya yoga. The yoga siddha research centre is currently gathering hundreds of ancient documents for translation and publication in electronic format. I am currently investigating whether any ancient siddha yoga medical texts still exist in the collections of the Indian government and private collections.

The more common form of "immortal yogi" doesn't actually physically live forever. Rather upon reaching a perfected state and fulfillment of personal spiritual tasks assigned, the master CONSCIOUSLY moves on to another life in another vehicle (body). He is called immortal in that he retains all the knowledge and capabilities of his former lives with no break in knowledge. In this case, physical death is a choice, not a necessity. A true master has mastered matter, life and death. He can leave the body or ascend whenever he desires to do so. Masters often elect to die by assuming the karma of their disciples. This is the greatest gift.

I mention all this not to sway anyone to a particular religion or belief system. I've attempted to use traditions from several modalities as examples. All religions will soon pass away anyway. My intent is to convey to the reader that life in perfect health and perfect consciousness is possible. Raising one's energy above the threshold of disease is a means of doing so as countless others have done before you. It's nothing new. All healing is self-healing. When the student is ready a teacher will appear! Which path you choose to walk is totally up to you.

When I began this book I promised to develop a Universal Theory of Disease, Rejuvenation and Immortality. I've attempted to weave it all into a comprehensive whole with some non-technical background so everyone can understand my meaning. To insure all the pieces of the puzzle aren't lost in a forest of words I feel it is best to summarize the main points at this time:

The Universal Theory of Disease, Rejuvenation and Immortality states that:

1) There is a direct correlation among cellular structure and longevity, immunity, mental functioning and spiritual capacity. This cellular structure can be measured by the corresponding bond angles and facets of the resultant stages or degrees of crystalline cellular structure attained. The greater the capacity of the crystalline cellular structure, as measured in MHz, the greater the immunity, longevity

mental and spiritual capacity.

2) Cells are immortal if all toxins are removed and the cells are routinely replenished.

3) The human body is composed of cells in an electromagnetic matrix and vibrates at its own unique frequency. At birth, cells are highly structured in the energy matrix. Loss of electromagnetic structure during ageing creates an environment for disease. All disease manifests in unstructured cells.

4) Each disease can only live in a specific frequency range. For example cancer is 42 MHz. Therefore diseases can be destroyed in 3 different ways. Energy to the diseased cell can be lowered, depriving it of its food and thereby starving it out (such as by Cancell). A disease can be destroyed by an equal and opposite current and shattered like glass using Rife technology or healing. Or disease can be terminated by raising the frequency of the affected area (providing structure) well above the frequency of the disease in question. All diseases tend to occur in lower frequency ranges.

5) Therefore adding structure to the energy matrix in the area of disease eliminates it. Only unstructured cells are open to disease.

6) As the cells gain structure, their crystalline shape and bonding angles change. This allows the cells to store and process more and more energy. For illustrative purposes the threshold of disease is assumed to be 75 MHz. This is an arbitrarily chosen value that may be in fact significantly higher or lower. As all diseases reside in the lower frequencies, once this level of energetic, mental and spiritual attainment is reached, the body is therefore immune to all diseases of this planet.

7) Cells that obtain their ultimate potential, a 72 pointed star

configuration, may become incorruptible or immortal. Even upon death of the body (if the vehicle chooses to die) the cells retain their perfect crystalline nature and do not deteriorate for centuries. For illustrative purposes the threshold of immortality is assumed to be at 90 MHz. This is a totally arbitrary number. Again, it may be significantly higher or lower. This state can be achieved only by one who has overcome all past life karmic situations and spiritual tests. These individuals are known as masters (of life and death) or "the pure ones." In India they are called simply "the Rishis" or seers from the word dris meaning "to see." In the West they are called "One Who Knows," which has the same meaning.

8) The work of Nobel Prize winner Albert Szent-Gyorgyi and Dan Winter suggests that there is a mathematetics of life and death centered upon what the Greeks called "**The Golden Mean**" or Pii (.618). A healthy cell is elongated and proportional to the Golden Mean, whereas a cancerous cell has a lower electrical charge and rounded shape. The wavelength structure of the emotions called LOVE and COMPASSION emanating from the heart chakra can realign the cells back to the Golden Mean. Therefore there is both an emotional and a mathematical component to health that has been lost to the public domain. Cancer is thus the mathematical opposite of the Golden Mean wave fraction.

9) Dr. Monte Greenawalt, DC, the founder of Foot Levelers, employs 30 research scientists. "His scientists have invented an algorithm that can diagnose and recognize prostate cancer and breast cancer non-invasively with 100% accuracy." He thinks we will eventually be able to detect cancer anywhere in the body non-invasively (Cracking the Millionaire Code, pg 78).

The Institute of HeartMath, is an innovative nonprofit research and education organization founded by Doc Childre. Using HeartMath technology, it is possible to bring the heart and brain into synchronization. Doc Childre has discovered that the electromagnetic strength of the heart is 5,000 times more powerful than that of the brain. He has mapped the effects of a loving and appreciative heart and their profound impact on health in several technical medical papers (www.heartmath.org).

10) To summarize, a three-step process is required to balance human health. First is the removal of toxins to create a cellular structure capable of storing more energy. Dr. Herbert Shelton, the originator of the field of orthopathy and principles of natural hygiene, maintained that the universal cause of all disease is toxemia (See http://www.drbass.com/disease-cure.html). (Several free downloads of Dr. Shelton's books are available at this address). Secondly, energy must be maximized from all available sources with particular emphasis on healing and expanding the energy matrix. And finally as the bodily, mental and spiritual circuitry rises above 90 MHz, access to higher dimensional knowledge and redirection of energy is acquired.

It is helpful to conceptualize the workings of the human body with a simple formula:

(E-T) x C= L

E = Energy

T = Toxins

C = Consciousness

L = Longevity

Understanding the dynamics of energy, toxins and consciousness opens the pathways to the human potential of immortality.

SO, WHERE ARE WE NOW?

It has taken me a couple of decades to discover some of the basic laws contained in the Universal Theory of Disease. And there may be others I have overlooked. Some adjustments may be necessary. In order to prove that a theory holds validity, it is essential to obtain independent confirmation by other researchers. If the same results can't be replicated by others, then it doesn't hold water. I was therefore overjoyed to find the research of psychiatrist and spiritual teacher David Hawkins published by Jasmuheen in Australia (www.selfempowermentacademy.com.au/htm/cia-education.asp). Hawkins embarked on an in-depth 20 year study to "calibrate levels of human consciousness." He published his results in 2002 in a book entitled **Power Vs Force**. Jasmuheen, a Taoist Master, used his 1-1,000 point kinesiology testing system and tested an additional 500 volunteers. Her work was in turn published in 2005 in her book **The Law of Love** (pages 222-229). The results of these two studies provide a road map of human consciousness that closely match those contained in my Universal Theory. "The threshold of immortality" may be a direct hit, while my proposed "threshold of disease" may be about twelve points off. It would appear that every emotion and hence every disease has a frequency range of it's own. If you follow the path of love and compassion, the next step is freedom from all disease. As Jasmuheen's observations and testing add a great wealth to human consciousness, I have added a brief summation of her findings here. As you'll see Jasmuheen went off the chart to show us where miracles begin.

200 & below Negative emotions of anger, fear, guilt or shame

200	Beginning energy of truth and integrity
310	Calibration for hope and optimism
400	Reason and Wisdom
500	Energy of love

540	Energy of Joy
635	Establishment of a Disease Free Existence
637	Ageing Free System begins
668	Food free and able to live on prana
777	Fluid free existence
909	Physical Immortality
1367	Dematerialization and re-materialization
1450	Ability to Perform "Classic Miracles"

So, the question remains, where are we now? According to Hawkins' research 78% of people test below **200**, while mass consciousness as a whole calibrates at **207**.

As of 2004, only 6% of the worlds' population calibrated at over **500**. Only 1 person in 10 million calibrated at over **600**. As the 635 and above range is where we see the threshold of disease begin, we can instantly see that humanity's current ability to survive is less than your odds of winning the lottery! The good news is that those who "live in love" and calibrate over **700** counterbalance the energy of 700 million people. Therefore we urgently need the 2,000 light workers who have volunteered for this task of raising the vibratory level of humanity to "wake up" and step forward at this time. Now is the time.

I propose that a great step forward in human evolution could be achieved simply by retesting subjects using an electronic scale such as measurement in MHz. This would provide a permanent, indisputable, scientific road map to human consciousness that anyone who chooses to could follow. As the Buddha said, "Ignorance is the root cause of all misery." Knowledge, wisdom and power are the antidotes to ignorance. No one would climb Mt. Everest, if no one knew it was there. Once it was discovered, mapped and conquered it became a popular destination. The same is true of the mountain of "the self." If everyone knew where it was, had a map of it, knew how to climb it and to conqueror it, then it would be successfully climbed more frequently to the benefit of mass consciousness.

In the final analysis, consciousness and health are intimately related. Healing can not begin at a level below 200 as that level is the beginning of truth. As on our MHz scale, **all major diseases live below 200 in the ranges of fear, hate, anger, and guilt**. Climbing the ladder back out to truth is the way out. Using the science of applied kinesiology we can test every meridian of energy and follow it back to each specific organ where negative energy patterns are stored. This can be used as a preventive measure to find energy blockages before they turn into a disease. If disease is already manifest, knowing the mental cause of it can lead to a more rapid healing process and possibly spontaneous remission in some cases. Louise L. Hay's famous little book entitled **Heal Your Body** contains a list of nearly 400 common diseases, their mental cause and affirmations to create new thought patterns.

Earnest Holmes, founder of Religious Science, used to say: "change your attitude, change your life." Levels of consciousness can be mixed. Perhaps there is that one nagging problem area in your life that needs attention and answers? Kinesiology is one method to get rapid accurate answers to the questions in your life. Hard wiring yourself into the collective universal mind is a way to access not only healing but "data." Great geniuses of history like Einstein, Freud, Newton and Descartes calibrate at **499**. Healers and saints calibrate at **540**. Choosing a path of joy, compassion and unconditional love will put anyone in the "zone" of love at **500**. Hawkins states that, **"In an energy field of 600 and above almost anything will heal**." Even the most desperate conditions can and have been healed. As in the example of Alcoholics Anonymous, accessing the power of truth has healed millions of lives.

"A total transformation of consciousness and liberation from the entrainment of lower attractor fields and a sudden emergence into higher awareness" is not only possible but common. What is needed is the willingness to lay the groundwork through prayer, study and meditation. You have the will, you have the power to become a healer. Study a course such as **A Course in Miracles**, or select a guru or teacher who is right for you. It is possible to raise consciousness by hundreds of points, instead of the usual 5 per lifetime. Edgar Cayce and Earnest Holmes frequently stated that there is no such thing as an incurable disease. Only you have the power to create the circumstances of your life. You can find the answers. David Hawkins book, **Power Vs Force** is a tremendous tool for transformation. I use it on a daily basis and recommend it highly. It provides a map of consciousness that makes the path to joy shorter.

The rules for using behavioral kinesiology are pretty simple and straightforward. First of all the person(s) testing must be above a calibration of **200**, the level of truth. Secondly all questions must be posed as a declaration of fact. Always begin by asking if, "I have permission to make inquiry into (topic) Yes/No." And you can ask the question several ways to check on its validity and to add depth to it. Either the one or two person method can be used. The two-person method tests the response using the resistance of the arm. The one person method uses only the thumb and forefinger of each hand to make an interlocked "O." If you test strong or YES the "O" remains unbroken and if you test "weak" or NO the fingers come apart.

As you are connected to the "universal databank" you may ask ANYTHING except questions about the future. Remember, the future is not yet formed. You can ask if your wife is cheating. Whether your stocks are overvalued. Is your favorite politician a dirty rotten liar? You can test for your personal calibration which is a real eye opener. And perhaps more importantly, you can calibrate everyone you know and every person you see on the Internet. Avoid anyone below 200 like the plague and as frequently as possible stay with those of your level. I especially like to test past life questions. If you have an attraction to a certain area of the world or a certain time period start asking questions about the period you lived in. Keep dividing the country in halves and narrow down the location where you used to live. Do a little research about the area and time frame and ask intelligent questions about what you used to do and who you were in that lifetime. If you find you were someone notable, read up on that life and further refine your questions. Eventually you may get to where you'll discover a half dozen past lives and see if there is a pattern to your incarnations and to those close to you. If there is a pattern you may ask if this is your life's work this time around. Is there something you're here to learn or to teach someone else? What is your source of inspiration in this life? Finding a photograph of yourself from a past life is great. Finding your previous autobiography is pretty fabulous as well. It gives an indication of your present strengths and weaknesses. You can draw upon your strengths to assist you in your present life. Standing upon your grave from 2,500 years ago is pretty exciting also. I've done it! Finding out your spouse was a Nazi tank commander in her past life explains a lot of things too. Time to call a good divorce lawyer! Using behavioral kinesiology is life changing. Use it to get well and to improve the quality of your relationships. It really works. You'll never have to accept a lie again. Just test and find out. You'll be amazed at what you find out.

Lastly, when you measure your spiritual calibration you may discover it isn't where you'd like it to be. No problem. There is a simple solution. Fake it until you make it! If you want to be a CEO, then just act like one. Create companies, make deals, and do the things CEOs do. Eventually, if you stick with it, your reality will catch up to your desires. There are several now famous Hollywood actors and actresses who were rejected hundreds of times, before they made it. The same is true in all walks of life. Spirituality is no exception to the rule. If you've read this far you're probably well above the average. However the path to enlightenment can be long. If you test anywhere below 500 just remember that a healer tests at 540. Learn Reiki or any other healing modality that feels right for you. The more you heal others, the more you heal yourself. It will change your worldview and your life. Becoming a master is a matter of intent. It doesn't matter where you start; only where you end up. I know at least one immortal who began as a Reiki master. If your ultimate goal is enlightenment and peace, just envision yourself with "the crown of enlightenment" on your head. This crown is made of bright sparkling diamonds shimmering with every color of the rainbow. If you can't hold this vision for long, then try just one big diamond. This is the Buddhist "diamond path" to enlightenment. You can also "walk through" the diamond to travel any place you'd care to see. I find it useful to perform this visualization when I wake up in the morning to get my day off to a good start and to deal with the stress we all encounter. It helps you stay "in the zone" of peace and harmony. Radiating peace and love is a choice you are free to make at any time. The worse your present situation is, the more it is required. You can make quantum leaps of hundreds of points in one lifetime if you are committed to doing so. Just reading **Power Vs Force** and committing it to memory may be worth an average of 35 points.

Part 6

I have been researching health, disease and comparative religions for the past 25 years. Back in 1989 everything in my life suddenly stopped. My wife left, then my job vanished, I got a new job and a girlfriend and then they both vanished. I found myself virtually broke, homeless, and alone. I started to house-set for a friend in an apartment with lovely Buddhist tapestries and good energy. I decided to be Zen about my sudden circumstances in life and stop and ask the universe what to do with myself. I felt that God was trying to get my attention and he certainly did.

I had learned from **Science of Mind** (www.religiousscience. org) that prosperity results from producing something the world really needs. Therefore I asked **"What does the world really need that I can provide?"** The answer was: "The world needs a cure for AIDS and cancer." Quite frankly I was at first surprised and then shocked by this answer. I didn't feel I was capable of the task or worthy of the job. So I decided to meditate upon it for 100 days. Everyday I walked down the hill to Fairmont Park in Philadelphia and sat on a rock overlooking the Wissahickon Creek as apparently some mystic master had done before me. Everyday the answer was the same, "proceed." Then I'd walk down the rest of the hill to the Valley Green Inn and have lunch where George Washington used to dine and ponder the future. Everyday I began to research different cures for AIDS and cancer. I had no preconceived idea of where the trail would lead, but I began the task on faith alone. One day, while sitting upon "my rock" overlooking the creek, an entire herd of deer gathered around me to graze. Quite a miraculous event inside a park in one of the country's largest cities. It was a wonderful sign I was on the right track and for the next 15 years I took every night job I could so I could read, study and research. I originally typed up half of a book entitled: THE AIDS REPORT: SUPPRESSED CURES FOR AIDS AND CANCER. I eventually discovered a greater theme, "the nature of all disease." And I decided that it would be wiser to focus on the solution rather than the problem. Of course the muck-raking journalist within me couldn't resist a few jabs. When I saw Drumvalo's article on perfect science water I felt that the last piece of the puzzle had arrived and that the time to share this information was now. Also, I felt compelled to add additional information about Earth Changes and Ormus. I've tried to blaze a trail wide enough and mark it well enough that anyone can follow it. However walking this path is totally up to you. All healing is self healing. All discovery is self discovery. Like the old gospel song says: "No one can do it for you."

It is said that all the events in our lives are either spiritual tests or karmic events. During the next 30 years, as the **END TIMES** unfold in more rapid profusion, there will be more than enough spiritual tests for everyone. Many will not pass, but will gain some valuable experience nonetheless. Someone once said that bad news comes in threes. The three biggest challenges will be: 1) The planned world-wide economic depression, 2) WWIII and 3) dramatic pole shifts and Earth changes where most of the Earth's surface will sink underwater to renew itself. (And cleanse the blood upon it.)

I have come forward at this time because being forewarned gives everyone the opportunity to be forearmed. Unfortunately, there is little time left to prepare.

THE BIG DIP

The world-wide economic meltdown will create catastrophic unemployment of 66.6% across the board. (Satanists like to sign their work). It will be higher in some places and in some categories. Over 70% of millionaires will be broke. The unemployed will be hard pressed to find food and shelter. If you know any of the arts of self- healing you won't have to worry about your health insurance. And opportunities for food and shelter will manifest, via the law of attraction. This is a case where all will reap what they have sown, both literally and karmically.

Edgar Cayce prophesized that "the big dip" (stock market crash) would occur in the spring of 2005; May and June would be periods of violent social upheaval; and that those with the means to do so would be wise to spend the summer in Canada. Maybe the 2005 prediction was just a typo, but the crash is long overdue. Gary Smith, a descendant of Joseph Smith, who founded the Mormon Church, has stated that **the Mark of the Beast will be visible by April 26th, Plus 40, 2006**. This event is astrological, where 2 dragon shaped constellations cross indicating the final countdown has begun. This would seem to indicate a lot of global negative events. I don't have a crystal ball, and I don't know exactly when "the crash" will occur. But I do know after 5 years of economic research that it is inevitable. It is wise to be prepared. 20 acres and a mule are infinitely better than giving control over your life to ANY government. You can eat a mule but you can't eat promises. **The poor are the plaything of the wicked**. And if you grow your own food it will taste a lot better without the 30,000 chemicals in it. Growing your own food is also an opportunity for spiritual advancement. I will eventually publish additional financial newsletters via my own website called **"Highlander Press"** to keep everyone abreast of situations before they unfold. The cost of accessing the site will be approximately $99/year, but will be free to those who donate to my disease research foundation or Aids Babies and Orphans (www.merkaba.org) or (www.aidsbabies.org).

WORLD WAR III

Warfare itself is nothing new. As long as there have been inhabitants on the planet there has been warfare. The first two world wars were planned events to bring about political and economic changes favorable to an eventual world takeover by the banking elite. That takeover only needs a WWIII to attempt its mission of what Hitler called "the final solution." According to Nostradamus, the 3rd anti-Christ will wage war for 28.5 years until he is destroyed by mother Earth. He'll catch the big wave so to speak. The good news is that the forces of light win. The bad news is that nearly 6 billion people may loose their lives unless the consciousness of the planet changes. The date for the beginning of WWIII encoded into the Old Testament is 2006 and is called "Mr. Bush's War." The new and improved "anti-Christ" is supposedly waiting for the call in his home in the suburbs outside London. A drawing of him is included in **Conversations with Nostradamus, Vol II.,** [28] along with a blow-by-blow description of WWIII. I can not attest that any of these items are true, but I believe in being prepared.

EARTH CHANGES

The Earth, like humans, has the ability to heal itself. It does this by earthquakes, tidal waves, volcanic eruptions, and by putting whole continents under water. You can view the predictions of Nostradamus at: (www.baproducts.com/cannon.htm). Another set of great maps are the I AM AMERICA maps from the ascended masters as given to Lori and Lenard Toye (www.iamamerica.com). Water washes away negative energy, particularly "battle energy," blood and pollution. The equation is very simple, the more blood, negative energy, and pollution there is, the more surface area that must be healed by Earth changes. It's that simple. **Everything that happens is a reflection of consciousness and it's interaction with the Earth**. All the repressed creativity of humanity has to go somewhere. When it is released by Earth changes, you won't want to be around. Edgar Cayce always used to say that "the future is as yet unformed." What DOES happen is a choice of freewill and how consciousness is either changed or not changed. For instance the Ascended Masters have said that either the people in the Middle East can learn to love each other or they can all die together. The choice is up to them. This goes for everyone else as well. All of the bloodshed on the Earth is like a pack of fleas fighting over the dog. It doesn't make much sense to me.

Nostradamus told us that only 250 million people would survive the next 30 years UNLESS consciousness changes. He didn't break the death toll down into categories of disease, starvation, war, or Earth changes. I however believe as many as half could be killed by warfare due to the use of biological weapons as this is likely to occur first. Biological weapons can kill as many people as an atomic bomb, but do it for the same cost as a six pack of beer. That's the difference. The problem is of course that once this Pandora's Box of plagues is open, there is no way to get them back into the box. That is why I have come forward at this time to inform the world that the spiritually mature individuals who desire to do so can attain an energy level above the threshold of disease and become naturally immune to all diseases of this world. It does take time, effort, expense, discomfort, and most of all discipline to learn. Now would be a good time to begin. Time is running out.

EARTH UNDER FIRE

There has been a great deal of speculation as to when and how the Great Earth Changes will commence (www.knowledge.co.uk/sis/resource.htm). The religious traditions of the West are founded on the eventual end of the world and the Last Judgment. After reading many thousands of pages on this subject I believe that the chronicles of the ancient Greeks hold the first key to understanding what is to come in the very near future. Plato and Herodotus tell us that the higher civilizations of the Earth were destroyed **"AT THE USUAL INTERVAL" by a** (microwave) **stream from heaven**. The interval between destructions is still in dispute as to whether it is 3,600 years, 13,000 years or 26,000 years (a great year according to the Mayans.) As the great year is completed on December 20 or 23rd 2012, we don't have long to wait to see which, if any, theory is correct. [29] Warning of impending cataclysm is seen in the form of a massive amount of comets and a "new" sun. The Hopi Indians refer to it as the Blue Star Spirit. The Egyptians called it the all-destroying eye of Re. This Blue Star, shining like 1,000 suns, may be a gigantic burst of microwave energy. LaViolette's **EARTH UNDER FIRE** [30] goes into great detail as to what happens when a **GALACTIC SUPERWAVE** crosses the path of Earth on its great cycle. A cosmic dust storm sweeps across the universe and blocks out the sun creating a flash-freeze. As the cosmic dust disrupts the workings of the sun and clogs up its energy, the sun eventually reacts with a violent explosion of its corona to blow the dust off. So what eventually occurs is a collision of the sun's explosive energy output with that of the galactic superwave. The resulting pole shifts, tidal waves, high winds, and extreme weather easily destroy MOST life on Earth. **The biggest problem is that the cataclysm is dual in nature. First there is a Great Winter and later the universe is consumed in Fire**. The whole process from start to finish may take up to 1,000 years (the 1,000 years of peace?) and then the cycle begins again. The enigmatic alchemist Fulcanelli believed that only the elite, **"the children of Elias,"** would survive and renew mankind. The "children of Elias" are described as those who have transformed themselves, i.e. created a perfect diamond body. These elite who developed the circuitry to handle the challenges of humanity "at the crossroads" may be the deciding factor whether humanity survives or not. The countdown begins when astrologically the dragons cross in the sky revealing the image of the Beast of the Apocalypse. [31] We've seen on TV (hurricane Katrina) how much chaos is created when the water level rises only 20 feet. Imagine what will occur when it rises 3,000 or more feet! As Roy Schneider said in the movie Jaws, "We're going to need a bigger boat!" My own personal guidance tells me that East Tennessee is the safest area in the USA when the time comes.

CENTERS OF LIGHT

My associate, David S. Devor (www.projectmind.org), originated the Project Mind concept. His stated goal is to gather the best minds in the world and train them in expanded consciousness. Then they would be able to solve some of the world's many inherent problems. I would like to apply this concept to medicine and permanently "crack" the nature of disease. What would happen if an Alan Dershowitz and "the dream team" were turned loose on cracking disease? It would spell the end for disease. In David's own eloquent words, here is how it would work:

"I am seeking scientists, so obsessed with their theories that, given special conditions that are the proprietary art of Project Mind, they will generate contemplation of unprecedented intensity such that their whole bodies will become Minds. I mean, literally, that every cell of their bodies will actively participate in higher mind, creative vision permitting the routine production of scientific breakthroughs.

Once the Project Mind method is accepted, it will proliferate in scientific institutions worldwide as more and more scientists allow themselves the intensity that for the pioneers of Accelerated Thought will be life or at least sanity threatening. In this way, matter, in a few short years, will be totally elucidated or, in other words, fully conquered. So you could characterize Project Mind as a "Mind Tank" rather than a think tank. This is the first of two original concepts of Project Mind.

The second is that all things, being formed by the same subatomic constituents, will become interchangeable so that things like sand and seawater, to which we are all totally indifferent, will be interchangeable with all other things including luxury items, expensive medicines, i.e. anything and everything. The result will be that, because of this interchangeability, we will become as indifferent to all material things as we are, today, to sand and seawater.

Unable to covet anything material, the only objects of our desires will be spiritual and thus we will all, without exception, awaken to an exclusively metaphysical existence whether we wish to or not. This will result in the rapid development of our, until now, vestigial extrasensory powers such as telepathy, prescience, and telekinesis etc.

Universal consensus as to the spiritual nature of reality will enable us to begin working on the true purpose of Creation, the coordinated, universal spiritual work of unifying all of existence into one conscious vessel worthy of face-to-face communion with the Creator."

To date hundreds of $ billions have been spent on cancer research alone with few or no results. The problem is that it is not in the financial interests of the drug industry to allow any cures to come to market although there are dozens or more available. To bring existing cures to market, and to establish once and for all the true nature of disease, a totally independent research foundation is needed. Therefore I am establishing **THE INDEPENDENT DISEASE RESEARCH FOUNDATION**. We will research 1) existing cures, 2) work to develop new cures, 3) bring cures to market, 4) develop improved agricultural techniques to promote health and enlightenment. 5) And train healers in Reiki and Sacred Merkaba. It is our goal to promote "Centers of Light" instead of hospitals. True health can not be separated from spiritual unfoldment, because lasting health is the end result of spiritual unfoldment. Those who would like to contribute research or volunteer your skills, please contact me at: fregol@bellsouth.net . To the fullest extent possible I'll test most remedies on myself before recommending them to anyone. I'll also try to accomplish our fundraising in the least painful ways possible. I may use a 5,000 product gift catalog for instance where the proceeds benefit the organization. I have decided to add a vitamin and mineral line. You may order directly from my website at: (www.dontforgettotakeyourvitamins.com/frego13358). This site is very educational and The Greatest Vitamin in the World is "scientifically designed to nutritionally support your body." As I personally believe in capitalism, there won't be any $1,000 spaghetti dinners with our foundation. None at all. Instead, you could EARN a $5,000 bonus selling vitamins that benefit us. Up to you.

As I've stated, a great deal of travel will be necessary to accomplish our goals. Therefore I'll be adding a travel franchise to our mix of products. Instead of getting micro waved spaghetti for a $1,000 donation, why not get 5 FREE Caribbean cruises annually and a 50% discount on all your travel needs for just a little more? (you'd pay room and port taxes only on your package) And if you love this type of business, you can start your own and make a six figure income. Why not make a donation that pays you back? Or gives you free Disney tickets and accommodations? Works for me. Who likes stuffy fund raisers anyway? Boring! If you believe in capitalism as I do, then let's be capitalists! If you believe in innovation, then let's be innovative in everything we do! Time is running out. We'll have to experiment and see which methods of fundraising are most cost-effective and bring the greatest benefit to all.

Most of the innovative doctors and inventors have been driven from the USA by Big Brother and have ended up in "medical havens" such as Tijuana, Mexico and occasionally the Bahamas. Even there the long arm of big pharma closes them down and kicks them out. Those who have stayed in alternative facilities in Tijuana have been pleasantly surprised by the difference in attitude. Instead of going someplace to die, it was more like a festival and a welcome home reunion combined. Their stay in Mexico was a celebration of life! Patients were happy and involved instead of being pushed through a medical assembly line that kicked them out after a few days.

A true Center of Light is like a "healing resort" where everyone comes to heal and have a good time while doing it. An oasis of love filled with a full spectrum of holistic doctors, healers, medical intuitives (www.drjudithorloff.com), yoga masters, natural foods, herbal remedies, healing waters and animals for the children. Patients come not only to heal but to be educated on transforming themselves and their health. There are no magic bullets here, only spiritual work. There aren't many clinics like this in the world. One I would recommend is **The Tree of Life Rejuvenation Center** run by Dr. Gabriel Cousins (www.treeoflife.nu). If you can't get to one, then start a healing circle of your own right where you are! Learn to become a healer and keep expanding your circle. Teach others. Grow a garden. Take charge. All you need is a majority of one.

The role of the Centers of Light needs to be greatly expanded. A great deal more can be done with the new tools and knowledge at our disposal. A rural Canadian farm setting with a minimum 15 acres of land and log cabin offices and living quarters would be an ideal start for our planned **Independent Disease Research Foundation** headquarters. I've located an ideal property in Nova Scotia near the town of Hawkesbury for under $10,000 USD. A 238 acre farm is currently available in the area for only $44,500 Canadian dollars and would be appropriate for larger scale agricultural research. I've also had a vision of a somewhat novel building for a healing training center: a circular building resting upon 4 great pillars. A library would line the outer rim.

A great deal of traveling will be required to complete the necessary research. A suitable 4X4, RV, or other modes of transportation for myself and our staff will be required. Once non-profit corporations are set up in the USA and Canada, project supporters will be able to donate funds, cars, trucks, planes, boats, computers, office equipment, and supplies as a tax deductible contribution. Like a bee going from flower to flower pollinating the garden, I plan to travel as frequently as possible to network with other healing centers and share our combined research and ideas. Working together we can raise the bar to a higher level and more lives can be saved. As soon as our website is up and running we'll keep you informed with regular installments and articles. Until then look for new articles on The Rumor Mill News Reading Room (www.rumormillnews.com). Welcome to the Winning Side!

The cost of getting one cure to market in the USA is approximately $840 million. The New World Mining System that I have developed could generate a gross of $1.5 billion annually and would take 5 years to establish. I created this system specifically to fund research into AIDS and cancer (and some archaeological research) I would be pleased to donate the necessary proceeds to the research foundation. Traditional mining methods can now also be employed as I believe Perfect Science Water is capable of totally neutralizing any wastes inherent in such systems. And crushed rock can be used for agricultural research. For more information about this method please read my article entitled, **"The Future of Gold Mining in the Post Depression Economy: Dig Gold or Dig Graves."** It can be found in the archives of the Rumor Mill News Agency Or go directly to: (http://www.rumormillnews.com/cgi-bin/archive.cgi?noframes;read=43395).

They say God gives each and every person a certain talent. He apparently gave me the gift of research. Now I would have preferred the "Tom Cruise" gene and a few $ million in cash if I had been consulted on the matter. But that isn't what I got (Just kidding, I know why I'm here). I've been a librarian since grade school and so far nothing has ever stumped me. Having cracked a few secrets of the Incas and Mayans, I concluded that the world didn't really need another historian and it would be best to apply what God gave me to do as Christ commanded: to **"heal the sick."** I sometimes go through 5,000 book titles in catalogs and let my intuition do the selection of what to read. When I feel a major migraine sort of pain, then I know that I've discovered a book of immense importance. Such was my feeling when I noticed **THE MYSTERIES OF THE GREAT CROSS OF HENDAYE: ALCHEMY AND THE END OF TIME**. If my third eye heats up or the top of my head heats up, then I know I've got a winner. When I do know a title of a book I want and can't find it, I've had books conveniently jump off the shelf for me at my feet. Somehow I always find the needle in the haystack even when there are 300,000 books in the warehouse. My friends call me "the bloodhound." For me every research task is like a detective story or spy thriller. I simply love the job.

When I wanted to take a Reiki course, the course moved to my street in Philadelphia. And there were a lot of streets in Philly. When I was on my way to Peru, a gentleman in the Miami airport told me of all the sunken lost cities in Lake Nicaragua, which I tracked down and published. When I've wanted to attend Sacred Merkaba classes, the check hit the door when I picked up the phone. Once when on a job in Ft. Lauderdale, I started singing the Outback Steakhouse jingle. So I listened to the call and went to the Outback. Sitting at the bar waiting for a table I had a meeting with a gentlemen creating an herbal AIDS treatment in Switzerland. Just last week while ordering lunch at the Jacksonville Naval Air Station a woman came over to me saying she was a psychic and that I should add medical intuitive Carolyn Myss to my list. Synchronistic events happen to me all the time (www.Myss.com). And I keep locating multi-billion dollar gold mines for sale. Apparently my ability to locate things doesn't just apply to books.

I will apply this same talent in finding the rest of the pieces of the puzzle of disease. I believe no one has found them for the simple reason that they looked in all the wrong places. Researchers love expensive toys and atomic accelerators and gadgets. With the exception of Rife's microscope and others, I feel the time would be better spent interviewing scientists, doctors, Essene Rabbis, Tibetan Medical llamas, Indian Ayurvedic masters, Chinese herbalists, Amazon shamans, or Chi Kung masters. Or checking out the Vatican library and the collection of ancient Tamil medical literature in India or digging in the caves around the Dead Sea. I believe history runs in cycles and therefore all basic human problems have not only occurred before, but have been solved before. I believe everything we need already exists. It is just a question of locating it and bringing it back. I am an Indiana Jones sort of guy and am ready to do the job. Whether the "job" takes me to Tibet, India, China, or to Shamans along the Amazon, I'm ready. Even New Jersey! I'm sure the universe will do its part and provide what info is needed at the proper time. With your help we will succeed. Welcome to the winning team.

CONCLUSION

William Shakespeare once remarked that "All the world's a stage and all the men and women merely players." Those who control the world theatre have a surprise ending planned. THEY intend to destroy the audience, the actors, the stage and the theatre. [32] In order to prevent this a new story line is desperately needed.

The bad guys think they have all the pieces neatly in place, so the world will fall in one big hostile takeover, like a game of dominoes. The obvious question is: "What if someone removed a few of the critical pieces?" Then the rest of the pieces wouldn't fall and mankind would escape enslavement.

Humanity has a choice of creating Hitler's New Man and accepting all the depravity that this entails or instead we could manifest a universal immortal, perfected man with a diamond body. You can sit on the couch, ride your Rascal into oblivion, or you can become a silent spiritual warrior. Unplugging yourself from the global control grid of the "octopus" only requires a majority of one. If you turn off the TV, unplug yourself from the grid, grow your own food, build your own home and heal yourself; no one will miss you except your doctor. But you'll know you've changed sides and reconnected with the life forces of the universe. Once you've learned to heal yourself, then teach 12 others. That is all that needs to be done over and over to change the consciousness of the world to a critical mass.

The powers of darkness have been working feverishly to hijack the planet to create their own personal fiefdom. They've used their computers to crunch every number, every reactive scenario, and track humanity's every move right down to the cellular level. What if humanity decided to transcend the problem instead of following the herd over a cliff? What if a new creative interactive story line was developed? A story line where the forces of light win! Welcome to the winning side!

So the problem is this: if the bad guys have calculated every reactive move of the global chess game, how can we win? The solution is pretty simple really when you think about it. Call in a ringer! The weakest link on a computer is the quality of the data. A computer can crunch numbers only within the parameters the programmers set for it. The bad guys have an Achilles heel, a weakness, a blind spot that can be exploited to maximum benefit. The forces of darkness can spiritually penetrate only six levels of reality or dimensions. They can not travel more than three levels above our three dimensional world. Six levels and they're finished. Evil by its very nature can not penetrate the highest dimensions of reality. Only the forces of love and light can travel to the 12th and 13 levels of reality. And what transpires there, all knowledge there, they haven't a clue. That is their blind spot and that is how we will defeat them. It is already happening in every area of life.

Jesus left us a road map to the higher dimensions in the Gospel of Mary Magdalene. Jesus said, "It is neither through the soul nor the spirit, but the nois (gnosis in Greek meaning knowing) between the two which sees the vision. There where is the nois, lies the treasure."[33]

The creativity, inventiveness, and right actions that Mary Magdalene exhibited are a Western spiritual model we can use to solve the problems of the tribulations to come. If, like Nostradamus, you have a clear vision (clairvoyance) of what the future will bring, you can head in the opposite direction. You have the time and opportunity to prepare to balance the situation. As Edgar Cayce said, "The future is not yet formed". Therefore, there is still time to rewrite the screenplay for this drama.

The Native American shaman Sun Bear used to say that if your philosophy doesn't grow corn, it's time to find a new one. The outlook, philosophy, religion and lifestyle you choose must be practical and scientific in light of what we expect the future events to be. The ability to raise one's immunity OVER the threshold of disease MUST take first consideration above all others. Increased physical and mental capacity play a major role in survival. The ability to endure great extremes of heat and cold are also very desirable skills. I've seen videos of Buddhist monks left in sub-zero temperatures with nothing but a loin cloth melt the snow and ice for 10 feet around themselves. Padmasambhava who helped establish Buddhism in Tibet melted the rock of his cave with his handprint as a symbol of his attainment of a diamond body. [34] I've read that a master can withstand temperatures of up to 2,400 degrees. Fire walking is a well known demonstration of this. Achievement of a diamond body structure has highly scientific and practical benefits at a moment in history when these attributes will be needed most. In ancient times every small town and hamlet in India had a Rishis to guide the people. India was then regarded as the most wealthy and wise country in the world. Nostradamus predicted that the elect who survive the coming changes would number only 250 million. It may be hard to believe but Nostradamus also predicted the use of "designer" biological weapons as the weapons of choice for use in WWIII. He specifically mentioned viruses that would kill males only and sterilize females. I believe that diligently working towards crossing the threshold of immunity is a very timely thing to do. None of us knows the hour and the time these events could occur. And if enough people should "awake" to their true nature, then a spiritual paradigm shift would occur to mitigate such dire predictions of the future. Either way, **perfecting your mind and body is a way to put yourself on "God's Schindler's list"** and to assist others.

Our current civilization bears the seeds of its own destruction. In the atomic age we are all aware of this. Fortunately, we also possess all the tools of our own salvation. Never before have all the tools for spiritual and physical advancement been so readily available. You don't have to ride a smelly camel 5,000 miles to Tibet or India to seek enlightenment. You can even begin your journey into enlightenment by correspondence course (www.yogananda-srf.org). Or you can check yourself into Yogaville in the Blue Ridge Mountains (www.yogaville.org). Fast planes, ships, trains, cars, make mobility easy by comparison. Phones and the internet make communications instantaneous. You can purchase products that all the wealth of the kings of antiquity couldn't obtain. So what are you waiting for? When the student is ready, a master will appear. The choice is up to you. **God's plan hinges upon people of service and industry to raise the mass consciousness of humanity to the next evolutionary level**.

EZE 33:6 BUT IF THE WATCHMAN SEES THE SWORD COMING AND DOES NOT BLOW THE TRUMPET TO WARN THE PEOPLE AND THE SWORD COMES AND TAKES THE LIFE OF ONE OF THEM, THAT MAN WILL BE TAKEN AWAY BECAUSE OF HIS SIN, BUT I WILL HOLD THE WATCHMAN ACCOUNTABLE FOR HIS BLOOD.

THOSE WHO HAVE EARS LET THEM HEAR.

In the light of God's unconditional love,

Lawrence F. Frego,

Reiki Master & Sacred Merkaba "Trinity" Healer

October 2nd, 2005

Appendix A

	Aids Patients	Cancer Patients
1) Toxins/Heavy Metals	10%	10%
2) Deficiencies	4%	3%
3) Mental Negativity	3%	3%
4) O_2/Ozone Deficiencies	17%	16%
5) H_2O, Hydration Issues	5%	4%
6) Bau-Biology/ Mal-Electrical Issues	13%	11%
7) Emotional Stress	3%	1%
8) Genetics	1%	4%
9) Diet	4%	5%
10) Exercise, lack of	24%	23%
11) Spiritual/Karmic Factors	3%	3%
12) Ormus Metals Deficiency	11%	15%
13) Sleep Deficiency	2%	2%

It seems that works of art are never totally finished. There is always something that could have been added, deleted, or improved. Leonardo Da Vinci carried the Mona Lisa around with him for over twenty years, but never got around to finishing it. Such is the case with this volume: there is always another discovery to be found, another cure, or a great insight lurking just around the corner of the conscious mind.

This hasty addition came about due to another experiment with behavioral kinesiology. I just can't seem to help finding more and more uses for it, as you'll see in book two. I got the brilliant idea one day to make a chart of the top ten health factors for a sick friend. As usual the chart greatly exceed my expectations. I believe that "diseases" get complicated and difficult to unravel as they build up layer upon layer. As the pile of symptoms gets higher and higher, it is difficult to see what was at the bottom as the root cause. Therefore I made a big list of all the various factors and using behavioral kinesiology came up with a percentage of involvement for each one. As the first chart went so well, I did another one for a friend with a cancerous brain tumor. Then it dawned on me that it would be extremely useful to have a chart or profile contrasting the average AIDS and cancer patients. The results were incredible for three reasons:

(1. They are almost identical.

(2. Oxygen and exercise deficiencies just jumped off the page at 41 and 38 percent. This trail led me to an unexpected discovery.

(3. Ormus deficiencies also were very notable at 11 and 15 percent. Ormus elements are normally found in natural sea salts, but not necessarily in refined salts. It turns out the role of salts in the body is much higher than one would imagine. It is a totally essential mineral that determines the hydration of the cells.

The problem with insights such as these is that they develop into even deeper mysteries. They open up another whole can of worms begging an answer. While it may be easy to conclude that modern industrial workers don't exercise enough, the simple answer just doesn't cut it. The practice of refining salt might explain that once again vital nutrients have been discarded at the expense of our health. Nothing new there as this happens all the time in man's futile attempt to improve on Mother Nature. But where the hell did all the oxygen go? Is it just a question of exercise or is there a more sinister reason? I believe there is!

WATER THAT KILLS

The answer to these problems may lie in the fact that most water delivery systems were built before World War 1. They weren't designed to handle modern pollutants such as benzene, arsenic, pesticides, or radioactive particles. Most of the pollutants we have to deal with today weren't even around ninety years ago. According to the Natural Resources Defense Council (http://www.nrdc.org/water/drinking/uscities.asp) nineteen major US cities have unsafe drinking water. Despite numerous clean water and safe drinking water laws, it is still millions of dollars cheaper simply to lie to the public. It is an issue no one wants to bring up as the solution would break the bank of cities already faltering on the brink of bankruptcy. In short the true condition of the water supply is one of America's dirty little secrets. Public water systems were NEVER designed to be one hundred percent safe. Ninety percent of public water goes for other uses such as agriculture, manufacturing, and firefighting. It would be totally uneconomical to make all water safe, when only ten percent goes into homes. The inconvenient truth is that each home should have its own water purification system. Homeowners have a false sense of security supported by a false bill of goods. If you really knew what was in your water you'd never drink it again. Ignorance is not bliss, it is a disease waiting to happen.

Even if your municipality has the newest reverse osmosis filtration plant, the water still has to go through old pipes and must kill 650 different nasty organisms. To do this municipalities use massive amounts of chlorine. It kills most germs and bacteria, but tastes like cow dung. It also hardens arteries; destroys proteins; irritates skin and sinus conditions; and aggravates asthma, allergies and respiratory problems. Chloroform is a powerful by-product of chlorination and causes excessive free radical formation (accelerated ageing) and mutation of normal cells. It causes cholesterol to oxidize. It's a known carcinogen. Another chlorine by-product is DCA or dichloro acedic acid. It alters cholesterol metabolism and has been shown to cause liver cancer in lab animals. The last chlorinated acid is MX, and is known to cause genetic mutations that can lead to cancer growth. All in all chlorinated water is the direct cause of nine percent of all bladder cancers, and fifteen percent of all rectal cancers in the US. Tap water should come with a warning label!

Even if you don't drink chlorinated tap water, your daily shower will give you the same dose of chlorine as if you drank eight glasses of it. Chlorine is absorbed through your skin and chlorine gas is absorbed through your lungs. The reason fans are required in bathrooms is to remove the chlorine gas before it becomes too dangerous. And who decides how much is too dangerous?

You can test the amount of chlorine in your tap water with a simple, inexpensive swimming pool test kit. Generally you will find that your household water has two to three times the recommended dosage for a swimming pool! You can prove the absorption of chlorine by filling two small glasses with tap water. Put your fingers in one glass and leave them there for three minutes. Then test both glasses with your pool test kit. The control glass will test positive for chlorine and the one that had your fingers in it will not. Your skin absorbed it all in only three minutes. The average customers' shower lasts ten minutes, so do the math.

I briefly worked for a water filtration company and conducted these tests in customers' homes. I never tested one that didn't have a high level of chlorine. I tested my own home and found out that it was just as bad as everyone else's! In the summer months germs and bacteria bloom in the warmer water. Therefore, the chlorine content is greatly increased, often to an intolerable level that smells like rotten eggs.

So where did all the oxygen go? I believe it reacts with chlorine and is lost to the bloodstream. Chlorine is highly reactive. This hypothesis would explain the complications with respiratory difficulties already observed. There are many thousands of scientific papers on the adverse effects of chlorine on river and pond life and their oxygen levels. Somewhere buried in these thousands of papers, I bet there are some on the effects of chlorine on the oxygen levels in the blood stream. I'm sure there is one in there somewhere, I just haven't found it yet. Respiratory difficulty and chlorine are a smoking gun, now we just have to find the rest of the body of evidence.

The bottom line is that the adverse effects of chlorine are high and a simple home water system starts at less than $500.00 at Wal-Mart. Better systems cost a lot more. If you are building a new home I recommend a top of the line system as part of the equity of your home. To read about the benefits of the latest systems with NASA spin-off technology see the following website (http://www.Aquasafeusa.com/).

WATER CURES

Water and salt are two of the most common compounds on Earth and perhaps the most under-appreciated. Most people would agree that chronic pain, rheumatoid arthritis, stress, depression, high blood pressure, high cholesterol, excess body weight, asthma, allergies and cancer are primarily caused by poor diet. According to the late Dr. Fereydoon Batmanghelidj, they'd be wrong! According to Dr. B, "You are not sick, you are thirsty."

Dr. B has written an amazing story of his discovery of the healing power of water. He was born in Iran in 1931 and educated in Scotland at the Fettes School and at London University. He quietly practiced medicine in his native Iran until 1979 when he was imprisoned and sentenced to death during the Iranian Revolution (the overthrow of the Shaw of Iran). It was while in prison that Dr. B discovered the healing power of water when he prescribed one glass of water to a fellow prisoner dying of acute stomach pain. He went on to cure over 3,000 cases of ulcers with his water cure. He was pardoned due to his work and discoveries. He later escaped to the United States.

Dr. B's discoveries on the healing effects of water while in prison began his life's work. Upon arriving in the United States he conducted extensive research about the mechanisms of water in the body. He established The Foundation for the Simple in Medicine, published his findings in medical journals and lectured to health professionals. His attempts to interest the medical lobby and the AMA were unsuccessful. There wasn't much interest in a healing method the public could have for free and that could potentially disrupt billion in profits. Dr. B decided after hitting the stone wall of establishment medicine that he would write a book and take his message about water and salt directly to the people. His first volume was **Your Body's Many Cries for Water**. It sold over a million copies. Five other volumes followed and are available directly from Tagman Press (www.tagman-press.com) or his website. Dr. B didn't mince any words about his findings. He clearly stated that water cures – drugs kill!

Dr. B made a number of startling findings that run contrary to popular medical opinion (http://www.watercure.com). He believed that the entire scientific paradigm about water was totally false and potentially fatal. The scientific community believed that water was essentially just a vehicle that active ingredients floated in. **Dr. B. discovered that water was actively involved in every bodily process and <u>even generated it's own electrical current</u>**. In often complex interfaces with the nuero-transmitter receptors and nerves of the body, water regulates the functions of the body. Lack of water or dehydration inevitably leads to disease. In very clear and concise language Dr. B describes the flow of water in the body, it's locks, dams, valves and the rather miraculous way it interacts. He explained the intricate survival mechanisms of the water system hard-wired into our DNA to survive draught. A number of aches, pains, and potentially fatal maladies are signals of thirst and dehydration. The body attempts to stay alive by using a severe water rationing mechanism, cutting off water from non-essential areas and causing pain, but saving critical life functions. Once this hits home, a whole new dimension of the healing potential of water and salt emerge! Who would have thought that water could be such fascinating stuff?

Dr. B tells how to treat the root cause of dyspeptic pain, stress and depression, high blood pressure, higher blood cholesterol, excess body weight, asthma and allergies. He sheds new light on cancer and AIDS. He tells how either the river rises or the bridge must be lowered to get the job done. Each process is a survival mechanism to compensate for lack of water in the system and to direct it to essential areas to maintain life.

Before proceeding to look at three of the most common conditions affecting health today in the Western world, I feel it necessary to divulge the secret root cause of all the aforementioned disorders. Someone once said that assumption is the mother of all screw-ups. Three false assumptions are responsible for untold millions of deaths and incalculable pain and suffering. The first false assumption we've already talked about: water is not a lifeless conveyor belt of materials, but **a generator of hydroelectric power**. This is one the main reasons for the rampant rise of what is labeled **chronic fatigue**. Most of us would never have guessed that one.

False assumption number two is one hundreds of millions of people make every day. Even exceptionally educated health conscious individuals fall into this fatal assumption. The health of the industrialized world is such a mess because we have all assumed that all liquids that contain water act like water. All liquids are NOT the same. **Assuming that <u>coffee, tea, soda, and alcohol</u> all do the same job as water can be fatal. These beverages lead to dehydration: they deplete the water reserves of the body**! Yeah- they do exactly the opposite of what most people think they do! I made this mistake myself while working at my ex-wife's dry cleaners and was surprised to see a cholesterol reading of 380! With long-term use of liquids other than water disease creeps in like a thief in the night. Your first warning could be dropping dead from a heart attack. It happens! The body is at least seventy percent water and needs eight to ten eight oz. glasses per day to maintain its reserve. The more you weigh, the more water you need. An easy test to perform is to take a urine sample and look at the color. If it is very dark yellow to orange, you're severely dehydrated. If your urine is clear to very light yellow, then you're hydrated. You can easily perform this visual check daily to be sure you're OK.

The last deadly assumption is that salt is a dangerous compound. Yes, too much of it could be, but the problem is most people don't get enough to regulate the proper storage of water in the body and become dehydrated. Half a teaspoon of sea salt a day will normally suffice to get your body back to normal. Larger persons need more. By monitoring your urine color, blood pressure, cholesterol levels, and weight you'll find out where you are. You can do all of these at home with periodic checkups and a full test panel with your doctor at regular intervals. Men have a built-in barometer in regard to these levels. If a man's metabolism is in a serious state of dehydration erectile dysfunction can result. Conversely once the body is rehydrated hardness improves dramatically (33).

Unfortunately fifteen billion gallons of soda are consumed annually. The average use among soda drinkers is 500 cans a year. Diet sodas contain aspartame and have over 92 different side effects. The one of the most unexpected revelations is that diet sodas make you fat! Dr. B explains this irony in detail. Most sodas contain generous amounts of caffeine and this can lead to high blood pressure, higher cholesterol, birth defects and some cancers. Plus there is the added bonus of benzene. Sodas are a sweet, tasty "Love Canal" of hazards and the highest source of calories most people consume. Long term use of beverages other than water result in a fat, burnt-out body. It is as simple as that. Now we can take a look at our top three conditions and take a look at the simple physics behind the conditions.

The body regulates blood pressure by opening and closing valves and increasing or decreasing their aperture. When there isn't enough fluid (water) to fill all the space allotted the aperture is decreased to increase the pressure. Otherwise gases could separate from the blood leading to "gas locks." Sounds fatal doesn't it? If enough water can't be squeezed from inside and outside the cells, then capillaries in less active areas are shut down. Sufficient water, salt, and exercise keep the water management system balanced and everything flowing properly. Conventional blood pressure medicines are diuretics that get rid of some of the sodium (salt), making the body more dehydrated.

Cholesterol is a whipping boy for many ills in the body, but it is just doing its vital job of maintaining normal cell functions. When the body has little water, the liver secretes cholesterol, a natural clay-like substance that clogs up the cell membranes. It does this as a survival mechanism to stop water loss of vital reserves. Dr. B. calls cholesterol part of the cell survival system. If the proper amount of water is taken, especially before we eat, then cholesterol won't be activated.

You have seen the impressive cholesterol-lowering drugs advertised on TV. As these powerful statin drugs treat a symptom and not the cause, the short list of side effects runs about nineteen pages. Personally I consider dropping dead from heart failure more than a side effect. You be the judge. As this is a vital issue to public health I recommend reading **Lipitor, Thief of Memory: Statin Drugs: Side Effects and the Misguided War on Cholesterol** by Dr. Duane Graveline. The long list of statin drug side effects runs 192 pages (http://www.spacedoc.net/statin_side_effects.html).

Water restoration, diet, exercise, herbs and chelation therapy should KO even the most advanced condition. Consult your holistic physician to assist you in formulating a workable plan tailored to your specific needs. Statin drugs are unnecessary except in the most extreme cases. That was their original intended application, but their widespread use resulted from profit motive and marketing, not sound medicine.

Americans seem to be putting on pounds with increasing regularity. Obviously, the American diet isn't the best, but again the answer is chronic dehydration. Over time the sense of thirst becomes less active and sometimes totally disappears. Even worse is that the sense of thirst is mistaken for hunger with constant overeating as a result. This can easily be combatted by having a glass of water at least a half hour before you eat and another two hours after eating. You should have the most water before and after your heaviest meal as water is needed for the digestive process. I tried this myself and lost several notches on my belt in just two weeks. I can see my ribs again for the first time in about twenty-five years. I was shocked how well this simple formula worked.

The bottom line is that if Dr. B is right then everyone else is wrong! Who do we believe? That is the question. The scientific facts laid out by Dr. B are in keeping with ayurvedic medicine. Ayurvedic medicine (www.amritaveda.com) has been around for at least 5,000 years. The smart thing to do now is to compare these discoveries to ancient medicine and see what else we have missed. Obviously, we have missed a great deal as four fifths of the world has little if any incidence of the diseases of industrial nations. The gap between what is ALREADY KNOWN and what Western medicine practices is great. With the great influx of older baby boomers coming to retirement age soon, now would be a good time to find some answers. Fast! I wrote this special chapter because I believe Dr. B was onto something big. I'd estimate that over a twenty percent savings in medical costs could be realized worldwide if Dr. B's discoveries were put into practice.

APPENDIX B

NOTES ON HEALING

Woody Allen said, "If you want to make God laugh, tell him you've got plans." Every time I think I've found all there is to find some new revelation occurs to me. The process appears to be endless.

The greatest revelation that has ever occurred in my life was the discovery of the secret healing method used by Jesus Christ and passed to the Knights Templar. The whole story is contained in book two: **THE DA VINCI CODE REVELATIONS**. This discovery first helped me cross over into enlightenment and eventually I was able to heal my injuries by accessing deep Christ level meditation techniques. I experienced several whole body healings as a big wave of energy traversed my body from top to bottom. My spiritual calibration rose to **1231** and continues to rise with the discovery of each new symbol. My back was healed by twin flames of fire energy that pulsated up my whole back to my neck and healed everything in it's path. Energy enters through the top of my head and seems to emanate from my hands as white light. I call this technique **"The Knights Templar Method of Accelerated Healing"** or **KTM** for short. I call it "accelerated healing" because it appears to have roughly double the healing energy of Reiki and can therefore heal in half the time. **KTM** may also be able to heal conditions that cannot be touched by Reiki as it's spiritual calibration is nearly double.

I realized I needed to test **KTM** in the field and went looking for the toughest case I could possibly find. My allegedly "terminal" brain cancer subject, Michelle, recovered and moved to Australia, leaving me with no one to work with. I was shopping the weekly two for one specials at Food Lion supermarket one day and saw a flyer for donations for a critically injured young lady whom I shall call Abby.

Abby was only 26 years old but had somehow survived cancer,

a bad back, a horrendous car crash, a coma, and a stroke. She had screws and rods in her right leg, and was paralyzed from the stroke on her left side. All she could do was lift her right arm and smile. She had massive injuries everywhere, a brain injury, and her liver was super-glued back together. Her stomach had been cleaned and repacked so many times, the doctors just left it open for easy access. When I first met Abby she had been in various hospitals in Jacksonville, Fl. for six months.

I had a couple of healing sessions with Abby and quickly realized this was the most complex case I'd ever seen. She had so many injuries and preexisting conditions I hardly knew where to begin. As she was in a great deal of pain from the car accident I first worked on all of her joints. After ten hours of healing work most of her pain was gone, her face was no longer paralyzed, and her left hand temporarily returned to normal.

As Abby's case was so complex I decided to try behavioral kinesiology in sorting it all out. First I obtained an estimated overall healing time of 100 hours. Then I further refined the process by dividing the front of her body into quadrants and made a chart. I didn't make a chart of her back, as her back injury and open stomach prevented me from turning her over. To keep it simple I divided the chart into ten sections as follows:

1) Head and neck
2) Left torso
3) Right torso
4) Left breast
5) Right breast
6) Stomach
7) Left arm
8) Right arm
9) Left leg
10) Right leg

Then using behavioral kinesiology I obtained an estimate in hours and minutes for each section. I got my calculator out and broke each section down as per healing time per session. The total healing time added up perfectly to 100 hours using KTM or 200 hours for Reiki. As spiritual calibration rises, the healing time decreases. Once again behavioral kinesiology appeared to have generated another map for me to follow. Several critical questions occurred to me; "How much of this condition is due to cancer and how much is from the accident?" How does one separate one condition from the others? What spiritual and karmic forces are in play? I just didn't have all the answers.

Whenever I get stuck or encounter a big new question to solve I go back to the drawing board and do more research on the problem. An Inner Traditions catalog immediately arrived and I decided to read Patrick Obissier's **BIOGENEALOGY: Decoding the Psychic Roots of Illness- Freedom from the Ancestral Origins of Disease** (34). After completing it I used some "mind mapping" techniques to sort it all out.

A NEW DISCOVERY

I eventually arrived at the figure of twelve (12) hours of healing to eliminate Abby's underlying cancer issues. **Ten hours for her uterus** where she had experienced cancer before and **two hours for her breasts**. Obissier's book stated that diseases are inherited from our ancestors and may go back thousands of years. So, I "ran the numbers" for Abby's mother and sister and again came up with twelve hours.

As Jon Voight's character Patrick Gates said in the movie National Treasure, "One clue leads to another clue, and that clue leads to another clue, and on and on." This situation was no different. This is how I arrived at asking the question as to how many hours of healing the "average" person needs to be fully well. Again the answer was **twelve (12) hours of KTM or 24 for Reiki**. That seemed to be quite a coincidence. Or was it? If all diseases are created by one's consciousness, as stated by Obissier, then perhaps this was the very number (or measurement of it) that I had stumbled upon.

Dis-ease can't just happen or manifest itself out of thin air. It requires raw materials from the physical, mental and spiritual realms. Diseases may even be good things that manifest themselves to save the life of the individual. It is a natural process and can work well when not interfered with by unconscious doctors. Chemotherapy immediately comes to mind as an example of how doctors treat a spiritual/emotional condition with a nuclear weapon. Perhaps our medical responses to disease are all wrong because our level of consciousness is too low?

I believe there is a "RESERVOIR OF TRAUMA" that is inherited by every living soul. This 12 hours worth of inherited trauma is the raw material from which dis-ease is manufactured. This is particularly true of cancer creation or manifestation. Removing this inherited trauma is also the first small step towards enlightenment. As discussed in book one, raising one's spiritual calibration beyond the threshold of disease is the ultimate solution to the problem of disease. If it is unconsciousness that creates dis-ease, then it is consciousness that can un-create it and heal it. As with all of God's creations, the system is perfect.

FOLLOWING THE TRAIL

Disease first manifests itself as an energy weakness and can be resolved by recharging the effected area with healing energy. One of the great deficiencies of conventional medicine is that it has no way directly to measure energy weaknesses over the entire body. MRIs are of some value in this regard, but a healer can feel subtle energy weaknesses in the body years before they are advanced enough to be measured by conventional means. Even worse, diseases or energy weaknesses spread along energy pathways or meridians and pop back out in unexpected places. I discovered this in the field when I worked on my neighbor Michelle. She had a case of allegedly "terminal" brain cancer and was told in October 2006 she would be dead by March 2007. Most of her brain tumor was surgically removed, but the area refused to heal. I worked on her entire body several times and eventually found a key to her illness. Apparently the weakness that created her brain tumor spread along the meridians down to her gall bladder. The trail led from the right side of her head, down the neck, crossed over her torso, went through the left breast and terminated in the gall bladder. I "followed the trail" and healed the entire system. It is essential to communicate with the subject and get continuous feedback as to where the energy is going and what it is doing. This assists the healer in following the trail back to the original source of the condition. A healer works <u>with</u> the subject not <u>on</u> the subject. It is a joint effort and co-creative process. Although Michelle completed only half the hours she needed before moving to Australia, she is still alive as of this writing.

It occurred to me that if I could make a healing estimate in hours for Abby using behavioral kinesiology I could make a general estimate for ANY disease. What had fooled me previously was that I wasn't aware of the pre-existing "reservoir of trauma" that I now believe everyone has. I needed to ask for an estimate in hours for the subject to be totally well and not just the mitigation of one symptom or disease. As I'd already created a chart of the physical co-factors for AIDS and cancer, I thought I would try to make a KTM healing estimate for various diseases. **To get an estimate using Reiki healing, just multiply by two**. Once the overall estimate is generated, I break the hours down for the specific subject into hours per quadrant. Then when healing be sure to recheck and follow the trail between the quadrants to be sure you've got all the affected areas along the meridians. The work isn't complete until EVERYTHING is removed and healed. It is best to think of disease as "**an energy system failure**" and not just a damaged spare part. We are not putting a new alternator into an old Chevy here. The trail of energy weakness can run literally from head to foot. Always think ENERGY and you'll be on the right track.

The averages below are theoretical averages for an "ordinary" subject with just one condition. Keep in mind that many subjects will have more than one condition layered one atop the other. The overall condition of every subject is therefore unique and must be treated accordingly. I will discuss how to deal with the different aspects of the body, mind and soul connection later in this chapter. First however lets establish a baseline of average healing times for common diseases. The averages are in hours using KTM as follows:

Average person	12 hours
AIDS	22 hours
Cancer stage 1	22 hours
Cancer stage 2	25 hours
Cancer stage 3	30 hours
Cancer stage 4	35 hours
Cocaine Addiction	22 hours
Heart Disease	32 hours
Stroke	35 hours
Parkinson's Disease	22 hours
Diabetes type 1	22 hours
Diabetes type 2	25 hours
Chronic Fatigue Syndrome	22 hours
Bi-polar Disorder	22 hours
Brain injuries	22 hours
Schizophrenia	38 hours
Alzheimer's Disease	35 hours
Multiple Sclerosis	50 hours

Moderate Auto Accidents	18 hours
Severe Auto Accidents	50 hours
Post Traumatic Stress Syndrome	52 hours

THE RESERVOIR OF TRAUMA

One of the reasons I made the above chart of average healing times is that on occasion I've had subjects that just didn't seem to respond well to healing. Normally every small item takes some energy for a few minutes and then is complete. Then I would move on to the next hand position and check that. It felt frustrating to work for fifteen hours or more with hardly any noticeable results. This was before I discovered the concept of the "reservoir of trauma." Now I realize that **the traumatic overburden must be removed first before one can connect with the underlying cause that we are seeking to heal and remove**. As in gold mining, you've got to remove tons of sand (the overburden) before you get to the gold at the bottom of the riverbed. This became apparent one evening when I was working on my difficult subject and we broke through to the cause; he heated up and started to sweat. He then fell asleep on the table and we finally began to make headway on his many injuries and surgeries.

The numbers above are only theoretical averages. Exactly how to proceed is best determined by the type and gravity of the particular situation. Time is of the essence in many conditions. The total hours are calculated to remove both the pre-existing "overburden of trauma" and the more newly formed trauma associated with the symptoms one may currently be experiencing. Completion of the healing regimen (in hours) above may or may not effect complete relief or remission of symptoms. The situation may require a higher spiritual calibration to unlock and remove the primary source of the condition. Old lifestyle habits that build up trauma must be replaced with more positive and nurturing habits. Healing will however remove the crushing weight of trauma being experienced and get the subject back to a neutral position where he may more easily and readily move forward physically and spiritually. Once the subject arrives at the neutral position or "square one," it is time to learn how to heal ones self and venture forth under your own steam. Just three (3) hours of self-administered healing per day adds up to over one thousand hours per year. Tremendous progress can be made in a year. An annual checkup by a master healer can assist you in monitoring your progress towards your healing and spiritual goals.

The hours of estimated healing time seen here are not set in stone. God didn't give them to me on Mt. Sinai or anything like that. They're just estimates. There are many different healing systems and techniques. I mention Reiki most frequently as a basic system because there are one million Reiki masters in the USA. Not only are there many types of systems, but different basic types of healing energy as well. According to Dr. Eric Pearl, the developer of "The Reconnection" Healing Technique, there are "hot" Earth energies, "cool" astral healing frequencies and direct angelic intervention (www.thereconnection.com) (35). You'll have to discover for yourself which type of healing energy is best for you.

THE ORDER OF HEALING

Healing has it's own divine order. I call it "the order of healing." It appears that divine intelligence knows what parts of the body should be healed and in what order to insure survival. It has been my experience that the major functions of the body are healed and preserved first. The brain, heart, lungs and kidneys all are healed first as these are most essential for the survival of the subject. The kidneys are one of the most frequently damaged organs, due to the current state of our environment. The spine, bones and issues of mobility come next. Improvement in digestion and other internal

116

organs come later. Reproductive organs and skin conditions aren't immediate survival issues and appear to heal last. Issues such as erectile dysfunction can only be reached by removing the entire pile of overburden (trauma) to get to it. Once the entire body is recharged and healed fertility improves dramatically. I believe the human body is wired to shield it's fight or flight capability and hence the life and survival of the organism.

BLOCKS TO HEALING

"**All illnesses have distress as their starting point, which (then) causes biological conflict.**" (36) A message is sent to the brain to get to work creating an illness. As genes contain inherited memories of ancient adaptations to old conflicts, illness can be considered genetic. The work of **Dr. Ryke Geerd Hamer**, a German physician, has been one of the first to deal with stress or trauma as a trigger to disease. Dr. Hamer actually used a CT scanner to identify how the brain adapts and creates illness. Traumatic events such as the loss of a loved one, bankruptcy, or loss of quality of life alter brain waves and lead directly to alteration of organs. Illnesses play a valuable role in balancing the body of an individual to adapt to life's challenges.

Illness and disease also fulfill a number of spiritual, karmic and educational functions. They ALWAYS occur for a reason and not at the random whim of God or nature. **The mind creates the illness or disease for a specific purpose**. Knowing that "inner work" is required to resolve illness is one of the biggest keys to its removal or neutralization. One must become attuned to the cycles of the Earth, life and death, as all things are temporary. The word therapeutic derives from the ancient Therapeutae of Egypt, (and the Essenes) which means "physicians of the soul." Complete healing requires total healing of body, mind and spirit.

It is necessary to put into plain terms why disease is with us: **people become very attached to their diseases and even define themselves as one who has a particular disease**. For example, members of Alcoholics Anonymous introduce themselves as, "Hello, I'm Robert, I'm an alcoholic." The same scenario is true with diabetics, drug users, or persons with cancer. They all define themselves as persons with this or that particular disease. I would like to remind you that you are NOT your disease: you are just a human being.

There is nothing better than a crippling disease to either spiritually educate, karmicly balance or simply punish your wayward mother. If you need to keep your husband from divorcing you and walking out, just roll the car over three times and maybe catch yourself on fire for some extra drama. That will slow him down for three years nursing you back to health. Who would pass up the opportunity for a multi-million dollar lawsuit and the opportunity to blame someone else for your life just to be well? If humans run low on their stockpile of diseases, they are forced to invent something else to use as a vehicle to accomplish their desires. Polio used to cripple millions of people per year until it was virtually eradicated. Therefore the human psyche called in extra cases of MS and car accidents to fulfill the need to be crippled. If you want to dissolve a disease, you must first determine its purpose.

Is it an "oh poor me" disease, or a "get out of work that I hate disease," or just the usual "I need more love and attention" sort of disease. All diseases have a reason. The spiritual reasons for most common diseases are cataloged in Christian Fleche's book entitled: **The Biogenealogy Sourcebook: Healing the Body by Resolving Traumas of the Past**. (This volume is due for release in July 2008). If you don't heal the cause you've accomplished nothing. Even if you had a magic bullet that instantly cured a disease, if the individual isn't done with it yet and totally released it then he can instantly create another one to replace it. Or maybe just get hit by a bus. When I worked with Abby I sorted out her past life experiences of murder, torture and hatred. Then I whispered in her ear, **"JUST LET IT GO!"** The next time she saw me at the hospital she said, "It feels like a tremendous weight has been lifted from me." Two weeks later she was released from the hospital and went home to her family.

BODY, MIND AND SPIRIT

Eradicating a disease is a much bigger chore than most people imagine. To finally, completely, totally get rid of one you must treat body, mind and spirit. Medicine and healing got divorced sometime during the period known as the enlightenment. Rational men of science wanted nothing to do with spiritual hocus-pocus and religious mumbo-jumbo. They wanted only hard science and facts. The time has come for medicine and healing to kiss and make up. This is the only viable way to treat all diseases. In order to deal with the issues of body, mind and spirit I've broken it down to a process I call "the triple threat" to disease. They work best in synergistic or complimentary fashion.

Physical Cures (the body) If we carefully dissect the problem into physical co-factors, as I have done for AIDS and cancer in Appendix A, we can get a better picture of how to remove a particular disease. I am confident that new physical remedies such as Ormus materials and oxygen will eradicate hundreds of diseases. Ormus and oxygen operate in both the physical and spiritual realms. Always remember however that magic bullets are of no value unless the root cause has been neutralized.

Spiritual Calibration (the spirit) Each disease "lives" on a certain electrical frequency which I have described in my Universal Theory of Disease. It also exists simultaneously at a certain spiritual calibration. If you raise your spiritual calibration beyond the threshold of disease or beyond the level the disease can tolerate then it is gone.

Healing (the mind) The final step is healing and removing the disease from your consciousness altogether. As in our traumatic overburden scenario, you'll have first to remove this to see what you've really got. During the healing process, the karmic overburden of the subject will also come into view. The more past life "junk" you're carrying around, the heavier you are. Sacred Merkaba Ascended Master healing is particularly useful for dealing with karmic issues affecting health. The higher the spiritual calibration of the healer the more rapidly the healing may occur. The higher the spiritual calibration of the subject the more easily it will be accomplished. Healing removes karmic and energetic blockages to health. **Healing operates on all three levels: body, mind and spirit.**

Solving a disease is like fitting three keys into the locks of a Spanish Galleon three-locked box. Working together the healer and the subject must use all three keys to get at the golden treasure (the gnosis) within. If you haven't yet found a physical cure, just work on steps 2 and 3. When your consciousness is high enough a physical cure will appear via the law of attraction. When you start seeing YOUR CURE everywhere you look, then you know it is meant for you. SEEK AND YE SHALL FIND. All you need then is the courage to "just do it." Once the initial "overburden" of trauma and disease is removed, it is then time for the subjects to learn how to heal themselves. The healer is not a crutch, but a guide and facilitator. The subjects must learn how to heal, stand on their own two feet, and take ultimate responsibility for their own health. It is wise to become a healer yourself and always keep plenty of energy in your "energy bank" just in case you need to make a sudden withdrawal. Someone once said that, "The only thing you can be certain of in life is uncertainty." If you go into the hole energy-wise, then you'll again accumulate a traumatic load or overburden. A smart investor keeps extra funds in his bank account for a rainy day so he doesn't go into the red. The same is true with energy. **Diseases such as cancer may be cyclical (astrological) and return again and again**. Earth energy and your emotional energy have highs and lows just like the tides. If you maintain your energy balance and keep some energy in the bank, you won't get caught short when an emotional low, such as cancer, comes around again.

METHODS OF HEALING

I have been engaged in healing for nearly eighteen years. I'm my best client as I was once totally banged up with 33 injured discs in my back. I have logged over 8,000 hours of treatment upon myself. Now I feel like Superman in comparison as my strength has increased by nearly 200%. I began with traditional Japanese Reiki and have found by experience that this is a great way to begin every healing session. Using the Reiki hand positions is an excellent way to start an initial assessment of any subject's needs.

Healing energy is somewhat like household electricity. We want to establish a circuit of a certain voltage and amplitude so we can recharge the subject's aura or body field. Therefore the first rule is to get rid of all metal objects on the subject's body. No rings, glasses, necklaces, earrings, piercings, bras, cell phones, or big metal belt buckles are allowed. We want to recharge the subjects, not their possessions. An energy buildup in a metal object can become painful on the skin.

We want the subject to be as comfortable as possible. I recommend baggy gym shorts and cut-off T-shirts. A blanket or sheet above and below the subject as they lie on a massage table maintains both comfort and modesty. I always try to maintain the dignity of the subject and to get them to relax and heal. Healing is a sacred activity. Acknowledging this with candles, flowers, photos of saints or gurus and incense is a nice touch.

The healing ability of each healer varies greatly. In general, the higher the spiritual calibration of the healer, the greater healing energy they will possess. Practice and experience also vary greatly. Normally a healer has a dominant hand and a weaker hand. The dominant hand is usually the one that is used to write with. The very center of the hand is the main conduit of healing energy and also a psychic receptor. A trained healer can "see" illness with their hands and inner vision. My energy is such that I can heal with the back of my hands as well as the front. Holding my hands together or even crossing my arms creates a healing circuit of energy. Energy from my hands on my chest penetrates through the entire body. I healed my back injuries by just putting my hands on my head or on my heart and letting the energy go where it needed to go. All that was required was a lot of patience daily over a period of many years.

I like to create a healing circuit by placing my dominant hand upon the affected area of the subject and then use my other hand as an electrical ground wire to generate the maximum current flow. I have also learned the hard way to treat every inch of my body AT EACH LEVEL of spiritual calibration. Whenever I obtain a higher calibration I start the entire process over again for as long as it takes to reach a plateau. I used to go out and take additional healing courses every time I felt like nothing was happening. I no longer have that problem as my healing energy seems to be continuously expanding as I keep discovering new healing symbols. The problem now is that my energy is increasing faster than I can keep up with it. I have healed so many systems and organs in my body that I have now exceeded my knowledge of anatomy. I may not know the names of the systems involved, but when they heat up like hot coals, I know they have been healed. **You may believe you are in perfect health and have the perfect Hollywood body, but I can assure you that there are one to two dozens systems in your body waiting like ticking time-bombs to go off**. Only by getting in there with self-healing and digging around will you discover what is actually inside of you.

Every part and every inch of the body is fertile ground for healing. There appear to be more nerves and meridians in the body than stars in the sky. Even elbows and ears have a surprising number of connections. What really hurts is when I suddenly hit a weak uncharged nerve or meridian that I've overlooked for eighteen years. Then I get ZAPPED with a little bolt of lightening that can run for several feet and go to unexpected places. Ouch!!!

In traditional Reiki we were taught to avoid sexual areas unless there was a clear-cut need such as breast cancer or a botched surgery. Frequently during breast augmentation surgery the ribs are broken or cracked in the rush for a speedy job. Given the prevalence of breast cancer and augmentation surgery I feel that every woman's breasts should be healed. Four women die of breast cancer every hour or 44,000 deaths a year in the USA alone. Over a million women are undiagnosed annually (http://wrongdiagnosis.com). There are approximately two million breast cancer survivors in the USA alone. (Men also get breast cancer, but you never hear about it. Men also need 12 hours of healing, particularly in the heart and lungs). Take a look at a radical mastectomy at: (www.breastcancer.org) and see how much of the breast is removed. Also note the extensive network of lymph nodes that seem to travel in every direction. Surgical removal of the breast and lymph nodes is a terribly disfiguring procedure and a major source of trauma. I believe breast cancer is easily preventable with thorough healing techniques. Even if it were just diagnosed early, it is 100% correctable with conventional means. I always check out the armpits of every subject and do a survey of all the lymph nodes and the neck. If I find a weakness I "follow the trail" to be sure I got it all. Following a trail of subtle energy can be difficult even for an experienced healer. I like to do this on bare skin whenever possible so I don't miss anything. The breasts, and in particular the nipple, are very major nerve and lymph node hubs of the body and need lots of work. The only "allegedly" terminal cancer subject that I've worked with drew so much energy from my hands into her breasts that it hurt my hands and I had to shake them out and rest. The cancer was supposed to have only been a tumor in her brain, but in reality the energy "trail" of weakness or low voltage ran from her head to her gall bladder. I followed the entire trail until it no longer consumed any healing energy and she is still alive today. A major deficiency of modern medicine is that it has no way to map systematic weakness such as this. A healer however CAN find all weaknesses and recharge them BEFORE they become a problem or life threatening.

In treating a sexual area of the body I find it best to treat the affected area last. First it is important to build rapport with a subject to get them to relax and to be aware of the healing taking place. I also feel that it is wise to remove all the other traumatic overburden first. This is a more cautious and less painful approach. Rushing in on any seriously affected area may be overwhelming and painful to the subject. A witness is also an excellent idea to maintain the spiritual nature of the work by real healers. A real healer has nothing to hide or no hidden agenda. Charlatans do. If you've never been to a healer before, ask for a fifteen minute healing sample to feel what they've got and see if they're right for you. Having two healers of different sexes also adds balance and increases the power of the healing. As in any endeavor, teamwork is a wonderful thing.

I believe that the concept of a genetic "reservoir of trauma" will greatly improve the effectiveness of healing cancer and all diseases. The only way to test a theory such as this is by testing it on real people in the field. This is how I discovered it in the first place. I would particularly like to work with "alleged" terminal patients. I would also like to donate a certain percentage of my time to organizations such as the Children's Miracle Network (www.thechildrensmiraclen etwork.org) as I feel miracles are possible.

THE WORLD'S GREATEST HEALER

The greatest living and accessible healer in the world that I am aware of is Joaa Teixeir de Faria, who is called John of God or Jao de Dios (**1350**). He lives at the Casa de Dom Inacio in Abadiana, 130 kms. from Brasilia, the capitol of Brazil. Tour guides are readily available to take you to him (www.Johnofgod-healing.com) or (www.Johnofgod.com). His services are free to all. He is a world renowned psychic surgeon and healer who is reputed to have treated fifteen million people. Jao has healed as many as 20,000 people in a day. He has healed notables such as the President of Peru and even Shirley MacLaine and Ram Das. The President of Peru awarded him the Medal of Honor in 1991 and threw a state dinner and a parade in his honor. I know of no other healer who has been honored and acclaimed in such a manner. He is rightly called "The Miracle Man of Brazil (37)." It costs approximately $ 1,600-$2,000 to fly to Brazil per person to meet with him. More than one trip may be necessary. Jao doesn't make house calls, so you'd have to visit him.

I MAKE HOUSE-CALLS

When I was a child doctors made house calls and knew you by name from birth. This custom has gone the way of the horse and buggy. I love to travel, heal others and do my research. I am willing to fly almost anywhere in the world and make house-calls for executives, professionals, sports figures, actors and others interested in my services. The average fee for Reiki Masters is about $50.00 per hour or $75.00 per session. The normal session is ninety minutes. As the Knights Templar method I've rediscovered takes approximately half the time for double the effect I feel a very reasonable rate would be $ 100.00 per hour or $1,000 per day for my services, plus room, board and expenses. A one week minimum would be required in most cases to treat an entire family. This is particularly true for international cases. Every subject's health data and personal information is totally confidential. I feel this is a very cost effective approach given the value of time lost to professionals of all walks of life. It is not cost effective to pass on a $10 million dollar movie deal or sit on the bench an entire football, basketball or baseball season. (My twelve year old son Chris is a baseball fanatic and has been playing little league for two years. In his attempt to be a power-hitter he tore up the ligaments to his rib cage and was in a great deal of pain. We were able to heal his serious injury in only one hour. He was back on the field the next day pain free).

Even for an average person, conventional medical costs can soar up to $300,000 for a serious accident, injury or disease. The drain on personal finances, stress, and time lost from work can be very destructive to one's way of life. This is totally unnecessary in my opinion. Therefore, I hope to establish the KTM as a new paradigm for healing and train practioners in this method. My personal services will only be available for a short period of time. The rest of my life will be dedicated to teaching and research.

HEALING IS A WAY OF LIFE

Our current medical paradigm barely acknowledges the role of healing and has consigned it to the outer fringes of an otherwise litigious society. Only a small minority of human beings have a healing consciousness and have a desire to get "reconnected" to the source of all healing. The healing effects of touch are outsourced to professionals, such as massage therapists. Touching is a frequently a taboo. The bottom line is that babies born without human touch nearly always die within a few months because touch is a basic human need. It is also a basic human asset that everyone has. I say, "Hug your spouse, hug your kids, and hug your dog and cat." Make the world a better place and hug somcone today. Ultimately healing is a way of life. Just a couple of hours of healing per day will change your life forever and of those around you. Sitting on the fence or sitting on your hands won't get you anywhere. Anyone can make it to **1420** just like Jesus. It just takes effort and patience. Do healing when you lie in bed, watch TV, or when sitting on the bus. I even do it in my sleep. I rest my hands on an extra pillow in the middle of the bed, clasp my hands together, create a healing circuit, and heal all night long. Do it anywhere and do it all the time. The minutes add up to hours and the hours to days. It's easy to log thousands of hours of healing annually once you make a commitment. Once you're well go heal someone else.

I began a healing regimen for my children before they were born. I healed them in the womb AND during birth. Every time they get a scrape or fall off something I am there to heal it. My daughter pulled a pan of hot water upon herself when she was two and had a large burn on her face. Ten hours of healing and it was gone without a trace. My children are exceptionally strong and have been sick only once in thirteen years. My son (and two daughters) climbed his first mountain when he was twenty-two months old and in diapers. He also rode a mule and a camel (naked) for the first time. By the time he was eight he could pick up my 220 lb. frame off the ground. The best time to heal your children is before they are born. If you do then your children will begin life with the spiritual calibration of a saint and healer (**650**). When they come of age you can teach them how to become healers. The best time to heal yourself is before you need it.

I saw a great bumper sticker recently that stated: **"If going to church makes you a Christian, does going to the garage make you a car?"** I thought this was pretty funny and timely. If dis-ease is created in our own minds, then healing can also be created there. It's just a question of taking responsibility for our actions and beliefs. You are the church and creator of your own destiny. Anyone can learn to heal and become "a Christ." The ancient alchemists believed that life was too short to achieve perfection. Therefore their first priority was to make the body strong so it would last and allow enough time to achieve wisdom and an enlightened golden body (38). The ULTIMATE SECRET of healing will be revealed in book two. The rest is up to you. My advice is to learn to heal and put a doctor out of work today.

APPENDIX C

TECHNIQUES OF PHYSICAL IMORTALITY THEY DON'T WANT YOU TO KNOW ABOUT.

There is an old joke that states, "If I had known I was going to live this long, I would have taken better care of myself." Leonard Orr, the father of Rebirthing, has put it more succinctly by saying that "The traditional practice of physical death and reincarnation is a needless interruption in our learning process." (39) Death is a waste of time. Why die and then come back and spend fifty years or more just to pick up where you spiritually left off in your previous life? Doesn't make much sense really. Imagine how much you could learn in one lifetime if you lived for hundreds of years. Death is just another bad habit like smoking. It may take 50-100 years to break this habit, but it can be done. Western society and medicine tend to be terribly ethnocentric and the accomplishments of the great sages are ignored. There are many immortals currently living and thousands recorded by name in Indian literature. As the techniques of physical immortality have a great bearing on curing all disease and are somewhat difficult to find I decided to add this chapter to make it easier for the student.

The methods and techniques of physical immortality have been closely guarded secrets held by those in power for thousands of years. As predicted in the Bible, these secrets are now available to the public domain as preparation for the End Times. I will shed some light on the two most reliable methods of immortality: Alchemy and Siddha Yoga. These techniques can be used to slowly climb "The Stairway to Heaven" which is discussed in more detail in book two.

Alchemy is often regarded as a myth or an old wives' tale. The powers that bc would like you to keep thinking that way. Alchemy has been around since the days of Adam and Eve. The tree of knowledge alluded to in the book of Genesis is actually a code word for alchemy. Alchemy was once the sole divine right of high priests and Pharaohs. Divulging the secrets of alchemy to the profane or uninitiated has always been punishable by death. The initiates of the Egyptian Mystery School in the Great Pyramid were taught the secrets of alchemy over a twenty year period. Graduates of the school became masters of the light. Those who failed either died, went insane or were imprisoned. When the Great Pyramid was first opened in modern times the floors of the main chambers were covered with white powdered gold. No one knew what it was and it was discarded. The Egyptian hieroglyph for white powdered gold literally means, "what is it?" This is the only hieroglyph contained in the Great Pyramid. White powdered gold is more commonly referred to as "manna from heaven," "The Philosopher's Stone" or simply "bread."

The secrets of alchemy were hidden from the profane by using arcane symbolism and intricate codes and ciphers. If you are interested in this subject I would suggest reading: The Tower of Alchemy: An Advanced Guide to the Great Work by David Goddard. However, as my focus is practical alchemy and curing all disease let us move on to how white powdered gold actually works.

There are two primary reasons that physical death occurs to most humans. The first is that DNA tends to degrade with age. Few are aware of the energy body much less how to fix it. Secondly, most of us are taught to assume that death is inevitable and to accept our fate. Religions play a major role in the support system for death.

We all start out life as an embryo in the womb with 46 base pairs of DNA per turn. Within a couple of weeks the number decreases to 34. By the age of two years old the number is down to 22 base pairs. At the age of 35 you're down to only 10 pairs of DNA turns. This lasts until age fifty and its all down hill from there as the DNA continues to degrade and replicate imperfectly. As the DNA imperfections increase so does aging until eventually the energy system fails entirely. Then you're dead. (40)

Those people who are fortunate to live in a high magnetically charged mountainous environment with an abundance of minerals tend to live over 120 years of age. Everyone else gets to become a life insurance company statistic. Life insurance companies aren't gamblers. They have maps of water mineral content that predicts quite accurately how long you will live and base their premiums accordingly. They don't tell you they are betting against you.

Daily consumption of white powdered gold keeps your DNA at or above the critical 10 pair limit. The body can then repair all DNA imperfections, manufacture or transmute missing minerals, and keep the body at a youthful 26 year old appearance. A youthful appearance can be maintained for hundreds or even thousands of years. Unfortunately, many alleged white powder gold formulas that are commercially available are fraudulent or contain impurities such as lead or mercury. Only with knowledge of the correct methods of manufacture can you either determine which products are genuine or make your own. Hank Kroll (www.alaskapublishing.com) provides a wonderful history of white powdered gold and recipes for many of the most common methods. Mr. Kroll's Philosopher's Stone: Key to Eternal Life is the best book on the subject I've ever read. It is fascinating reading even for the layman. I recommend it highly. It is the ultimate how to book on Ormus materials and contains lists of suppliers to obtain all the materials you'll need to manufacture white powdered gold at home. I would recommend establishing a very firm spiritual understanding before attempting to use white powdered gold. And always remember the most basic rule- GO SLOWLY. Never push yourself or your body faster than it wants to go. Wait until you've reached the plateau of the level you're on before attempting to go to another one.

Conquering death requires a firm spiritual, mental and physical understanding of how the human organism actually works. Without this knowledge the body becomes more and more dense annually and death is inevitable. Although alchemy and yoga do overlap at the highest point there are four basic laws of spiritual purification that everyone must understand in order to become an immortal. These spiritual practices are: 1) Breath, 2) The name of God, 3) Fire purification and 4) Water purification. Although I have completed approximately 8,000 hours of healing, the aforementioned practices appear to heal the aura in ways that no other form of healing can.

The ultimate causes of death are stuck energy, psychic dirt, and negative mental conditioning. These lead to emotional problems and eventually manifest into physical illness. Leonard Orr teaches that breath, birth, money and death are all part of a single cycle. Spiritual purification requires the removal of the basic traumas of humanity. These traumas are 1) birth trauma, 2) parental disapproval syndrome, 3) unconscious death urge and 4) past life trauma. Leonard Orr used spiritual purification techniques to eliminate eight major diseases from his body including cancer and heart disease. It normally takes fifty to one hundred years to overcome death, so it is best to start early.

The ancients spoke cryptically of the four elements of earth, air, fire and water. Westerners seem to regard this as just another silly superstition. However these are the keys to understanding the purification of the aura and physical immortality. In order to be in harmony with the Earth we must live consciously like Henry David Thoreau. We must master food, be aware of the subtle energies of the Earth, and our place within it. Fasting, vegetarianism, exercise, massage, body-work, and developing our divine career allow us to be in harmony with the Earth. Farming is the most spiritual profession.

Incorrect breathing keeps our negative psychic energy in place. Deep conscious breathing at least twenty times a day blows out all the old stale air and keeps our consciousness clear. Alternate nostril breathing eight times on each side of the nose helps to clean out the nadis (energy) system. This takes approximately 90 days to see the benefit. Lack of oxygen (and/or exercise) is one of the most major causes of disease. I would rate it at approximately 30% of all the co-factors of diseases such as cancer and AIDS. Western medicine classifies the breathing of too much oxygen as hyperventilation syndrome. Leonard Orr sets the record straight by saying that hyperventilation is not a disease, but a healing process. It is the correction for breathing incorrectly all your life. More energy or prana means more life. It takes some practice to adjust to techniques such as "The Breath of Fire" in Kundalini yoga. It is quite life changing. Alchemists believe that we breathe Ormus materials in the air and that is the source of prana. If you can't afford white powdered gold, then yoga is an affordable alternative.

Fire purification is one of the fastest methods of getting rid of negative energy. Fire is as important as food, but is virtually unknown in Western circles. When you stand next to a fire your aura is purified by the flames. An open flame can heal many kinds of disease, including conditions that even a Christ level healing can not touch. I was quite shocked to discover that I needed 33 hours of fire purification even after 8,000 hours of healing. Once you initially clear your aura with fire purification about twenty minutes a day are required to maintain a pure state. Immortals traditionally sleep by their fires daily to keep themselves clear. An advanced technique is that of the five fires ceremony. Four fires are built in a square pattern about three to four meters apart. The yogi sits in the middle and stares at the sun, which is the fifth fire. An advanced yogi can eventually stare at the sun all day without injury. This is not a technique for beginners as blindness could result. Leonard Orr calls the five fires ceremony an immortality machine as it is the most rapid way to purify the body. The ceremony can also be done with the fifth fire being the moon. Throughout the orient priests maintain fire temples that have had a continuous fire burning for sometimes hundreds of years. They are always open so anyone can come to purify their aura at any hour of the day or night. If you don't have a fireplace or outdoor fire pit, you can start initially with twelve candles and work your way up. I purchased a wonderful fire pit made in India from Wal-Mart for $49.00. Fire purification is a wonderful treatment for depression. Sit by the fire and feel your cares melt away. The health benefits of fire purification have never been studied in the West. It would be interesting to see which diseases are most easily cure with this method. Lastly, the fire ceremony is also a positive alternative to war. Nuclear war is a mass purification of many thousands of souls and their death urge. It is better to purify yourself consciously by your fireplace, than to be purified unconsciously by war and death.

Every time you immerse yourself in water you are literally bathing your aura. As your aura circulates in the water it is purified. It is recommended to perform a water purification twice a day. Pure rainwater is the best type of water for the ceremony as it is very charged with energy. Clean ocean water is also excellent. A hot tub or bath can be used provided the water is clean. Swimming pools with chlorine or stagnant bodies of water are to be avoided. Sitting in hot water for hours and performing a rebirthing ceremony is an excellent way to become clear. Rebirthing instructors are available throughout the USA and Europe. Just contact Leonard Orr to find one near you.

As death is a learned response it is necessary to purify the thoughts of the mind. As we average 50,000 or more thoughts a day the job of purification can be a big one. The traditional method of mental purification is to repeat the name of God over and over. The name of God in Sanskrit is: Om Namaha Shivaiya. This mantra is used daily to still and cleanse the mind. Prayer beads with 101 beads can be used to keep track of your repetitions of the mantra. The mantra is used while performing both water and fire ceremonies. It is best performed out loud in a deep resonant voice.

Leonard Orr has studied with half a dozen different immortal masters. The most well known immortal is Babaji, who maintains an ashram north of New Delhi. Immortals are naturally reclusive, but traditionally attend festivals in September. Leonard makes periodic pilgrimages to India as does Sondra Ray (www.SondraRay. com). Complete details on all the above techniques are contained in Leonard Orr's ground breaking book: Breaking the Death Habit: The Science of Everlasting Life. Or you may write to Leonard at: Inspiration University, P.O. Box 1026, Stanton, VA. 24402. Phone (540) 885-1026. Or on the web at: (www.rebirthingbreathwork. com). Leonard's books are the best in the field and he writes with passion, knowledge and a sense of humor. Leonard reminds us all that, "Death is a grave mistake."

The ancient solar meditation techniques used in Siddha Yoga are also taught in the Western Christian tradition of Jesus Christ. While the secret oral teachings of Jesus, known as the "paradosis" (41) were lost after his death, these teachings have been reclaimed at The Jamilian University of the Ordained of Reno, Nevada (www.jamilian. org). The original teachings of Jesus and the Essene Brotherhood were revived by the prophet Jamil Savoy (1951-1953). He was known as "The Christ of the Andes" (42).

The solar meditation techniques called cosolargy, have been updated for the new millennium and are available via a five-hundred hour correspondence course followed by instruction at the university. Those who successfully complete the correspondence course and instruction in the secret oral teachings of Jesus are eligible to be ordained as a reverend in the Jamilian Order.

Biography

Lt. Lawrence F. Frego, USNR (ret.) is a retired Naval Intelligence Analyst, electronics materials officer and special warfare officer. Mr. Frego also served in the US Coast Guard as an enlisted man and was a search and rescue boat coxswain. He is currently the CEO of Highlander Gold Mining Co., Inc. and other mining ventures. Mr. Frego graduated The State University of New York at Potsdam with a BA in history and education. Post graduate studies in education were at the University of North Florida. Mr. Frego joined the Explorers Club in 1994. Mr. Frego is a Japanese Reiki Master in the Usui tradition and a Sacred Merkaba "Trinity" Healer. He served as Vice chairman of the Libertarian Party of St. Johns County, Florida and is a founding member of the American Liberty Foundation. Currently Mr. Frego resides in St. Augustine, Florida. You may contact the author at: fregol@bellsouth.net.

It took over 25 years to research the information in this book. If you enjoyed this book and found it useful a donation of $15 or more will help to continue the work outlined here. A check for only $1.00 will put you on our mailing list and we'll keep you informed of updates and new articles. Be sure to include your internet address and phone number.

THE GREATEST VITAMIN IN THE WORLD

TRY US 100% RISK FREE
VISIT OUR WEBSITE TODAY!

Educating yourself about nutrition is important to your health and well-being. Please check our website and learn the shocking truth about many of the vitamins on the market today!

WHEN YOU VISIT OUR WEBSITE YOU WILL LEARN:

About 40% of North Americans are currently taking a multi-vitamin and do not realize they may be causing more harm than benefit!

DID YOU KNOW?

Most vitamins on the market today use synthetic vitamins rather than whole vitamins straight from vegetables and fruits because synthetic vitamins are much cheaper to produce.

INTRODUCING
THE GREATEST VITAMIN IN THE WORLD

The Greatest Vitamin in the World nutritionally supports the body by using only the highest grade-

Whole Food Vitamins (not synthetic)
Chelated Minerals (most absorbable)
Probiotics (critical for the body's health)
Enzymes (critical in digesting food)

-along with other nutrients that are scientifically proven to nutritionally support your body!

TO ORDER VISIT US AT OUR WEBSITE:

http://www.dontforgettotakeyourvitamins.com/frego13358

FDA Disclaimer

The statements made about the effects of the products discussed in this book have not been evaluated by the Food and Drug Administration. Special dietary and nutritional supplements such as these products are intended for special dietary use. They are not intended for use in the treatment, cure, prevention or mitigation of any disease or disorder. They are intended to be used as part of an overall healthy lifestyle program that includes proper diet and exercise. Only your doctor can diagnose and treat any disease or disorder. Before starting to use any nutritional supplement it is important to check with your doctor.

Second disclaimer: This book is intended for educational and informational purposes only. The author is not a doctor, nor does he claim to be one. The author does not endorse products or websites. The author affirms that he has no financial interest, stock, considerations or received any compensation from any of the companies listed in this book except as noted.

ENDNOTES

1) **Jim Marrs**, *Rule by Secrecy: the hidden history that connects the trilateral commission, the freemasons, and the pyramids.* **(New York: Perennial, 2000)**

2) **Laura Knight-Jadczyk**, *Secret History of the World and How to Get Out Alive.* **(cyberspace?: Red Hill Press, 2005)**

3) **Paul LaViolete**, *Earth Under Fire: humanity's survival of the apocalypse.* **(Schenectady, NY: Starburst Publications, 1997) pgs 16-21.**

4) **Sir Laurence Gardener**, *Genesis of the Grail Kings-the pendragon legacy of Adam and Eve.* **(London: Bantam Press, 1999)**

5) **T. Lobsang Rampa**, *The Hermit* **(London: Corgi, 1971)**

6) **Kevin Trudeau**, *Natural Cures "They" Don't Want You to Know About.* **(Kinsdale, Ill: Alliance Publishing Group, Inc. 2004) pg 209.**

7) **Paramahansa Yogananda**, *Autobiography of a Yogi.* **(Los Angeles: Self Realization Fellowship 1946) page 478.**

8) **Arline Brecher & Harold Brecher**, *Forty Something Forever: a consumer's guide to chelation therapy and other heart-savers.* **(Herdon, VA: Healthsavers Press 1992.)**

9) **Marcus Laux**, *Is "Modern" Medicine Killing You?* **(Potomac, MD:**

Naturally Well Publishing, 1995.) pg 66

10) Leonard Horowitz, *Emerging Viruses: aids and ebola- nature, accident or intentional.* (Sandpoint, ID: Tetrahedron Publishing Group 1999)

11)   Kevin Trudeau, Ibid. page 186.

12) Des Griffin, *Fourth Reich of the Rich.* (South Pasadena: Emissary Publications, 1976)

13) Gerald F. Foye, *Royal R. Rife Humanitarian Betrayed and Persecuted.* (Spring Valley, CA: R.T. Plasma publishing 2001) page 35.

14) Anonymous,. *Handbook for the New Paradigm.* (Carson City, NV: Bridger House Publishing, undated) page 145.

15) Anonymous, *Handbook for the New Paradigm.* page 170.

16) Gerald F. Foye, Ibid. Page 88.

17) Gene Savoy, *Project X: the search for the secrets of immortality.* (Indianapolis: Bobbs-Merrill, 1977)

18) Paramahansa Yogananda, *Autobiography of a Yogi.* (Los Angeles: Self Realization Fellowship 1946) chapter 46 "The Woman Yogi Who Never Eats", pages 443-453.

19) Gael Crystal Flanagan & Patrick Flanagan, *Elixir of the Ageless You are What you Drink.* (Flagstaff, AZ: Vortex Press 1986)

20) Christopher Bird, *Secrets of the Soil.* (New York: Harper and Row 1989)

21) Sir Laurence Gardener, *Lost Secrets of the Sacred Ark: amazing revelations of the incredible power of gold.* (London : Element 2003) pages 112-119, 173, 363, 364.

22) Jay Weidner & Vincent Bridges, *The Mysteries of the Great Cross of Hendaye: alchemy and the end of time.* (**Rochester, VT: Destiny Books 2003**) **page 70.**

23) Paramahansa Yogananda, *The Second Coming of Christ: the resurrection of the Christ within you: a revelatory commentary on the original teachings of Jesus.* (**Los Angeles, CA: Self-Realization Fellowship 2004**)

24) David Pearson, *The Natural House Book: creating a healthy, harmonious, and ecologically-sound home environment.* (**New York: Simon & Schuster, 1989**)

25) Jay Weidner & Vincent Bridges, *The Mysteries of the Great Cross of Hendaye: alchemy and the end of time.* (**Rochester, VT: Destiny Books 2003**) **page 274.**

26) Mark Amaru Pinkham, *The Return of the Serpents of Wisdom.* (**Kempton, Ill: Adventures Unlimited Press 1997**)

27) Marshall Govindan, *Babaji and the 18 Siddha Kriya Yoga Tradition.* (**Montreal: Kriya Yoga Publications 1991**)

28) Delores Cannon, Conversations *with Nostradamus- His Prophecies Explained, Vol II.* (**Huntsville, AZ: Ozark Mountain Press 1990**)

29) Laura Knight-Jadczyk, Ibid, pages 198-220.

30) Paul LaViolete, Ibid.,

31) Jay Weidner & Vincent Bridges, Ibid., page 360.

32) Anonymous, *Handbook for the New Paradigm.* (**Carson City, NV: Bridger House Publishing, undated**) **page 1.**

33) Steven Lamm & Gerald Secor Couzens, *The Hardness Factor.* (**New York; Harper Collins 2005.**)

34) **Patrick Obissier**, *Biogenealogy: decoding the psychic roots of illness.* **(Rochester, VT: Healing Arts Press 2003)**

35) **Eric Pearl,** *The Reconnection: Heal others, heal yourself.* **(Carlsbad, CA: Hay House, Inc. 2001)**

36) **Patrick Obissier, Ibid., Page 4.**

37) **Heather Cumming & Karen Leffler,** *John of God: The Brazilian healer who's touched the lives of millions.* **(New York, NY: Atria Books 2007)**

38) **David Goddard,** *The Tower of Alchemy: An advanced guide to the great work.* **(Boston, MA: Weiser Books 1999) Pages 2,3.**

39) **Leonard Orr, B**reaking the Death Habit: The science of everlasting *life.* **(Berkeley, CA: Frog, Ltd. 1998) Page 110.**

40) **Gene Savoy,** *The Millennium Edition of the Decoded New Testament.* **(Reno, NV: The International Community of Christ 1983)**

41) **Gene Savoy,** *Jamil: Child of light & messenger of God.* **(Reno, NV: The International Community of Christ 2008)**

BIBLIOGRAPHY

Adam. 2006. *Dream Healer: A true story of miracle healings.* New York, NY: The Penguin Group.

Adam. 2006. *The Emerging Dream Healer: A guide to healing and self-empowerment.* New York, NY: The Penguin Group.

Adam. 2007. *The Path of the Dream Healer: My journey through the miraculous world of energy healing.* New York, NY: The Penguin Group.

Altman, Nathaniel. 2000. *Healing Springs: the ultimate guide to taking the waters.* Rochester, Vt.: Healing Arts Press.

Anonymous. Undated. *Handbook for the New Paradigm.* Carson City, NV: Bridger House Publishing. phone (800) 729-4131.

Balch, Phyllis A. 2000. *Prescription for Nutritional Healing 3rd Edition.* New York: Avery/Penguin Group.

Batmanghelidj, Fereydoon. 2000. *ABC of Asthma, Allergies & Lupus: Eradicate Asthma Now – With Water.* Falls Church, Va: Global Health Solutions.

Batmanghelidj, Fereydoon. 1991. *How to Deal with Back Pain and Rheumatoid Joint Pain.* Falls Church, Va: Global Health Solutions.

Batmanghelidj, Fereydoon. 2005. *Obesity, Cancer & Depression: How water can help cure these deadly diseases.* Falls Church, Va: Global Health Solutions.

Batmanghelidj, Fereydoon. 2003. *Water: for health, for healing, for life; You're not sick, you're thirsty: Water & Salt: Your healers from within.* Falls Church, Va: Global Health Solutions.

Batmanghelidj, Fereydoon. 2003. *Water Cures, Drugs Kill.* Falls Church, Va: Global Health Solutions.

Batmanghelidj, Fereydoon. 1992 & 2000. *Your Body's Many Cries for Water: A revolutionary natural way to prevent illness and restore good health.* Norwich, UK: Tagman Press.

Bear, Sun & Wind, Wabun, 1992. *Black Dawn, Bright Day: Indian prophecies for the millennium that reveal the fate of the earth.* New York: Simon & Schuster.

Bird, Christopher. 1991. *The Persecution and Trial of Gaston Naessens: the true story of the efforts to suppress an alternative treatment for cancer, AIDS, and other immunologically based diseases.* Tiburton, CA: H.J. Kramer.

Bird, Christopher. 1989. *Secrets of the Soil* New York: Harper & Row.

Brecher, Harold & Brecher, Arline. 1992. *Forty Something Forever: a consumer's guide to chelation therapy and other heart-savers.* Herdon, VA.: Healthsavers Press.

Brennan, Barbara Ann, 1988. *Hands of Light: a Guide to healing through the human energy field: a new paradigm for the human being in health, relationship, and disease.* Toronto: New York: Bantam Books.

Cannon, Dolores. 1989. *Conversations with Nostradamus- His Prophecies Explained Vol. I.* Huntsville, AZ.: Ozark Mountain Press.

Cannon, Dolores. 1990. *Conversations with Nostradamus-His Prophecies Explained, Vol .II.* Huntsville, AZ.: Ozark Mountain Press.

Cannon, Dolores. 1994. *Conversations with Nostradamus- His Prophecies*

Explained- Vol. III. **Huntsville, AZ.: Ozark Mountain Press.**

Carter, James P. 1993 *Racketeering in Medicine: the suppression of alternatives.* **Norfolk, VA: Hampton Roads Publishing.**

Clark, Hulda Regehr. 1993. *The Cure for HIV and AIDS: with 70 case histories.* **San Diego, CA: ProMotion Pub.**

Clark, Hulda Regehr. 1999. *The Cure for All Advanced Cancers.* **Chula Vista, CA: New Century Press.**

Clark, Hulda Regehr. 1995. *The Cure for all Diseases: with many case histories.* **San Diego, CA: ProMotion Pub.**

Clark, Hulda Regehr. 1993. *The Cure for All Cancers: including over 100 case histories of persons cured.* **San Diego, CA: New Century Press.**

Cumming, Heather & Leffler, Karen. 2007. *John of God: The Brazilian healer who's touched the lives of millions.* **New York: Atria Books.**

Cousens, Gabriel. 1986. *Spiritual Nutrition and the Rainbow Diet.* **Boulder, CO: Cassandra Press.**

Dubois, Charlotte & Lubecki, John. 1988. *The End of Cancer.* **Fair Oaks, CA: UNIC.**

Dyer, Wayne D. 2006. *Inspiration- your ultimate calling.* **Carlsbad, CA: Hay House, Inc.**

Flanagan, Patrick & Flanagan, Gael Crystal. 1986. *Elixir of the Ageless You are What You Drink.* **Flagstaff, AZ: Vortex Press.**

Foye, Gerald F. 2001. *Royal R. Rife Humanitarian Betrayed and Persecuted.* **Spring Valley, CA: R.T. Plasma Publishing.**

Gardener, Laurence, Sir. 1999. *Genesis of the Grail Kings-The Pendragon Legacy of Adam and Eve.* **London: Bantam Press.**

Gardener, Laurence, Sir. 2003. *Lost Secrets of the Sacred Ark: Amazing Revelations of the Incredible Power of Gold.* **London: Element.**

Gardener, Laurence, Sir. 2003. *Realm of the Ring Lords-The Myth and Magic of the Grail Quest.* **Gloucester, MA: Fair Winds Press.**

Goddard, David. 1999. *The Tower of Alchemy: An advanced guide to the great work.* **Boston, Ma: Weiser books.**

Goldberg, Burton. 1993. *Alternative Medicine- The Definitive Guide.* **Fire, WA: Future Medicine Publishing, Inc.**

Govindan, Marshall. 1991. *Babaji and the 18 Siddha Kriya Yoga Tradition.* **Montreal: Kriya Yoga Publications. (www.babaji.ca).**

Graveline, Duane. 2004. *Lipitor, Thief of Memory: Statin drugs and the misguided war on cholesterol.* **Haverford, Pa: Duane Graveline.**

Griffin, Des. 1976. *Fourth Reich of the Rich.* **South Pasadena: Emissary Publications.**

Haas, Elson M. 1996. *The Detox Diet: The How-To and the When-To Guide for Cleansing the Body of: Sugar, Nicotine, Alcohol, Caffeine, Chemicals, and More.* **Berkeley, Ca.: Celestial Arts Publishing.**

Haigh, Charlotte. 2005. *The Top 100 Immunity Boosters: 100 Recipes to Keep your Immune System Fighting Fit.* **London, UK: Duncan Baird Publishers.**

Hansen, Mark Victor & Allen, Robert G. 2005. *Cracking the Millionaire Code.* **New York : Harmony Books.**

Hawkins, David R. 2002. *Power Vs Force: the hidden determinates of human behavior.* **Carlsbad, CA: Hay House.**

Hay, Louise L. 1988. *Heal Your Body: the mental causes for physical illness and the metaphysical way to overcome them.* **Carlsbad, CA.: Hay House, Inc.**

Heimlich, Jane. 1990. *What Your Doctor Won't Tell You.* New York, NY: Harper-Perennial.

Holmes, Ernest, 1997, 1938. *The Science of Mind.* New York: G.P. Putnam's Sons.

Horowitz, Leonard. 1996. *Emerging Viruses: Aids and Ebola- Nature, Accident or Intentional.* Sandpoint, ID: Tetrahedron Publishing Group.

Horowitz, Leonard G. & Puleo, Joseph S. 1999. *Healing Codes for the Biological Apocalypse.* Sandpoint, ID: Tetrahedron Publishing Group.

Icke, David. 1999. *The Biggest Secret- The book that will change the world.* Wildwood, MO: Bridge of Love Publications USA.

Icke, David. 1996. *I AM ME I AM FREE- The Robots Guide to Freedom.* Newark, UK: Bridge of Love.

Jasmuheen 2005. *Harmonious Healing & the Immortals Way.* Noosa Heads, QLD, Australia: Self Empowerment Academy.

Jasmuheen 2005. *The Law of Love & It's Fabulous Frequency of Freedom.* Noosa Heads, QLD, Australia: Self Empowerment Academy.

Knight, Jadczyk, Laura. 2005. *Secret History of the World and How to Get Out Alive.* Cyberspace?: Red Pill Press.

Kroll, Henry. 2002, 2005. Philosopher's Stone: Key to Eternal Life. West Conshohocken, PA: Infinity Publishing Co.

Kun, T. 1993. *Project Mind- The Conscious Conquest of Man & Matter Through Accelerated Thought.* Indian Rocks Beach, Fl. :Unimedia.

Laux, Marcus. 1995. *Is "Modern" Medicine Killing You?* Potomac, MD: Naturally Well Publishing. (www.drmarcuslaux.com & Naturally Well Newsletter).

LaViolete, Paul. 1997. *Earth Under Fire- Humanity's Survival of the Apocalypse.* Schenectady, NY: Starburst Publications.

LeLoup, Jean-Yves & Rowe, Joseph. 2002. *The Gospel of Mary Magdalene.* Rochester, VT: Inner Traditions International.

Marrs, Jim. 2000. *Rule by Secrecy: the hidden history that connects the trilateral commission, the freemasons, and the pyramids.* New York, NY: Perennial (www.jimmarrs.com).

McGraw, Philip, C. 1999. *Life Strategies: doing what works , doing what matters.* New York, NY: Hyperion.

Murray, Michael T., 1999, 1994. *Natural Alternatives to Over-the-Counter and Prescription Drugs.* New York: W. Morrow.

Murray, Michael & Pizzorno, Joseph. 1998. *Encyclopedia of Natural Medicine.* Rockland, Ca.: Prima Publishing.

Murray, Michael & Pizzorno, Joseph. 2005. *The Encyclopedia of Healing Foods.* New York, NY: Atria Books.

Murry, Steve. 2003. *Reiki the Ultimate Guide: Learn sacred symbols & attunement plus Reiki secrets you should know.* Las Vegas, NV: Body and Mind Productions.

Noah, Joseph. 2002. *Future Prospects of the World According to the Bible Code.* Boca Raton: New Paradigm Books.

Null, Gary. 2001. *The Complete Encyclopedia of Natural Healing: a comprehensive A-Z listing of common and chronic illnesses and their proven natural treatments.* New York, NY: Bottom Line Books.

Obissier, Patrick. 2003. *Biogenealogy: Decoding the psychic roots of illness.* Rochester VT: Healing Arts Press.

Orr, Leonard. 1998 Breaking the Death Habit: The Science of Everlasting Life. Berkeley, CA: Frog, Ltd.

Pearl, Eric. 2001. *The Reconnection: Heal others, heal yourself.* Carlsbad, CA: Hay House Inc.

Pearson, David. 1989. *The Healthy House Book: creating a healthy, harmonious, and ecologically-sound home environment.* New York: Simon & Schuster.

Pinkham, Mark Amara. 1997. *The Return of the Serpents of Wisdom.* Kempton, Ill.: Adventures Unlimited Press (www. adventuresunlimitedpress.com).

Rampa, T. Lobsang. 1963. *The Cave of the Ancients.* New York: Ballantine Books.

Rampa, T. Lobsang. 1971. *The Hermit.* London: Corgi.

Rampa, T. Lobsang. 1956. *The Third Eye- The Autobiography of a Tibetan Lama.* New York: Ballantine Books.

Rampa, T. Lobsang. 1965. *Wisdom of the Ancients.* London: Corgi Books.

Rogers, Sherry A. 2002. *Detoxify or Die.* Sarasota, Fl: Sand Key Co. (www.detoxamin.com).

Savoy, Gene. 2008. *Jamil: Child of light & messenger of God.* Reno NV: The International Community of Christ.

Savoy, Gene. 1983. *The Millennium Edition of the Decoded New Testament.* Reno, NV: The International Community of Christ.

Savoy, Gene. 1977. *Project X: the search for the secrets of immortality.* Indianapolis: Bobbs-Merrill.

Stein, Diane. 1995. *Essential Reiki- A Complete Guide to an Ancient Healing Art.* Freedom, CA: The Crossing Press, Inc.

Sutphen, Richard. 1986. *Sedona: Psychic Energy Vortexes.* Malibu, CA: Valley of the Sun Publishing.

Trudeau, Kevin. 2004. *Natural Cures "They" Don't Want You To Know About.* Hinsdale, Ill: Alliance Publishing Group, Inc.

Trudeau, Kevin. 2007. *Weight Loss Cures "They" Don't Want You to Know About.* Elk Grove Village, IL: Alliance Publishing Group, Inc.

Vogt, Douglas B. 2007. *God's Day of Judgment: The real cause of global warming.* Bellevue, WA: Vector Associates.

Wallach, Joel D. & Lan, Ma. 2004. *Dead Doctors Don't Lie.* Bonita, CA: Wellness Publications, LLC.

Wallach, Joel, D. & Lan, Ma. 1994. *Rare Earths: forbidden cures.* Bonita, Ca.: Double Happiness Publishing Co.

Weidner, Jay & Bridges, Vincent. 2003. *The Mysteries of the Great Cross of Hendaye: Alchemy and the end of time.* Rochester, VT: Destiny Books (www.adventuresunlimitedpress.com).

Weinland, Ronald. 2006. *2008 God's Final Witness: The prophesied end-time reveals the demise of the United States and the beginning of man's final war.* Cincinnati, OH: the-end.com, inc.

Yogananda, Paramahansa. 1946. *Autobiography of a Yogi.* Los Angeles: Self Realization Fellowship (www.yogananda-srf.org).

Yogananda, Paramahansa. 2004. *The Second Coming of Christ: The Resurrection of the Christ Within You.* Los Angeles: Self Realization Fellowship.

INDEX

158

161

XYZ

BOOK TWO

THE DA VINCI CODE REVELATIONS:

A ROADMAP TO HEALING AND ENLIGHTENMENT

BY LT. LAWRENCE FREGO, USNR (RET.), HKT.B

To Jasmuheen

Those who serve only themselves,

Serve another master,

Those who unselfishly serve others truly serve God.

FORWARD TO BOOK TWO

In 1990 I made a promise to God to search for cures for AIDS and cancer. The result was the first part of this book. Having accomplished this goal after 25 years of health research I decided to give cracking **The Da Vinci Code** a try. Contrary to the opinion of many doubters, there really is a Da Vinci Code and I miraculously was able to decipher it. Due to God's grace, I was given the secrets of the healing methods used by John the Baptist, Jesus and the Knights Templar. Using these ancient, secret symbols of the Templars I healed my own injuries and maladies in a rather spectacular fashion. Now I am 200% strong than before. My spiritual calibration has increased 600 times to the level of the "Christos Frequency."

This volume has many potential solutions to the 2,000 year old mystery of the life of Christ. The story unfolds more like a spy novel than a history, replete with many twists and turns. It is also a true story of hope and enlightenment for those who despair and have lost their way. "The Way" shown by Jesus, and his apostles, both men and women, blazes a trail across the centuries for us to follow back to God and his grace. Once "The Way" is understood, ANYONE can become enlightened and eventually attain the level of "A Christ." **Becoming attuned to the Christos Frequency is the ultimate healing method on this planet.** That is why it is found here in a health book. My experiences in using the "Knights Templar Method of Accelerated Healing" are contained in Appendix B. Attaining the level of the Christos Frequency is just a matter of perseverance and hard work. Sit back and enjoy the journey on this modern day quest for "The Holy Grail."

Namaste,

Rev. Lawrence Frego

INTRODUCTION: A SIMPLE PREMISE

The truth of the Da Vinci Code won't devastate mankind: it will save it!

What do you do next after spending 25 years researching cures for AIDS and cancer? Minds can't just sit idle you know! Well, crack The Da Vinci Code of course! It seemed to be the most tantalizing unsolved puzzle in the world at the moment. As I was a history major and well versed in research, I thought I'd give it a shot. Little did I know that my Da Vinci Code project would turn into a real life detective thriller and would change my life forever.

It all began innocently enough. I was more than a little miffed that so many seemed to relish debunking the issue of Christ's descendants. Debunking <u>The Da Vinci Code</u> has become a national sport, like football or soccer. Those of us who are aware that we are descended from Jesus and Mary Magdalene <u>aren't amused</u> by all of this! Therefore I thought I would enter the fray and see if the issues could be resolved.

I didn't have any preconceived ideas about what I might find or where the trail would lead. Like a bloodhound, I like just to pick up the trail and follow it until I arrive at the destination. The only game plan I had was to use behavioral kinesiology to steer me in the right direction whenever the normal trail was obscured. I considered the whole project as an intellectual exercise and as a test case to see what could be done applying the data from the collective unconscious in a new and novel way.

Applying this simple formula, it wasn't long before all hell broke loose spiritually speaking. I quickly found myself on new and challenging ground with more and more major revelations appearing miraculously on a daily basis. I was initially shocked and then overwhelmed! However I felt it was my duty to keep digging until I got to the bottom of it all. It was clear to me that millions of people were seeking answers and that I had an opportunity to deliver them. So, I rushed in where others feared to tread.

As I wanted to proceed in a logical, orderly, and consistent manner, I felt that an initial map of consciousness must be drawn. It's always helpful to have a baseline before proceeding into the unknown. And the rules of engagement had to be laid out so everyone could duplicate the results, if any were found. Therefore my first task was to design a chart of several dozen famous persons, both living and dead, and plot their spiritual calibrations using behavioral kinesiology. To my amazement a very clear pattern emerged with some obvious links to other data, and more than a few surprises. My perspective was on another level and didn't match those of David Hawkins. My questions were somehow different and therefore revealed much new information.

I started researching by purchasing 30 books on the subject to establish a baseline of the issues involved. The collection grew and grew as the work progressed. The works of Margaret Starbird and Sir Laurence Gardener proved the most useful. The first lead I followed was the similarity between the calibrations of the apostles and the Knights Templar. After some searching I found a missing link between Christ and the Templars.

After examining the preliminary evidence, it became clear to me that there were numerous alternative scenarios to every basic question posed in The Da Vinci Code. I tested the validity of the various scenarios and a whole new range of possibilities again literally jumped off the page.

Drawing from the baseline data, I was eventually able to crack the real Da Vinci Code. I discovered the hidden elements encoded into Leonardo Da Vinci's Last Supper and gained the secret symbols used by Christ and the Templars to heal the sick. The next day a photo of the real Holy Grail arrived in the mail and I decoded the symbols on it also. You might say I downloaded the information directly from the Holy Spirit to achieve enlightenment. I hadn't expected to achieve enlightenment in such a rapid fashion and had planned on studying for several more years to do so. God had other plans! My spiritual energy rose 250 times over a two week period and just "blew my socks off!" While this was the most challenging and physically uncomfortable spiritual progress I've ever experienced, the results were well worth it. My health and well being has improved dramatically.

From my new perspective and dramatic rebirth, I tried to look at the situation as Jesus and Mary would have experienced it. A little known 2,000 year old biography of Christ presented itself and eventually the larger picture emerged. I saw for the first time the fail-safe plan of Jesus and Mary to save the world. Proving this was at first difficult, but eventually I discovered the trail of the Christ descendants is clearly marked in the coats of arms of Europe's noble families.

Following the clues Christ left for us enables the sincere student to achieve enlightenment. To insure the trail is easy to follow, I have plotted it out mathematically. Achieving enlightenment is the ultimate key to health and the salvation of the planet.

This book is a roller coaster ride of historical and spiritual truth. Living it has changed my life forever and revealed my spiritual destiny. I sincerely thank Dan Brown for initiating this modern day quest for the Holy Grail. He has woken up an entire generation of spiritual seekers. My findings may shock many, but in the tradition of Mahatma Gandhi, I feel the truth must be told forcefully even if it offends. And like every good mystery novel, this book has a very dramatic surprise ending! I hope you enjoy this as much as Dan Brown's novel. It was both a pleasure and an epic adventure for me.

As this book brings to light so many hitherto unresolved mysteries of immense importance I wanted to make it immediately available to everyone. Therefore I decided to add this to my existing book so everyone could have it as a free bonus book. It is my sincere wish that this material makes the world a healthier, safer, happier place. The more enlightened souls we have on this planet the better. This book's goal is to make the process of enlightenment easier to achieve.

THE PLOT THICKENS

I generally dislike novels as they are usually pretty boring fare. Consequently, I haven't read one since forced to do so in American literature while at Potsdam State College thirty years ago. I prefer lost cities and ancient mysteries as a rule. That is why I joined The Explorers Club (www.explorers.org/). However, Dan Brown's The Da Vinci Code intrigued me. It sounded like a compelling mystery novel and after all the uproar and controversy it generated, I simply had to read it. I had to know what all the fuss was about. I watched the movie twice just to get up enough nerve to get through the novel and thoroughly enjoyed it. The book was quite a page turner and everyone agrees on that, but no one seems to agree on the basic theme of the movie. Nor does anyone seem to agree on anything else. As the novel brings up a large number of "heretical themes" the Roman Church would rather leave undisturbed, it was no surprise to me that a number of books appeared debunking The Da Vinci Code as history. I think it fair to say that debunking The Da Vinci Code has become an international sport, like soccer and football. Poor Dan Brown. No one has risen to his defense. To add insult to injury, the authors of **Holy Blood, Holy Grail** attempted unsuccessfully to sue him for stealing their intellectual property. New lawsuits are in the works. The lawyers are circling like sharks on the fresh scent of blood.

Fortunately for Mr. Brown, I have always been a passionate student of history. All the cast of characters in his novel are allegedly my ancestors and I have been studying them for decades. I am the descendant of over a thousand kings and queens. It's pretty easy actually, as they're all related to each other. If you get one royal line in your pedigree, you get them all, back to the Pharaohs of Egypt. They all liked to keep the money and power in the family business so to speak! Unfortunately, no one had the foresight to leave me anything in their wills. I'm a card carrying member of **The Somerset Chapter, Americans of Royal Descent**. More importantly for this story, I am a member of **The Order of the Crown, Descendants of Charlemagne**. Therefore I am in the line of those pesky Merovingians who supposedly married into the Grail family. I couldn't resist joining **The**

Magna Charta Barons either, and have fourteen of them including the St. Clairs of Rosslyn Chapel. Finally, as I am a descendent of the founders of the Knights Templars I recently joined **The Hereditary Knights Templars of Britannia**. It took over forty years of research to get into the first three aforementioned organizations. Trashing Dan Brown is one thing, but trashing my ancestors is another thing entirely. Eventually I began to get pretty ticked off and decided to investigate the themes posed by the novel and see if I could come to Dan Brown's aid.

My first book, **An End to All Disease** (www.authorhouse.com), was released on July 24th (2006), and I excitedly called my old buddy of twenty years, David Childress at **Adventures Unlimited Press** (www.adventuresunlimitedpress.com). I told him about my plans to vindicate Dan Brown and he told me that in fact Dan Brown was inspired to write the novel after reading David's lengthy introduction to an 1842 reprint of **The History of the Knights Templars** by Charles G. Addison. According to the court documents of the aforementioned trial, Dan Brown named David Childress as the inspiration for the novel. I am not shocked very easily, but this bit of information did catch me totally by surprise. So, for starters, let's clear Mr. Brown of stealing the theme of the novel from the authors of **Holy Blood, Holy Grail,** and we'll take it from there to clear him of all the rest.

I have examined a number of the books attempting to crack or decode the Da Vinci Code mysteries. I can sum them up quite simply by saying that they haven't. I am not going to name anyone in particular as I believe all do their best to the limits of their understanding. They meant well, but the reason that none of the debunkers has cracked the code is lack of qualifications. All the PhDs and titles of the physical world look very impressive on books and articles, but are of no value in cracking themes of this nature. Only an enlightened initiated individual can crack themes pertaining to ancient secret occult societies. To make an analogy, let's say that it would be quite improbable for a high school student in the 7th grade to crack the mysteries of a TOP SECRET nuclear government facility that requires clearance ten levels above the President of the USA, just to get to the snack bar. In this instance, unless you had six PhDs in nuclear physics, there really isn't much point in speculating what is in there. The same principles apply for the subject at hand. Their greatest sin, however, is that none of them even looked at the latest evidence by distinguished and eminently qualified authors such as **Sir Laurence Gardener** (www.graal.co.uk/).

Sir Laurence Gardener has published a treasure trove of books on the Grail Family. If you haven't read everything written by this knight, then you aren't informed on the subject. His classic, **Bloodline of the Holy Grail: the Hidden Lineage of Jesus Revealed**, filled in all the blanks where others feared to tread. Sir Laurence's latest book, **The Magdalene Legacy: The Jesus and Mary Bloodline Conspiracy** was written specifically to take the reader into the world of occult secret societies and explain its many mysteries and codes. The Bible was NEVER meant to be read by the common man. It is an encrypted history written by insiders "who knew the mysteries" and had no intention of revealing the greater mysteries to anyone but themselves. Unless you have the keys to the encryptions or are otherwise an enlightened person from another tradition, you're wasting your time trying to figure it out. It would take a great deal of time by an experienced code breaker and linguist just to figure out one paragraph. Fortunately Mr. Gardener is a knowledgeable man, a Knights Templar who shows us all the way inside this secret world. It's an incredible story and I will refer to his works as a starting point throughout this book. **Then using my own spiritual experiences, I will reveal some of the world's greatest mysteries.** In order to accomplish this goal we must first have a shared language: a means of communication that is precise. We'll need a system with the precision of mathematics as mere language is inadequate for the task. And this system must be very simple and easy to use in daily life. As the late American Indian shaman Sun Bear used to say, "If your philosophy doesn't grow corn, it is time to find a new one."

BABY, I'VE GOT YOUR NUMBER

Gratefully, such a system already exists and has been tested for accuracy millions of times. It is called behavioral kinesiology. The complete system is covered in David Hawkins' brilliant work, **Power Vs Force**. I first read about it in Taoist Master Jasmuheen's book, **The Law of Love**. I wrote to Jasmuheen and she granted me permission to use her material in my book. I am deeply grateful for this, as I feel this is the greatest system to come out in the last few hundred years. I've been using it daily and have made a number of shocking discoveries, that I will reveal here for the first time in print. Mr. Hawkins was correct when he predicted it had a multitude of untried uses and could be used to crack anything, including history. But first I must explain what the system is and how it actually works.

Every thought, word, and deed that ever happened in the history of the universe is recorded in the collective unconscious memory. Edgar Cayce and others call this collective memory by its ancient name: the Akashic records. For the sake of simplicity we'll refer to this solely by the name of the collective unconscious. Experienced psychics have the ability to tap into this body of knowledge and relay it to others. However, everyone on this planet and all the others in the universe, are all plugged in to the same collective unconscious. Like a computer program running in the background of your mind, it is ALWAYS there. You have only to become aware of this fact and know the very simple procedure for accessing all this data on any subject.

Computer language operates with a system of (+^{s}) pluses and (0^s) zeros. The collective unconscious operates with a language of either yes or no. Anything that increases the strength of the body is a YES. Anything that decreases the strength of the body or causes it harm is a NO. All you have to do to get a yes or no answer from the collective unconscious is a simple resistance test using your arm or your fingers. In the two-person method, the tester tries to pull down the outstreched arm of the test subject while presenting the test question. In the one-person method, the thumb and forefinger of each hand are locked together and one attempts to pull the fingers apart while asking the test question. If there is strength and resistance (the fingers go strong) that is a yes. If the fingers easily slide apart and go weak, then that is a no. That's all there is to it.

There are only a few small rules for using the behavioral

kinesiology system. The system is normally based on a numerical range of 0-1,000. 1,000 is assumed to be the spiritual calibration of Christ. A tester must have achieved a spiritual calibration of 200 or above on the scale to successfully administer a test. This is called the level of truth. Questions can not be asked about the future, as the future hasn't formed yet. Anything that is happening in the present time or the past is fair game. Before you ask a question, you must first ask permission and wait for the reply. And the question must be worded in a positive format. Just ask permission and then ask the question in a direct and straightforward manner. That is all there is to it.

Calibrating the various levels of consciousness provides a new road map to the mind and the parameters of human experience that few realize even exist. I was terribly enthusiastic about the system as it appears to validate my own Universal Theory of Disease. Jasmuheen has extended the system somewhat to incorporate the outer realms of spiritual experience. This is highly relevant to our discussion here today. The basic system parameters or levels of consciousness are as follows:

200 & below   Negative emotions of anger, fear, guilt or shame.

200   Beginning energy of truth and integrity

310   Calibration for hope and optimism

400   Reason and Wisdom

500   Energy of love

540   Energy of Joy

635   Disease Free System begins

637   Aging-Free System begins

668   Food Free and able to live on prana

777   Fluid Free existence

909   Physical Immortality

1367   Dematerialization and Rematerialization

1450   Ability to perform "classic miracles"

I was extremely excited about this map of consciousness because it shows that there is indeed a threshold of immunity at 635 and a level of physical immortality at 909 as I had predicted there would be in my book. The bad news is that only 1 person in 10 million calibrates over 600. The good news is that anyone who calibrates over 700 can counterbalance the negative energy of over 700,000 people. The beginning calibration of healers and saints starts at 540. Please commit these numbers to memory as we'll be using them frequently as we go along in this book.

After using this system for a while and getting comfortable with it, I realized that it could be used to generate any number of other maps of consciousness. I started to spiritually calibrate every famous person, living and dead, I could think of. It was so much fun, so fascinating, and so revealing, I even did it a few times driving down the thruway (Not recommended). This ability is quite irresistible. It obviously could open a whole new approach to sociology and the social sciences, not to mention psychology. Its potential uses are unlimited, as discussed in Hawkins' **Truth Vs Falsehood**. My very first map of human potential using the famous and the dead was a real eye opener revealing a greater truth than I had expected to find. Let me show you what I got and then I will analyze what I feel the results are and how this could shape the future of mankind and society. For starters, like Jim Carey's hilarious movie, LIAR LIAR, it would certainly put a lot of politicians out of work and force them to get real jobs. My map of the spiritual calibrations of the famous and the dead are as follows:

1450	Jesus upon leaving the tomb
1420	Babaji
1350	John of God, Brazil
1242	Lord Shiva
1240	Lord Krishna
1218	Marshall Govidian, Siddha yoga master
982	Buddha
980	The Dalai Lama
980	Gary Smith
974	Guardian of the Ark of the Covenant, Axum, Ethiopia
964	**Mary Magdalene, highest calibration in that lifetime**
944	Margaret Starbird
943	"David", a Kabalistic Rabbi
934	Mary Baker Eddy
933	**Mary Magdalene upon her marriage to Jesus**
933	Edgar Cayce, the Sleeping prophet
923	Yogananda
921	Mother Theresa
880	"Adam," a Canadian healer
821	Grand Master, Hereditary Knights Templars of Britannia.
780	Jasmuheen
733	Gordon-Michael Scallion
730	Dr. Wayne Dwyer/St. Francis of Assisi
722	Lori Toye
703	Gandhi
703	Mohammed, the Prophet
700	**Beginning of Enlightenment**
650	Dr. Gabriel Cousins
650	Sir Laurence Gardener, Knight
650	Average calibration of G.M., top 20 Knights Templars
650	Average calibration of Reiki Masters in the USA.
650	Steven Spielberg
643	Thomas Jefferson
642	**Donald J. Trump**
642	Andrew Jackson
632	Gen. George S. Patton

623	Elizabeth Claire Prophet
622	***** DAN BROWN *****
622	Little Pebble, Australia
621	Joan of Arc
620	King Arthur
617	David Koresh
552	Bill Gates
540	**Saints and healers, above this number**
522	**Leonardo DaVinci**
499	Albert Einstein
499	Sir Isaac Newton
435	Martin Luther King
433	John Lennon
433	Martin Luther
423	Tom Cruise
422	Abraham Lincoln
420	L. Ron Hubbard
333	George Washington
333	Clara Barton, Founder of the Red Cross
244	John F. Kennedy
214	Marilyn Monroe
213	Mel Gibson
212	Average 4 year seminary student
207	**Average Joe/Jane**
206	My dog, "Mini-Roo"
200	**<u>Threshold of Truth</u>**
182	**cocaine addicts and alcoholics**
182	Al Gore
175	The Pope
175	George W. Bush
175	Adolph Hitler
175	Richard Nixon
175	Napoleon Bonaparte
175	Franklin Delano Roosevelt
175	Stalin
175	Lenin
175	Mussolini

175	KKK, Grand Master
175	Anton LaVey, Founder of Church of Satan
175	Walt Disney
175	Michael Jackson
175	Benjamin Franklin
175	Ted Bundy
175	Jeffrey Dahmer
175	Bill Clinton
172	Genghis Kahn
144	Hilary Clinton
124	Vlad the Impaler, aka Count Dracula
123	**Anti-Christ entity & below**
111	**THE ANTI-CHRIST (A Palestinian)**

First, I would like unequivocally to state that I had no preconceived ideas on how this exercise in consciousness would pan out. None whatsoever! However it appears to have collated itself very neatly into groups that are immediately recognizable to anyone. There are the avatars of the world at the very top, the higher prophets, and the great souls of mankind all in the range of enlightenment. From **540-700** we have the range of saints and healers. Many of the great geniuses of the world calibrate around **500**. Below this we see the ranges of reason and optimism and the individuals there seem to fit very well. Unfortunately only 22% of the world's population calibrates over **200**. Below **200** there would appear to be a real can of worms I call the "psychopath zone" at around **175**. Their main defect is that they are all below the level of truth and are at odds with the creative forces of the universe. In short, they are the group called "in service to self." We see all sorts of strange bedfellows when we enter the zone of hate and revenge at **175** and below. There are war mongers, Nazis, Communists, serial killers, pedophiles, Satanists, clansmen and mass murderers. Liars of all sizes and descriptions. The anti-Christ wannabees and the real article are all on the bottom of the pile. A word of caution: DON'T DWELL ON THOUGHTS AT THE BOTTOM OF THE PILE. If you go there even for a moment, balance yourself back up by dwelling on the avatar range for a while. Spend some extra time "at the top" and miracles will begin to happen in your life. If you want a miracle to happen, focus at or above the 1,000 level ranges (Christ level range). I received one just by making this map.

I am not going to elaborate on any of the "service to self" psychopath group as I would prefer to go on living for a while longer in my present incarnation. All I will repeat is that **the zone of hate and revenge makes strange bedfellows** and leave it at that. I specifically didn't calibrate any TV evangelists as the 175 zone was already full. My calibrations seem to be much more "compassionate" than those assigned by David Hawkins. I can only infer this discrepancy is due to my own inherent nature. I also asked some questions differently and in a very specific way. This methodology was particularly true in regard to my questions about Jesus "the Nazorean" and Mary Magdalene, "the Magdal eder". This may explain why my answers were different, as I was more specific.

What is most important about this exercise is that you learn how to do it yourself and not take my word for it. It is more important to learn how to fish than for someone to give you one. **The underlying cause of the world's problems is simply a HUGE lack of discretion.** Very few people can discriminate between the false prophets and the real ones. It is very obvious to me that the masses of humanity are oblivious to their surroundings. How else can we account for the fact that nearly every country in the world uses Satan's money, instead of honest money: gold and silver, but they don't know it! Now you can calibrate anyone and act accordingly. Just because you're a loving human being doesn't mean you have to be a sucker. **Life demands discrimination.** Demanding that those you deal with stay "within the truth" is a justifiable action. That is why Alcoholics Anonymous works. They have learned to stay in the truth!

I found it quite interesting that the system could be so precise! I wondered why old Genghis Khan was three points lower than all the others, even Hitler. Not much difference in my book. Genghis apparently was responsible for the death of a great holy man calibrating at **1250**. This event lowered the spiritual calibration of the whole world at the time and hence his additional three "bad points."

The calibration for the prophet Mohammed also seemed too low (**703**) for such an important figure of such vision and great wisdom. The obvious answer to me appeared to be whether his involvement in warfare in any way was responsible for this lower score. His highest calibration in that lifetime was **943** or that of a higher prophet. His score was indeed lowered by involvement in warfare and its inevitable karmic consequences. David Hawkins also came to this exact same conclusion. I feel this is a valuable observation. For those of you who may feel that I am "anti-Muslim," I assure you I am not. I am also a descendant of the uncle of the prophet. Remember I mentioned that all royal lines are linked! The royal Spanish lines descend to the Princes of Arabia. The Spanish and Moorish lines mixed when the Moors invaded and ruled Spain. English monarchs had a talent for marrying Spanish princesses to prevent war with Spain. The lines go back to some very interesting rulers.

The calibration of David Koresh was also puzzling as something told me he didn't really deserve such a high rating. What I believe happened is that he got his high spiritual rating by taking a tempting shortcut: Satanism. Sometimes spiritual seekers want the quick and easy way to the top and are willing to sacrifice their principles for glory and power. Such is the case with David Koresh. He succumbed to the temptation and his personality became "cracked" or a split personality. One side was good and one evil. Evil got the better of him and destroyed many of his followers. There is a lesson here that one must ask twenty hard questions and not rely on just a spiritual calibration alone. Always ask all the hard questions before giving any measure of control over your life to anyone else. Just because someone has a high spiritual calibration doesn't necessarily mean they aren't psychopathic. Psychopaths can hide anywhere at any range. Always remember the symbolism of **"the wolf in sheep's clothing."** They are devious and cunning. They create false personas deliberately to throw everyone off their track. Just because some are loved by the public doesn't mean they aren't pedophiles, selling drugs, or making snuff flicks. Everyone who ever met Ted Bundy said he was such a sweet and charming guy. Until he kills you of course. The devil always has a handsome face and a sweet voice. Remember: twenty tough questions! That's my rule of thumb for sorting out the wolves from the sheep.

Spiritual calibration can be used as a starting point therefore into asking questions about history, as they leave a trail to be followed. We can trace a spiritual heritage from one age to another via the trail of calibrations of its practitioners. If our target person "pops up" in the saint and healer range for instance, we can sometimes trace back to the lifetime and exact person where this calibration was "earned." There are six billion people on the planet today, but only a few thousand great saints and healers. Christ had only twelve apostles and about 600 full time followers. This narrows the range down considerably when we are seeking answers in this general area. Is it a coincidence that the average calibration of Christ's apostles was **650**, the same as the "average" Knights Templar? **Is there a spiritual "trail" from Christ directly to the Templars right down to the present day?** Does this trail lead to famous individuals we know today? The answer to all of these questions is YES! They do. We'll get to this in a little bit, but first we need to make a more general map of the major starting points on the larger trail of enlightenment itself. This is one of the <u>world's greatest secrets</u> and it is essential knowledge if we are going to sleuth history for answers.

THE STAIRWAY TO HEAVEN

There are many references to "ladders" and climbing "the stairway to heaven" in the Bible, freemasonry and other occult texts. Actually there are two stairways to heaven, the other being a joy ride in an alien spacecraft. To clarify, I am not talking about that one. The stairway I am talking about involves slowly raising the spiritual calibration of the seeker towards the goal of enlightenment and beyond. Less than 1 in ten million achieve it, but it isn't too hard to do once you know how to accomplish it. Anyone can do it; it is just a question of desire, patience and perseverance. The achievement of enlightenment requires a spiritual plan.

As any wilderness guide or Boy Scout will tell you, before you plot a course to somewhere, you must first know where you are. The same holds true on the spiritual frontier. If you are above the level of truth, you may simply ask, "At the present time, my spiritual calibration is? Above **100**? Above **200**? Above **300**? And so on until you hit it. If you're an average Joe/Jane, you're in the **207** range. If you get a yes for above **200** and a no for above **300**, then you start to break it down and "walk it back up." Am I currently above **210, 220, 230**, etc? Wherever you stop, just walk back again. Ask about above **200, 201, 202, 203**, etc. until you get a yes. If it appears that you are below **200**, then ask a Reiki master to do it for you to establish your baseline calibration and work from there.

Every level of emotion and every disease has its own special frequency. Disease lives in low frequency "survival emotion" or base chakra emotions. At the very least we want to get out of the lower end of the human spectrum, above the level of truth and on our way towards the threshold of all disease and into enlightenment. Once we achieve enlightenment, we are literally "born again" in the truest sense of the word. A whole new heaven and a new Earth suddenly appear as if we had lived our whole lives in a fog bank.

I began my spiritual journey by reading all the works of Edgar Cayce. No one else had any answers to my health issues and he did. I credit the Edgar Cayce remedies with saving my life during the extremely difficult and painful period following my car accident in San Francisco in 1983.

Eventually I learned about Reiki, as I noticed a book about spiritual nutrition by Dr. Gabriel Cousins, a Reiki master. When I saw it I "knew" it was the one for me. I found Reiki master Suvarna Hannah, was treated three or four times, and then was off hiking the Andes with a backpack.

Reiki calibrates on the average as follows:

264 Reiki One

273 Reiki Two

323 Reiki Three

I did Reiki for about ten years and then felt the urge to move higher. I had many healing experiences and they are told in more detail in my first book. As usual I was looking for more. So I flew to Copenhagen, Denmark to have my aura "balanced" by Anni K. in an incredible four hour session. The results are as follows:

373 Aura Balancing in Copenhagen, Denmark

I was surfing the Rumor Mill News one day (www.RumorMillNews.com) when I noticed an article by Gary Smith about Sacred Merkaba Ascended Master training. As I still had a few kinks left in my neck and back, I thought I'd give it a try and see what happened. I had no idea how powerful an experience it would be.

384 Sacred Merkaba, ascended master training, level one

403 Sacred Merkaba, ascended master training, level two

These courses continue on through seven levels starting with level three at **444**, and then **464, 494, 514, 534** respectively. However as I didn't have the time or funds to complete these I had to seek out another way.

During the course of my research into the nature of disease I came across a book entitled: **The Mystery of the Great Cross of Hendaye: Alchemy and the End of Time**. When I saw the book my head "heated up" and I recognized it as something major in my quest for health knowledge and spiritual enfoldment. In a nutshell the book stated that the use of gold powders (Ormus) during the End Times would determine the fate of the Earth. I looked into 140 different formulas, but one made by Ambrosia Technology "spoke to me" as being the one for me (www.liquid-chi.com). Again when I saw the name of the formula, "Vulcan's Treasure," my head REALLY heated up and the energy started to pour forth, so I decided to try it. As I had been reading so much about Ormus and gold powders, I decided to do the entire regimen and see what happened. Needless to say, all hell broke loose and I started to heal all over my body. The details are in my first book. The calibrations are as follows:

Upon reading Jasmuheen's **Law of Love** and then David Hawkins' **Power Vs Force**, I found my initial spiritual assessment to be at **693**. This high number may have resulted from taking a formula called "The White Dove," a very powerful healing Ormus formula that calibrates at **720**. (I've tried many of them on an experimental basis.) I figured I would probably stay there quietly at **693** for years until I was initiated into yoga or some other momentous event. I could have just gone and sat upon Chimney Rock in Sedona, and absorbed an energy of **712** or Mt. Shasta, CA. at **912**. Not bad for sitting on one's butt! Few Westerners are aware of the incredible power of "sacred mountains" such as Mt. Kalais that comes in at **932**. I had also considered using various gold powders from Ascension Alchemy, as they have incredible properties. Their products range from a low of **722** with Hudson's Best to a high of **922** with Chrysalis 8. Their ascension acceleration line of products do just that. Their products are of the highest character and purity. I only used one a decade ago and had a Kundalini rising while doing so.

My spiritual plan was to complete the levels from Ambrosia Technology and then when ready start the levels from Ascension Alchemy and get myself "over the top" into enlightenment. That was the plan. I figured, "Heh, I have only seven points to go, right?" However, God had other plans. I had to stop on the last bottle of Merlin's Chalice as the healing intensity was too much for me. In particular, my teeth were killing me. I have a few cracked and chipped teeth and my new intense healing energy was going right to it in an attempt to heal them all. So I had to stop there, take pain killers for a few weeks, and just back off and let things settle on the new level. Healing takes its own sweet time and can't be forced or pushed. I had broken my hand in seven or eight places in the Coast Guard during a little scuffle with a guy nicknamed "Tree." In case you never met him, he was the twin brother of "jaws" in the James Bond movies. Really stupid idea on my part! I was doing Reiki for many years but it never got to my broken hand until about seven years later. Then it finally dealt with the traumatic remnants there. So, I have learned to be patient and to treat every inch of my body upon reaching each new level of healing. When it is time, a new way to reach a new level will appear. What happened next many would describe as a miracle. No one could have been more surprised than I was.

The small town of St. Augustine, Florida is "a quaint drinking village with a fishing problem." There really isn't much to do here unless you either drink or fish. Due to the beautiful beaches however, some interesting and fascinating people come to town from time to time. Millions of tourists come here annually. Eccentric billionaires, the New York Social Register crowd, movie stars, ghost hunters, psychics, famous authors, playwrights, Robert Ripley, a couple serial killers and Spanish conquistadors all have called this place home. Movie crews love it. Part of the movie "The Celestine Prophecy" was shot here, right where I am sitting now. Then they all go home to someplace else. So then, it's back to diapers, cats, dogs, hamsters, Chuck E. Cheeses, and other mundane fare unless you can find something interesting to do. And go to church of course.

To beat the monotony, my mother used to do genealogy, clean up graveyards, and host psychic classes. I got into the rhythm of this in the winter months as there is nothing else to do here. I took Reiki classes and psychic classes with the late "licensed" psychic, Kay Mora. We always had a wonderful time and made dozens of new friends. I'd also run off on an expedition to Peru, Bolivia, Brazil, Panama or somewhere whenever I could, meaning when I had money. I'd also travel for classes and other spiritual work. I even visited Istanbul twice, and popped into Copenhagen and London as well. Working on the research for my book took up a lot of slack time for 25 years.

When I finished it last month, the movie "The DaVinci Code" came out. I saw it twice, despite the best efforts of a couple of protestors out in front of Blockbuster waving signs. I never figured out exactly what it was they were protesting. If I were doing the protesting, I'd protest why Robert Langdon never put a huge "lip lock" on Sophie Neveu. I would have, had it been I. Of course the movie has some other major flaws, besides the neutering of Tom Hanks.

All together my mom, sister, and various cousins have put more than a total of 100 years worth of research into our family genealogy. It has been a major family obsession. My cousin Lenice Watson had decided she wanted to join **The Order of the Crown, The Magna Charta Barons, Americans of Royal Descent, The Plantagenet Society and the Descendants of the Order of the Garter.** Like a super-sleuth she flew all over the world and tracked all the ancestors down. And of course she sent all the work to me and my mother and we all caught "the bug" as well. (We used to get invitations to stay with the Queen of England annually, until all this terrorist stuff happened). Kind of like "gold fever" except more expensive. We acquired a few thousand new cousins and they all pitched in also. As I had all the paperwork, books, and charts going all the way back 6,000 years on some lines, I figured I'd be a natural to really crack The Da Vinci Code once and for all. The pile of material we have must be over five feet high, not counting the thousands of photographs going all the way back to our thirteen Revolutionary War veterans.

I started collecting the relevant books, such as **The Templar Revelations** and **The Magdeline Legacy: the Jesus and Mary Bloodline Conspiracy**. I had a pile of 30 books in short order. However, books are only a base line. The rest of the story lies in the collective unconscious and I wanted to probe there also to see what might "pop up." I have on occasion seen the future. Usually only when it is of immense importance and charged with energy. More frequently I can "see" the past. Sometimes when the information is extremely important to me personally, I see the past lives of people when I touch them. Kind of like Johnny Smith in The Dead Zone, except in reverse. This began to occur more frequently after I took the second level of Ascended Master training. I have always seen past lives when doing Reiki since day one. The fifth level of gold powders, Phoenix Fire, seemed to open the floodgates of past life memories for me. I got a couple dozen of them in a two week period. Wow! Really good ones too, except for being burned at the stake a few times. And losing my head a few times, etc. How about taking a lion to lunch? No wonder I hate Rome! Bummer!! I gathered enough information about myself to plug in information about the others around me. And I figured out my soul's purpose. It appears that since the opening up of America I've been here primarily, and waiting only an average of five years before reincarnating back. So much to do and so little time to do it I guess! Ever have that "urge" to go to the Alamo? If you do, it's because you were killed there just as I was. Some lives are daring adventures. And some are not, but who cares about those anyway? I'm only going to reveal one exact name out of over 250: **John B. "Texas Jack" Omohundro**, as that was a fun lifetime, I look exactly the same in the photos and it is a good illustration of how past lives work (www.texasjack.org). All the rest I feel are my business and no one else has "the need to know." I will only describe them in general terms.

Although spiritual calibration is so simple to use and so much fun, I've found it is the most useful tool for past life associations. Although I learned it only recently, I find myself doing dozens of them per day. Especially fun on dating websites, as you can pick out all the saints and ax murderers. Quite the challenge when it is revealed to you that many of the people in your life are those who've murdered you in the past in hideous ways. Or that you've murdered them. I think this is something that happens when one begins to get to the bottom of what I call "the karmic barrel." If you've cleaned up all the easy stuff, then there is nothing but the hard stuff left to handle. The higher in spiritual calibration you go, the harder the tasks become. However there is a solution. I make it a rule never to confound anyone with a problem without giving them a possible solution. All you have to do is ask the question and you will receive the answer! If you find yourself surrounded by murderers from past lives, have multiple health issues, financial issues, keep crashing cars, or any other negative issues, there is a solution. It may not be easy, but it is the answer. What is necessary is to list your current problems and then ask "What spiritual calibration is necessary to dissolve them?" Our Science of Mind minister, Reverend Elizabeth Claire, notes that most of us go through life like little angry bees in a bottle. Always angry about our circumstances in life and buzzing against the glass of life, when all we have to do is ascend upwards and fly out the top of the bottle. As I appear to have hit a patch of heavy karma that's been going on unresolved for many thousands of years I asked the question as per how much was needed to resolve it. The answer was **920**. I just happen to know a gifted healer in Turkey who is of that exact calibration and plan to have him assist me with the job. Like a Qi Gong Master, he can move people from across the room with his hands. When I saw him do it I was very impressed. So, that seemed like a very logical solution to my problems.

In the course of doing all this research and looking for answers, I decided to calibrate all the avatars at the upper range and see who was who. I spent a lot of time calibrating the lives of Jesus and Mary Magdalene at various times, places, and circumstances to find answers. I also calibrated all the apostles and various saints to see who had been doing what and where. I also calibrated John the Baptist and all the other players in the grail story. I continued to use spiritual calibration as a research tool and spent a lot of time in the area above **920** and into what I believe is **"the Magdalene frequency."** Then it happened! I was caught totally by surprise!

THE PASSING OF THE CROWNS

Like death itself, enlightenment comes in like a thief in the night. No one knows the exact hour of either. One day a couple of years ago I was lying in my bed dreaming half in and half out. I had sort of a dream about a multitude of ascended masters in their skeletal forms with their clothes in rags from the grave. If you've seen the ghostly pirates in "The Pirates of the Caribbean," you know what I'm talking about. I could only identify one of them as El Morya, as he had a turban on his head. Each ascended master came up to me with a golden crown of a different size and shape and then placed it on my head. In this dream I received about a dozen crowns from various ascended masters. Obviously they were all dead, but I am very much alive, so I felt that the task now falls to me. I've received lots of info about crowns and their metaphysical significance in the past. The purpose of a crown is to hold the gems in place over the third eye and the head to keep the proper "vibration" of the wearer. Same principle as the Breastplate of Aaron, except it works on the crown chakra instead of the heart chakra. In any event, I blew it off and didn't pay much attention. I get interesting things all the time.

The next day after "the crown passing ceremony," I received something totally different and unprecedented in my present life experience. As mentioned earlier I had been calibrating events in the lifetimes of Jesus, Mary Magdalene, John the Baptist, Leonardo Da Vinci and the apostles. I was also thinking very intently about the possible meaning of the **"John gesture"** in Da Vinci's famous painting, **"The Last Supper."** I'd been trying to crack it for a few weeks. In my half asleep, half awake state, I got the urge to raise my left index finger in a John gesture, while lying there in bed. (I am left handed and my left hand is my primary healing hand). When I raised my finger in the John gesture, I received an imprint of **"the healing activation code"** on it. Then I received the correct symbols of John the Baptist/the Knights Templars to use to download massive amounts of healing energy. Somehow I had been initiated into the mysteries by the Holy Spirit.

This incredible flow of energy coursing through my hands just blew out all the old energy in my left hand, like gout leaving the body. It hurt a bit, but I knew the benefits would soon follow as this happens at every level. A bolt of electricity ran along a nerve or meridian of energy in my right arm. It hurt like hell and just blew out everything there. As I had both hands on my heart during this, my heart then had a "sonic boom" and popped out a wave of energy about a foot from my chest. It was a scary ride there for about 10 seconds, but as soon as I realized I'd opened my heart chakra and wasn't going to die or anything, I calmed down. My spiritual calibration shot up 10 points to **703**, which is the beginning of enlightenment. Wonderful news, but there are 750 more levels to go. I figured this was enough excitement for one day, so I got up and cooked dinner. This was the **26th of July 2006.**

The next day Maurice Cotterell's **JESUS, KING ARTHUR, AND THE JOURNEY OF THE GRAIL: the Secrets of the Sun Kings** arrived in the mail. This book has a photo of the legendary Holy Grail on the cover and very detailed blueprints of it inside. (1) It's incredibly beautiful! I was thinking about it when I went to bed and while asleep I "remembered" the encoding on the Holy Grail. Then all hell broke loose metaphysically speaking. My head felt as though I had diamonds for hair, chakras in my left ear blew out and I had a blaze of past life experiences all flash by. Thousands of years worth in sixty seconds. Got a hell of a headache as my head was engulfed in light. I felt as if someone had put my head in a microwave, shut the door and pushed COOK ON HIGH. My eyes were "irradiated" and burning. My eyebrows were jumping and twitching as if they were downloading a program. It felt as though my head and eyes had been irradiated and burned for a couple of days. When I went to work and listened to the radio, I felt like Stevie Wonder on crack. I was out dancing in the rain. I was in ecstasy for days. Then I got crabby and irritable for a few days. I was wondering if I had been reincarnated as a blues musician for a while. Every piece of music just went right through me. My spiritual calibration shot up from **703** to **742**, then **832** in a couple of days, then up to **943**. What a rush! In the last "installment" of this energy I felt that I could see "into" the future as in a dark glass. I saw large tanks there firing shells in the desert in Israel. My vision had a sort of 3D quality to it for days as if I were seeing things from the viewpoint of an IMAX theatre. Time just seemed to "slow down" and I could touch it. My head and third eye were "hot" for weeks. This all took place in just a week's time, so it was quite an adjustment. All sorts of aches and pains "came out," hurt like hell and healed; then calmness settled in. I can breathe effortlessly now. My arms are so much stronger. I experienced another "body wave" healing that cleared my whole body and just blew everything out. I lost some weight and am standing much taller now. The energy is soft like talcum powder, but very powerful. I'm still releasing blocks of energy in my hands and elsewhere all the time. Sometimes it's rather painful, but I am used to it. The pain and discomfort generally lasts for only ten seconds, but the benefits last forever.

Why have I shared all this information with you? First of all, I want everyone to know that ANYONE can do this. The good news is that the energy flow to the planet is about 43 times stronger than it was before. Christ is reputed to have said that everyone would be able to do greater feats than he. The bad news is that this is because it is the End Times. It's time either to learn or to be in deep manure. Therefore I want everyone to be encouraged to begin, because without small steps there can be no journey. Secondly, the past life "remembrances" and associations I've made are directly related to this story. I remembered the secrets of the Templars because I was one. I remembered the secrets of the grail because I was there when Christ passed it around to his followers. The last supper took place in my parent's house in that lifetime when I was nine years old. I believe Christ taught me the symbols personally and that is how I remembered them. I was not an apostle, but knew them all well. (I know them in this life as well). I was too young at the time to be one. But I was a member of the 600 who followed Christ in that lifetime and have suffered a martyr's death many times as a Christian. And finally, if you'll forgive my vanity, I am tired of people kicking my ancestors around in this life. So, I thought I'd give everyone the other side of the story. You can do with it what you will.

The whole issue of past lives and karma is the hidden determining factor of history. In the West we live in a culture that has done its best to erase this knowledge from the masses so they can be controlled and robbed. What is left of the Bible has been edited over 26,000 times. It calibrates at only **500**, because it has been cut in half. If we were in a culture such as that of India that is immersed in reincarnation as a religion and way of life there would be no big Da Vinci Code story. The people on the streets would calmly say, "Oh, Dan Brown must have had a past life in that period and therefore wrote about it now." My friends that is exactly what happened. **When Dan Brown read about the Templars something clicked and he "remembered" being one on the subconscious level. He remembered because he was one of the original nine Templars who camped upon King Solomon's Temple in that time period. He wrote about the Grail family and the Grail, because he was the apostle known as St. Jude. His name is carved on the Holy Grail. So he has a right** to write a novel if he damned well wishes to. He is fulfilling his spiritual mission in this life by creating an interest in the spiritual world. Ultimately, he is part of the preparation process for the next coming of Christ. He is doing his job and I think he has done it well. The people hunger for the truth and he has created the desire for the masses to look for it again after 2,000 years of lies, murder, torture and repression. Looking from the perspective of one who was burned at the stake during the Inquisition in a previous life, I have no intention of white-washing the activities of the Roman Church. They bear a great deal of responsibility for the mess in which the world currently finds itself. We are still in the darkness they created. Let's call a spade a spade and be done with it. I guess this puts me firmly out there on the limb with Shirley MacLaine (www.shirleymaclaine.com) but the time has come. Socrates used to ask, "What is truth?" With the very simple suggestions I have provided here, you can look for it yourself. Don't take my word for it. That is the lesson. Get off your butt and look for it. Everything is recorded in the collective unconscious for you to read.

HISTORY IS A LIE EVERYONE AGREES ON

As a history major at Potsdam and Fredonia State colleges in New York state I learned the rules for researching history. Rule # 1 is that "history is always written by the winners" and the losers usually get killed. Therefore history is "a lie that everyone agrees on." In order to find out what really happened one must dig, dig, dig, until all sides of the story can be presented. Only then can a balanced picture emerge.

A fundamental rule in solving any crime is to "follow the money." Money, as we know, means both power and control. The "details" of the ruthless pursuit of power is the most fundamental key to solving this historical puzzle. The story of Jesus and Mary Magdalene, the Roman Empire and the Catholic Church is a classic example of the victors attempting to rub out all traces of the vanquished. As David Icke says, "It's all about control."

Jesus the Nazarene was of the line of King David and Solomon and therefore had legitimate title as a priest-king of Israel. Likewise his wife Mary Magdalene, the high priestess, was descended from the royal house of Israel, the Hasmonaean House of the Maccabees. As man and wife they posed a direct threat to the Roman occupation and conquest of Israel. As priest (rabbi) and priestess, they posed a threat to the established temple cults of the time. Therefore those in power, both religious and secular, wanted them both dead. They and their zealot compatriots, otherwise known as apostles, were branded "subversive" and marked for death. After the execution of James Boanerges, Mary Magdalene decided to flee to Gaul in 44 AD. The apostles were implicated in the death of King Herod-Agrippa 1st of Jerusalem, and had to flee for their lives, but not all of them made it out alive.

The great Jewish revolt occurred in 66 AD and was put down by a massive Roman army which slaughtered 6,500 inhabitants of Jerusalem and enslaved the rest. Emperor Vespasian issued orders that anyone from the royal house of David be found and killed. All records of the royal genealogy of Jesus and Mary were burned. Roman authorities wanted no competing claims to their unholy rule of Israel. All blood relatives of Jesus, known in Greek as "the Desposyni" or "heirs of the Lord," were forced to flee in all directions. Jerusalem was left a burned out ruin of a city for over sixty years as an example to all who choose to oppose the rule of Rome. The Romans wanted to rule the world and would let no one live to get in their way. It was a very simple scenario: kill all opposition.

In similar fashion, the Desposyni posed a threat to the control of the Roman Catholic Church. The descendants of Jesus and Mary, as well as those of Jesus' four brothers (James, Joses, Simon, and Judas) and at least three sisters (Mary, Salome, and Joanna) all had a greater entitlement to rule the church than those claiming apostolic succession. The Roman church had direct competition in what became known as the Eastern Orthodox Church, which was run by blood relatives of Jesus and their descendants. Even worse than that, some of these bishops of the Eastern churches were women, in the tradition established by Christ. Meanwhile back in France, where Mary Magdalene came ashore in Provence, churches dedicated to the Magdalene were springing up all over. Hundreds of them. The descendants of Christ wanted to become bishops in the Roman Church in 318 AD and move the Church back to its roots in Jerusalem. Needless to say, the Church threw them out on their ears. When Emperor Constantine made Christianity a state religion, he set himself up as both a god and an emperor. He didn't want anyone around claiming to be a descendant of "the son of God" either. A unified church and state had no room for a legitimate competing line of priest-kings. When the Roman Empire collapsed, the Popes stepped into the vacuum as the new priest-kings and did their best to conquer the world where the Roman emperors left off. The Catholic Church had its own army, navy, banks and palaces. It claimed superiority over all the kings of Europe. The Roman church ruled nearly half the world until the British Empire supplanted it. The last 2,000 years has been an endless attempt to erase the memory of Jesus and Mary and their blood relatives and descendants. They stood in the way of empire building, as did pure the sect of the original Christian faith: the Cathars of Provence. The church would attempt to destroy them all. However, like the French resistance fighters of WWII, the Desposyni, the Cathars and the Knights Templars all went underground and kept on fighting to survive to this very day. This is their story.

THE HOLY GRAIL

We must ask ourselves what was so special, unique, and powerful, that the greatest army in the world would fear one man, one woman, and twelve rag-tag followers? Why would a religion that was in business for several thousand years be worried about a small sect of preachers and healers? Why would a church supposedly founded in the name of this man be concerned that remnants of his original teachings survived over a thousand years later? Are these teachings so radical that they could topple churches and governments even two thousand years after the death of the founders? What is this body of secrets that untold thousands have died to protect?

The first mistake that most researchers into the Holy Grail and the Sang Real (the Royal blood) make is that they don't know where to begin the search. The first key lies in ancient Babylon, as this was the home of the Anunnaki or "those who came down from heaven." This race of beings came from what was called the tenth planet and periodically comes to Earth when the Earth is in close proximity approximately every 3,600 years. As the Earth had become more or less depopulated after the flood, it was necessary to create more workers to perform the tasks of "their lords," the Anunnaki. Consequently seven males and seven females were created in test tubes of half human and half Anunnaki stock from Lord Enki. The resultant "Adama" and his partner, Eve, were to be the work force to serve their rulers. The first "Adama," called Adapa, became the first anointed (by Enki himself) priest king to manage the kingdom and lands (plantation) of E.den along the Tigris and Euphrates Rivers. He was to build cities and "manage" the people and instruct them according to the will of the Anunnaki. In short he was the first bureaucrat and paper-pusher, although clay tablets were the writing media of the time.

The Anunnaki were said to be immortals, but after a period of time on planet Earth their longevity began to fade. They intermarried to preserve their special bloodlines, but this also was insufficient to maintain their immortal status. To revive their longevity, they created hormonal extracts derived from the sacred blood of the females. This extract was called "The Star Fire." It is the original holy blood and the bloodline referred to is that of the extraterrestrial master race of the Anunnaki.

Again, after a period of time, The Star Fire extract was insufficient to continue the task of immortality. White gold powders were created to assist. These powders are what we could call today alchemical gold powders or Ormus materials. As these powders were substitutes for the original Star Fire extracts, they also acquired the name of Holy Grail or Sangraal. In truth, they were originally designed to preserve the holy blood of the Anunnaki priestesses or Queens. A figurine of a Sumerian Goddess figure from 5000 BC, shows either their very obvious reptilian features or their distinction as the ugliest women who ever lived. You can decide for yourself. See Gardener's very informative **Genesis of the Grail Kings: the Pendragon Legacy of Adam and Eve.**

It is from <u>this</u> "royal" bloodline, through the pharaohs of Egypt, that the tribes of Israel sprang, leading to the royal house of King David. The DNA of the House of David still bears its proportionally higher evolved Anunnaki structure. In short it is better able to store larger quantities of higher frequency information. It has a higher electrical capacity than "ordinary" humans. Ultimately, it is more spiritually capable, more expandable and better able to evolve into new DNA forms. It is eleven strand DNA as opposed to the more "human" eight strand DNA. It can store more light!

The use of specific Ormus materials, such as white powdered gold made in the ancient manner "of the Gods of heaven," can speed up the cellular communication process as much as 10 million times. Gold in this form is a super-conductor of electricity. The knowledge of making Ormus or alchemical powders was preserved in the ancient mystery schools of Egypt and India. The great pyramid of Egypt is approximately 38,500 years old. Its true history is recorded on The Emerald Tablet by Hermes, its builder. The Emerald Tablet is made from pure gold Ormus glass. In one of its alchemical powdered states, gold becomes a glass (This is the same Ormus glass used in the great cathedrals of France during the renaissance). The mystery schools of India also preserved this knowledge as the immortal yogis survived the flood by inhabiting the Himalayas.

The individual known as Jesus was a descendant of this very special line of the royal house of David. He also was an initiate of the Egyptian (Pyramid) mystery school of Osiris. While in India Jesus became an initiate of the mystery school of Shiva. He was also associated with the Essenes of Qumran who lived along the Dead Sea. The Arabic word asayya is of the same root and means physician. The Essenes were a sect of alchemists and mystics (a mystery school) who made Ormus products derived from the salts of the Dead Sea. As white gold powder "heals" or converts DNA into its correct structure and opens the initiate "to the light." Those who master it are therefore physicians or healers. Alchemy was a tradition in the family of Jesus as his father Joseph was a "master of the craft" or master of high alchemy as was his brother James. Jesus consequently became "enlightened," became aware of who he was and of his purpose upon the Earth. However, the secret of his true purpose has been kept from us, as to do so would set us free from the bonds of tyranny. I will reveal this in due time as we proceed.

THE CHALICE OF ARDAGH

The chalice known to history as "the Holy Grail" was taken to England by "the Joseph of Arimathea" (St. James the brother of Jesus) approximately six years after the crucifixion. The chalice was used by St. James at Glastonbury, England during the founding years of his missionary church. It was kept at various monasteries on a rotational basis to protect it for nearly 1,000 years. It is believed to have been buried for safekeeping during the period of Viking raids and there remained lost for nearly another 1,000 years. In 1868 the so-called Ardagh hoard was found in an ancient earth fort called Reerasta Rath in County Limerick, Ireland. Paddy Flanagan and Jimmy Quinn were digging for potatoes on land rented from an order of nuns who owned the property. The treasure consisted of two chalices, one quite magnificent, the other a cheaper version from a later date, and four silver brooches. The hoard was sold for 50 pounds to the Bishop of Limerick and then later to the Royal Irish Academy for 500 pounds in 1873. The chalice was originally dated to around 750 AD due to inscriptions of the names of the apostles and its association with the other items found. Upon closer scientific study it was seen to be more representative of the La Tene III style from the Eastern Mediterranean circa 150-50 BC. The carving and script having been identified as a crude later edition possibly made around 500 AD with what appeared to be a nail point.

The Ardagh chalice is currently on display at the National Museum of Ireland in Dublin (http://www.museum.iel). However even to begin to understand the complexity of its manufacture or the incredible esoteric content it conveys a full set of blueprints is required. Such a set is contained in Maurice Cotterell's book: **Jesus, King Arthur, and the Journey of the Grail: the Secrets of the Sun Kings**. The mystery begins with an inventory of its intricate parts,

354 in all. The main bowl is spun silver, eight panels are made of gold plated bronze, some of the inlaid matting is made from copper, and some from bronze. There is a lead ring, a quartz crystal, glass studs and wax decorations on its solar emblems. I would estimate that it took twelve men sixteen months to make it, not counting design planning time. NASA would be hard pressed to duplicate it today at enormous expense. Perhaps upwards of a million dollars in today's money. Not exactly the work of a poor carpenter turned preacher from the sticks. It is an incredibly brilliant work of art conveying ancient esoteric information that I feel existed tens of thousands of years ago. The decoding of it reveals that the chalice was created by a perfected being: a Sun of God. It contains the super science of the sun, the solar wind and the next "end of the world" in complex mathematical calculations. And finally to drink from it the thumbs must be placed through the two dragon handles and come into contact with studs resembling nails. The result is what Cotterell calls a "virtual crucifixion." It's construction, content and message all identify it as having been made by Jesus, the Alpha and the Omega or the morning and evening star. This would also indicate that the crucifixion was a planned event as the Grail would have been in the planning stages at least several months before it's lengthy construction. As mentioned earlier in this book, it contains both the "activation codes" and the symbols required to raise the spiritual calibration of the initiate towards enlightenment and "a Christ" level of consciousness. As it represents "the light," it glows in the dark from the quartz crystal in the base. I can think of no other object on Earth that so nearly perfectly fits the description of The Holy Grail. Maurice Cotterell promised to deliver the secrets of the ancients in his book and he certainly did deliver them. See the following website to view the chalice: (www.celtic-weddingrings.com/ardagh-chalice.asp).

There is however a missing dimension of the Holy Grail that was never explained by Cotterell. How does a silver chalice glow in the dark? The only metal that I am aware of that glows in the dark is WHITE POWDERED GOLD (Ormus gold). I believe there are five ormus elements blended into the silver chalice that account for its electrical generating capacity and therefore the ability to glow in the dark. I believe the five elements represent the 5th civilization to come as this one will soon pass away. The blend of ormus elements acts as a superconductor to generate the small electrical current needed. The calibration/frequency of the grail is **999 or THE CHRIST FREQUENCY**, as it says on the encoded base. The resultant frequency raises the spiritual calibration of the initiate from **666**, the level of a man to **999, the level of a Christ**. The **666** represents the baser instincts of man. The lower chakra survival instincts of reptilian (brain) nature of man. The **666** "mark of the beast" is the threshold of, or cutoff point between, human nature (reptilian brain survival instincts) and the beginning of the path to enlightenment on the way to becoming **"a Christ."** In effect the balanced ormus elements frequency acts as a **TRANSFORMER "INTO THE LIGHT."** Therefore, only Christ himself could drink from it and receive **"the 999 effect"** via the nail studs on the chalice. Only Jesus ever drank from it and became a perfected being. This knowledge is essential to our understanding of events centered on the crucifixion.

THE DESPOSYNI

The Sang Real or Holy blood is also associated with the family and descendants of Jesus. If Jesus had five brothers and four sisters, that would be a total of 10 counting Jesus himself. Certainly not uncommon for the day. Such a number would multiply rapidly except for the fact that all of the "DESPOSYNI" or dispossessed "heirs of the lord" were marked for death by the Romans. The Temple priests were also more than happy to see them all executed. **Edgar Cayce's Story of Jesus** goes into some detail about the tribulations of the early Christian sect and how they tried to elude all their numerous enemies. Given the circumstances, it is no surprise that Mary Magdalene fled to Provence, France around 44 AD in an effort to keep herself and her children alive. Therefore the very first reason that we hear little about the children of Jesus and Mary Magdalene is that they essentially were on the run from those who would kill them. Simple enough story line I believe. However their movements are encrypted into various stories of the bible, so those with "eyes to see" would know, and those who meant them harm wouldn't know.

One of the codes used by the Essenes was the Atabash cipher. To use the code, the first eleven letters of the Hebrew alphabet were exchanged for the last eleven letters. All twenty-two letters were then reversed. So those "with a need to know" the true meaning of the coded message, the phrase, "for those with eyes to see" was placed before the message to be decoded. The keys to the various codes used are referenced in the plain text. An example of the key code to the Atabash cipher is Mathew 19:30, "But the first will be last, the last will be first." Obviously, when the plain text is translated into another language all the codes are lost in translation.

As Jesus was continuously a hunted man his code name was "the word of God." So when it says that the "word of God" went to Gaul or elsewhere, it is the code word for Jesus actually going to Gaul or Malta in the flesh. And if matters weren't difficult enough to track the whereabouts of everyone, great use of sacred or monastic titles were used to designate individuals. We have distinctions such as "a Mary," "a Joseph" and "a Sarah" (high priestess or princess). In short, we have little idea of who all the players in the story really are, as they are normally only mentioned by their titles. And the titles repeat as each succeeding generation takes over the titles of their fathers and mothers. To preserve the history of the descendants of Christ, symbols and codes were used in art, literature and numerous paintings to keep the knowledge alive, but only to those with a need to know. Attempts to murder the Grail line have been ongoing for the last 2,000 years. The first child of Jesus and Mary, Tamar "the Sarah," (princess) was apparently killed in Rome along with her husband St. Peter. In the year 208, the Emperor Septimius Severus attacked the Vienne Estate where Mary Magdalene had lived and murdered 19,000 Christians in the area. The next major onslaught was the Albigensian Crusade of 1209 when Simon de Montfort and a papal army of 30,000 soldiers descended on the south of France to destroy the Cathars. Many Cathar aristocratic families were Christ descendants and the Catholic Church wanted them all dead. Torture was used to induce confessions as to the secrets of Jesus and Mary and the whereabouts of the Grail bloodline. These confessions were recorded and are still in existence in the archives of the Holy Inquisition.

This persecution has continued to modern times with Hitler's extermination of six million civilians and Stalin's extermination of perhaps forty million. Even Saddam Hussein has played his role in exterminating a branch of the ancient Johnnite tradition called "the marsh Arabs." There is more yet to come. If the anti-Christ is allowed to realize his full expression, he will certainly attempt to exterminate all of Western civilization and totally eliminate any traces of the bloodline. He will seek to continue where Hitler left off.

The whole issue of the marriage of Jesus and Mary Magdalene is heretical to the Orthodox Catholic Church for a very simple reason. The orthodox church of Rome seized the power of the Christian religion and made a fortune doing so. It's all about the money! If they were ever to recognize the descendants of Christ, then they would be admitting that the power to rule the masses of followers doesn't belong to them. The money would go elsewhere. As stated earlier, Desposyni descendants have petitioned the Church of Rome to become Bishops of the church, but were thrown out on their ears. Theoretically, each Pope of Rome has passed down the rule of the church to the next generation by a laying on of hands. The question remains as to whether this has any legitimacy. Clearly the answer to that question is NO! If any of the Popes had been conveyed the true power of Christ, then they would be able to do the miracles he performed. They would understand the mysteries and be able to heal the sick as Christ commanded. They would understand High Alchemy. Clearly they don't possess any of these abilities. The surviving apostles themselves called the emerging church, "a religion for fools." The 4th century treatise known as "The Apocalypse of Peter" called the church of Rome "a dry canal." It is no surprise therefore that the church sought to murder the descendants of Christ with crusades and inquisitions. They stood in the way of their power and money. This can be confirmed in the collective subconscious by taking the average spiritual calibration of all the popes of history.

Not surprisingly the answer is **175** or the level of hate and revenge, right on a par with Hitler. In particular, the inappropriately named Pope Innocent III, who was responsible for the Albigensian Crusade, tested at a low of **125**. This is nearly a complete "anti-Christ level." Right down there with Vlad the Impaler! These are the true colors of the Church of Rome. Check them yourself. The REAL successors of Christ are to be found elsewhere.

Given this background, it is not surprising that the descendants of Christ and Mary Magdalene went underground. They had to go underground to preserve their lives and those of future generations. Jewish law of the period was very strict and very clear about the duties of parents. One of the five laws of Judaism was that children be married by the age of twenty. A Rabbi in particular was required to be married in order to be able to understand family life. Preserving "the seed" of Israel is an issue seldom understood today in an age of overpopulation. At the time there were many Jewish laws designed to propagate the line of Israel. Even "the covenant with God" we call circumcision, was designed to minimize masturbation and wasting "the seed of Israel." Homosexuality was on a par with being unmarried as no offspring were produced to the detriment of Israel. Abstinence from sex was considered nearly as bad as murder at the time. Margaret Starbird discovered that the mindset and the laws of the Jewish faith were so vehement on reproduction **that even a criminal sentenced to death could not be executed until he had fulfilled his obligation to Israel to produce a child. If this is correct then Jesus could not have been crucified under Jewish law unless his wife was pregnant! (2)**

Sir Laurence Gardener explains that a dynastic (royal) marriage in this time period was totally different from what we celebrate today. First of all, the sole purpose of marriage was to procreate. At all other times, the bride and groom were celibate for very specific periods until they had permission to try again. The first marriage was a probationary affair and not even formalized as such until three months after the betrothal ceremony. The whole marriage was not legally binding until the wife had conceived. If she did produce an heir, then a second marriage ceremony occurred. In the event a wife was barren, the husband had the responsibility of finding a new wife who could conceive and produce an heir. (3) Gardener has managed to find all the complex clues to the dynastic marriage of Jesus and Mary Magdalene within the bible itself. It is not surprising that few today understand the customs of the times, but Gardener has done a brilliant job of unraveling the codes. Those who debunk Jesus and Mary have failed to realize that manuscripts describing the life and times of Mary Magdalene still exist. I was extremely impressed that Gardener managed to find a copy of the six volume Rabanus manuscript (Rabanus Maurus, 776-856) at Oxford University. (4) *The Life of Saint Mary Magdalene* contains information dating back to the 4th century.

Royal houses have the burden to produce an heir, otherwise their kingdoms crumble. It's that simple! Anyone who has ever studied history knows the problems kings have had with producing a male heir. The troubles of Henry VIII immediately come to mind. The Sultans of Turkey solved the problem by having 500 wives. And to insure there were no squabbles over territory all the male heirs were murdered upon selecting a successor. The heir problem has been going on for many thousands of years. It is totally inconceivable that the union of the royal houses of Israel in the form of Jesus and Mary Magdalene wouldn't be interested in producing an heir. Furthermore, the prophecies of the Old Testament couldn't be fulfilled unless Jesus was married. The definition of "a Messiah" is one who is anointed. To be anointed is to be chosen by a queen and anointed (and crowned king) as her husband. The sacred marriage of the sister bride and the anointed king assures the protection of the land and the people. Due to the presence of an occupying Roman army at the time, the land and the people of Israel were in great need of protection by a messiah. As we all know, the efforts to repulse the Roman Army were unsuccessful. Several of the apostles were murdered and all the remaining disciples were forced to flee to safety. And the grail family hid out in the backwaters of France.

I have summarized above several of the logical reasons why Jesus and Mary had children. The REAL reasons have never been published until now. To understand this concept fully we must go back several thousand years in time to ancient Babylon and the Anunnaki fathers. They created a special brand of humans, or I should say "super humans," out of their stock. All efforts were employed to maintain this pure strain of kings through the generations with some success. Eventually we arrive at the House of David. The Davidic kings employed both spiritual and alchemical means to preserve their uniqueness and "spiritual capacity." Their DNA was superior to that of their more ordinary counterparts and they wanted to keep it that way. The continued use of alchemical gold powders removes imperfections in the DNA. The powders increase the energy-carrying capacity of the cells turning them into "superconductors." Needless to say the royal family alchemical tradition of the House of David, over thousands of years, produced offspring genetically superior to any other. When we combine the increased genetic DNA capacity with the knowledge of how to activate it to its fullest electrical (and spiritual) potential, the end result is what Maurice Cotterell calls "a supergod." In the Indian tradition we call such a self-realized person an "Avatar," a Sun of God, or a messenger of God. The choice of names is rather arbitrary. **The bottom line is that we achieve a human in the flesh with the ability to achieve miracles or calibrating on the 1,250 level. As it took several thousand years to achieve this level of purity and spiritual capacity on the physical level, it would be unthinkable to destroy it by not producing a line of offspring and sharing this stock to uplift the overall genetic strain of humanity. Only by such measures would humanity have the ability to save itself during the End Times. <u>Without this increased spiritual calibration for "discretion," the ability to detect the false prophets from the true prophets, humanity would in all likelihood become extinct! And that is why Jesus and Mary Magdalene produced three heirs: to save humanity from itself. The previous four civilizations completely destroyed themselves when they achieved the level of technological and nuclear sophistication we currently enjoy. The absence of the counterbalance of the divine feminine principle always leads to tyranny and self-destruction!</u>**

The forces of darkness would like to keep you a slave your entire life and insure that you never find out that you have the "kingdom within" to draw upon in the times of trouble. That is their plan. Therefore the various "myths" of Christ and his family were created to keep you in the dark. The Roman Emperors wanted to set themselves up as living Gods, and blend Christianity into a pagan hybrid religion that would put all people under their direct control. And that is exactly what happened. Christ became the dead celibate savior and poster child of Imperial Rome. But as the Koran says, **"THEY KILLED HIM NOT!"** As **Jesus II was born in AD 37** and **Josephes was born in AD 44,** the children of Jesus would put a big hole in the story of his death in AD 33! That is one of the several reasons they have been erased from history. The heirs of Christ and Mary were threats to Rome and to the Church of Rome. They were also the rightful rulers of Israel and eventually of France. **And most importantly, without the genetic contribution of Jesus and Mary, there would be no hope for humanity at the End Times. That is what the forces of darkness would like to keep from you!**

The Da Vinci Code implies that only one person is "the Holy Grail" or the only direct living descendant of Jesus and Mary. If you do the math for 2,000 years, with a generation being about twenty years, and the tradition of very large families in the past, you should arrive at a figure of around 3 billion descendants. Factor in lots of wars, disease, high infant mortality, the Inquisition, the black plague, and famines and you get **1.5 billion descendants** who survived. The attrition factor cuts the potential in half, but it appears that **everyone in Western civilization is an heir to Jesus and Mary!** Test the question yourself and see what you get. I've tested it a dozen times and always get 1.5 billion. It is incredibly obvious that no one has done the math or little real research into this matter. Just the "card carrying" members of **The Order of the Crown, the Descendants of Charlemagne,** number 28,000 strong. While this is the much talked about line of the Merovingian Kings, there are over a dozen other major lines from England, Scotland, Wales, and Ireland. I can only surmise that the quick buck artist debunkers have never actually looked at any genuine genealogical material.

You could prove this yourself by the laborious process of researching your family tree back 2,000 years. That takes LOTS of time and expense. If you calibrate above 200, you could just simply ask the question: "Am I a descendant of Jesus and Mary, Yes or No?" Or you could take the Jesus DNA test using a sonic method at the following website: (www.thetruejesus.org). It takes about only seven minutes and if you get a reaction, then you're a descendant. About ten years ago my group of Reiki Masters was doing a practice channeling session with Kay Mora. When I asked a question about what was significant about my life that was unknown to me at the time I received the statement, **"You are the Lion of Judah."** (i.e. a Christ descendant, see **Rev. 5:5.**) And I had a vision of a beautiful gold ring to make with two lions, the Star of David, and a diamond in the center of it. I didn't pay too much attention to this at the time and I've never gotten around to making the ring. But at least now I understand the significance of the statement. Perhaps I should put the ring into production so others can know who we are. I believe symbols of our faith are important. We all share a common past.

I realize all this is pretty shocking to the average Christian and Jew alike. It shocked me too! **It appears that Jesus and Mary had a fail-safe plan for humanity. It wasn't implemented by dying, but rather by living. As they have shared their DNA with humanity, it can be accessed via meditation. We call it DNA memory. The whole story is right inside you; but you've never looked there before for it.** The first time I accessed a genetic memory of the lifetime of Moses, I about fainted! I saw little Moses floating down the Nile in his basket, just like on a TV screen. I was speechless. It is better to prepare yourself for these events by increasing your spiritual calibration, than to allow them to happen unexpectedly. As the energy of the End Times is much higher than before, more and more people are having "unprepared" episodes of accessing genetic memory with bizarre results. Between ten to forty individuals a year experience sudden unprepared genetic memory flashback. This happens so frequently in Jerusalem, Israel, that it is called "The Jerusalem Syndrome." In this scenario a tourist suddenly sees himself as John the Baptist or Jesus, takes his clothes off, starts preaching to the poor, and ends up in a mental ward. So, like an unplanned Kundalini rising, you should decide now whether you'd prefer a controlled planned genetic memory event, or you'd rather wait and have one find you instead. It's up to you. You have the capacity to become an elect of Christ and Mary, or you can just plod along and let the breeze take you where it may.

JESUS, SON OF MARY AND JOSEPH

Hugh J. Schonfield's book, **The Passover Plot**, made some waves in 1965 by proclaiming that Jesus had planned his own execution. The recently discovered "Gospel of Judas Iscariot" would seem to confirm this theory. If Jesus had asked Judas to betray him, then the whole crucifixion was a planned event. Judas was just following orders like a good soldier. If so then Judas wasn't the villain he is portrayed to be. Nor is Jesus exactly what we've expected him to be either. We're wrong on both counts. Perhaps it is because we haven't discovered the deeper spiritual meaning and purpose to all these events. I see the events quite differently now than I used to as a young altar boy. I believe **Jesus had a very concrete spiritual plan to save humanity**, but it has never been revealed until now. Using the collective unconscious, we'll take a look at it for the first time in a new light. I have calibrated the major events in the life of Jesus as follows:

343   The birth of Jesus

423   At age 13

513   At age 21

833   Upon returning from India and Tibet

833   Prior to his marriage to Mary Magdalene

933   Immediately after his marriage

933 Just prior to his crucifixion

999 Upon drinking from the Holy Grail

1,450 Upon leaving the tomb after three days

The details of this small chart reveal some incredible facts. First of all, Jesus didn't just jump into his role as a savior as a baby. He had to use "the way" and build up his spiritual calibration just like the rest of us mere mortals. It climbs rather predictably from school to school with a major increase in consciousness gained while in India and Tibet. As his beloved Mary Magdalene, the high priestess, calibrated at **933** prior to their marriage we can see the results of the sacred marriage or "heiros gamos." The calibration of **933** is high enough to cancel out the negativity of approximately 1.2 million people. However if there were 45 million people on the planet in the year 33 AD how would the rest be saved? In short, the world needed a miracle and a savior to cancel out all the negativity of the world's population. **933** wasn't enough "juice" to do the job! What was needed was a calibration of **1,450**. The ability to perform the most major of miracles: to save a world. And that is exactly what Jesus had planned. However he didn't do it by dying exactly, he did it by living again.

A few years ago a good friend of mine sent me a copy of T. Lobsang Rampa's book, The Third Eye (5). The book describes in detail the very rigorous methods used by Tibetan lamas to increase their spiritual calibration and psychic potential. As Lobsang was on the fast track to become a medical lama and clairvoyant, when he was eight years old the monks drilled a hole in his skull to allow "the third eye" center to be more transparent and increase his clairvoyance. He worked his way up through the various degrees and became a medical lama. The final degree however required the ultimate sacrifice: death itself. The aspirants to the highest degrees of potential in this world are required to be "dead" for three days and then return. This is called the initiation of "**THE LITTLE DEATH.**" The Tibetan abbots lock the aspirant in "the cave of the ancients" for three days, and have them drink a formula that essentially puts them in a coma for days. The cave is several hundred feet below the Portola Palace at Lhasa. While "dead" or nearly so for the three days, the soul travels through all the levels of reality (of consciousness) and gathers experience and information. The soul is tethered to the body by a silver thread while it is out exploring the universe. If the cord breaks: you're dead and you fail. Your body is cut up and fed to the buzzards and that's the end of it. However, if the aspirant is "the right stuff" and spiritually advanced enough to complete the task, then he comes back to life as a new person. This new person has gained the experience of a million years in three days and calibrates hundreds of times higher than before he "left" on his sojourn to the stars. This is a planned "little death" where you stop breathing for three days as opposed to the "big one" in which you're dead and buried in a more permanent manner. The Tibetan monks have been performing this initiation for thousands of years. I believe that Jesus learned of this procedure while in Tibet and performed it at Calvary to "save the world." Using "vinegar and gall" (snake venom) he initiated the rite of "the little death" and was removed from the cross within only two hours and put into the tomb. As Jesus had performed this initiation before in previous lives, he only needed but an hour to perform it again. His brothers revived him, treated his wounds, and placed him at the monastery of Qumran on the Dead Sea to recover from his ordeal.

Obviously we must ask ourselves whether such an event is possible or not. Is there anything in modern experience to lend some validity to such a conjecture? In modern scientific terms we call this experience "**the near death experience.**" Elizabeth Kubler-Ross and others have written extensively about it. You may even have seen a TV show dramatizing the experience of those who died, went down the long tunnel towards the light, and for whatever reason decided to come back instead of crossing over to the other side. Those who have experienced this phenomenon relate how they gained insights into the spiritual realms and many have brought back information. Some may have found themselves thrust into the calibration of enlightenment upon their return. I have calibrated the average gain in consciousness at **211** or about 42 lifetimes of experience. While that is an extremely impressive gain in consciousness, those who are prepared for such an event realize much higher gains. If you prepare for an initiation rite all your life, then your results will be proportionally higher. I feel that is what Jesus did. He prepared.

My mother had one of the unprepared varieties of near death experiences. Shortly after I was born she went into the hospital for some surgery. She was "accidentally" given penicillin by the hospital staff and she was violently allergic to it. Consequently she went into a coma for three days and a priest was called to give her the last rites. When the oil from the last rites was placed upon her head she sat bolt upright and knocked over the nun who was holding her arm. The priest and nun left silently. Mom was BACK! Since this event she has maintained her link "to the other side" and on occasion receives prophetic dreams. She "knew" I would be in a car accident at eighteen by the time I was eight. She saw the policeman coming to the door of our house to tell her just as it in fact occurred. I totaled the car during an ice storm the day before Christmas in 1969 in western New York. She "saw" the Kennedy assassination, the Reagan assassination attempt, and even did a show once for **Unsolved Mysteries** about her psychic adventures. She has run into a lot of ghosts who wouldn't shut up while the St. Augustine Historical Society was cleaning up the graves of the early settlers. My favorite story however is when she predicted the death of my step-father Dan. He was going to Germany on Army National Guard maneuvers for two weeks and my mother saw a vision of his death. She gathered up the courage to tell him about it and warn him NOT to go out for a ride with his army buddies on a certain day. If he did, a car would come suddenly over a hill and kill all of them. On the day in question she sat by the phone at the appointed hour. My step-father Dan has a large collection of grandfather and grandmother clocks, all of which he made by hand as a hobby. They all require being wound up by hand and none of them uses electricity. At the appointed hour all the clocks in the house STOPPED. My mom figured that perhaps he hadn't listened to her and that they were all dead. A few moments later the phone rang from Germany and Dan said he had decided to stay home just in case and called to be sure mom wasn't worried. The moral of this story is that indeed a near death experience greatly increases spiritual calibration, clairvoyance, and prophetic ability. I know because we have all lived it my entire life. I've had quite a few experiences myself.

Fortunately for the world, Jesus survived his near death experience and accomplished a great deal for humanity during his LONG life. I believe that Jesus lived to approximately 85 years of age. It is generally accepted that Jesus was 33 years of age at the time of the crucifixion. This would indicate an additional 52 years. The first obvious question to ask would be why? Why 52 more years? Again, we have to go back to the true purpose of what any Avatar is here to accomplish. The purpose of any Avatar or spiritual teacher is to set the people back on the path of righteousness. The more frequently the people lose their way, the more frequently an avatar must reincarnate upon the Earth to help the people overcome their overindulgence in the trap of materialism. The Earth is a dense medium, full of pitfalls, and it is extremely easy to get stuck in materialism and lose total sight of spiritualism and "the way" back to God. As the spiritual calibration of the people of the Earth sinks lower and lower, they get more and more stuck. They lose their ability of "discretion" and can no longer tell the difference between the false prophets and the true ones. The more serious the condition of the Earth, the longer the Avatar needs to stay to straighten it all out. In ancient times an average person didn't enjoy the longer lifetimes we currently enjoy. Back then the average person was dead at less than fifty years. And that is the reason: Jesus remained upon the Earth an entire three generations so that the entire population of the Earth would have an increased spiritual calibration and get the Earth back to an even keel.

Naturally, the people of the Earth have the built-in tendency to run amuck and require an Avatar to come back sometimes in as little as 200 years or less. Then the world has to be "straightened out" all over again and again, and again. Maurice Cotterell's research indicates that the ancients believed that the "son of God" has been here many times. Some of these incarnations include Krishna, Tutankhamen, Buddha, Ch'in Shi Huangdi, Jesus, Viracocha, and Lord Pacal of the

Maya. In each of these instances, the incarnation was known as the morning and evening star or Venus. Codes relating to perfection and righteousness were also synonymous with each incarnation. The codes are extremely complicated; hence I recommend that the reader consult the texts directly. Like the grail, the codes relate much material about the super-science of the sun and astrological data. (6) I believe there is ALWAYS at least one Avatar, ascended master, or master of the 7 rays "on duty" upon the Earth to help keep it in balance, plus thousands of "the goodly company" as assistants. It is essential that the spiritual calibration of the Earth be kept at above **200** or the level of truth.

THE GREAT TRAVELLER

We are currently in exactly the age of materialism that the ancients talked about. Except this one is worse as the logical outcome of the selfishness of man is extinction. There are many prophecies as to the return of Christ from the apostles themselves, to that of St. Columba of Ireland, and even Nostradamus. Nostradamus said that Christ would return as a "great scientist" and help the people establish colonies in space far away from a doomed Earth. St. Columba predicted that the second coming of Christ would occur on the Island of Iona or the Sacred Isle in the Hebrides of Scotland. He built his monastery there for that reason and also because he believed that one of the children of Mary Magdalene and Jesus was born on the island. This individual may have been Josephes, born in 44 AD, the only line to survive persecution, and therefore essential to our story. It is a Scottish tradition in the area of the Hebrides that indeed Mary and Jesus traveled there. I will continue to research this legend as my ancestors were the Lords of the Isles of Ulva and Mull and are buried on Iona, the burial place of the kings. If this is true, it would explain why all the kings and queens of ancient Scotland and Ireland were buried there. They would have wanted to have been buried on ground walked upon by Jesus and Mary.

Buddhist tradition refers to Jesus as "the great traveler" and asserts that he was well known in Lhasa, Tibet and elsewhere. I believe there are documents and manuscripts written in his hand there today. It was extremely difficult to travel across continents at the time, but there were caravans along very established, but dangerous, trade routes. The Mediterranean Sea however was a mere lake to the sophisticated mariners of the time. Sea power was at its peak in 500 BC as shipbuilding was the arms race of the ancients. In fact modern shipbuilding didn't surpass the ancients until about 1850, as some of the ships built in ancient times were as large as aircraft carriers. I was quite surprised to read of all the kings of Israel who escaped the Babylonian destruction of the country by traveling afar. There were Jewish settlements and kingdoms in Gibraltar, Spain, France, Britannia, Scotland and Ireland. Of particular interest is the warrior princess of Ireland, known as Teia Tephi or Tamar (by Gardener). She was the daughter of king Zedekiah of Jerusalem and was married to Eochaidh the High King of Ireland. She passed away in August of 534 BC. Her autobiography has survived and can be ordered at: (http://jahtruth.net). It is quite central to our understanding of events to acknowledge both the advanced state of sea power in ancient times and the string of Jewish kingdoms all along the Mediterranean Sea routes. Jesus "the traveler" and the apostles couldn't have gotten around the known world so well if these routes and settlements hadn't been in place.

The main problem in tracking the whereabouts of Jesus, Mary and their "Grail children" is knowing where to begin the search. There were large Jewish settlements in France as we know. This is where Mary Magdalene and her daughter Tamar arrived from Egypt with twelve other saints in an open boat. This event is celebrated annually in the South of France and relics of the saints are paraded by the church in the town of Saintes Maries de la Mer, France. However this doesn't account for all the so called "missing years" of Christ or tell us where he may have lived during all that time. The missing years are the key to the whole story.

As is usually the case in solving historical mysteries, a longer view of history provides the solution. We have to ask the logical question: "Where would Jesus hide?" Remember there was a death sentence on his head and none of his relatives were too popular with the Romans either. **They were ALL MARKED FOR DEATH**. That is the key. Logically we would think that the followers would hide out in someplace "off the grid" of the Roman Empire. France would be OK for a while as the Grail family had royal protection. But if things got too hot, a better place would have to be found.

The word "British" is not English, but Hebrew, meaning "the People of the Covenant." This refers to the Covenant between God and the children of Israel handed down by Moses. The British coat of arms refers to the twelve tribes of Israel symbolized by the Lion of Judah, and Christ symbolized by the unicorn. Likewise Ireland was called Hibernia in ancient times meaning "Hebrew's new land" or the land of Heber/Eber in descent from Abraham. Hibernia or Iberia (Spain) also means Hebrew's land. The Celts are believed to be descendants of the lost tribes of Israel. If you look at a picture of Britannia, she is holding an olive branch that comes from Jerusalem. She is a representation of Queen Teia Tephi, the Princess of Jerusalem. Lastly, the meaning of the term Hebrides also means Hebrew's Isles. The bottom line is that there were many kings and queens in the British Isles of Israeli descent who would welcome Jesus and Mary with open arms and afford them protection in times of trouble. And most importantly, at the time England was off the Roman grid. The Roman conquest of Britain didn't begin until 43 AD and was a forty year process. The Romans didn't have any luck conquering the pesky Scots and called it quits at Hadrian's Wall. They decided that discretion was the better part of valor and left the formidable Scots (and the Irish) alone. We therefore have a "safe haven" for Jesus Christ and Mary in the Hebrides and Ireland. This is memorialized in Scotland on the Island of Mull at the Kilmore Church in a stained glass window of Christ and the very pregnant Mary Magdalene (www.buyimage.co.uk). (Click on "Isle of Mull" and go to photo #25 to view the stained glass window of Jesus and Mary Magdalene). Mull is but a few miles from the sacred Isle of Iona and Ulva, the home of my ancestors. How Jesus Christ and Mary got to Britain takes both some explanation and some hard evidence.

Joseph of Arimathea's exact relationship to Christ is somewhat sketchy. He is described as the "rich Uncle" of Jesus, the great uncle, and as James, the brother of Jesus by Gardener. Gardener maintains that "the Joseph" is a spiritual title often adopted and that Arimathea is a town. Last names weren't in common usage in ancient times and individuals were often designated by places, occupations, or characteristics. This also protected their true identity from those who would do them harm. I believe that Gardener is correct, but in any event it is commonly believed that "The Joseph of Arimathea" was an exceptionally rich man involved in the tin trade between Cornwall and the rest of the Roman Empire. Some believe he was so rich that he had an entire fleet of ships at his disposal. Tin was "the" industrial commodity of the time as it was used to make bronze. And bronze was used to make everything, but especially swords, lances, arrows, ship fittings and other implements of war. In short it was indispensable and at times worth more than gold. Phoenician fleets sailed as far as America, Peru, and even Australia to get it as one ship load was equivalent to a ship load of gold. Those who owned tin mines were rich, connected, well traveled. They had many resources at their command. Kings and queens of necessity had to patronize them; otherwise in times of war they could be cut off and hence defeated and killed. Joseph was not just a mine owner, but also a "minister of mines" to the empire. Therefore, I believe that Joseph of Arimathea was the richest man of his day and age. That fact alone explains many things.

Mary, the mother of Jesus, was connected to British royalty as well as to that of Israel. Joseph, her husband, was a "master of the craft" in metals and alchemy. Apparently, Joseph of Arimathea was also, and Jesus was well acquainted with the metals industry and alchemy. As the tin mines were located in Cornwall and this was "the family business," the family spent a great deal of time there. Hence, it would be logical to assume that Jesus spent many of his alleged "missing years" in Britain and grew up there. I think they are "missing" to hide the facts of the family of Jesus and the ancient heritage of Britain itself. Jesus often accompanied Joseph (his father) on mining business; and art-work of the Cornwall mining area shows Jesus on a "tunic cross" as a young lad and not as a crucified adult (http://

asis.com/~stag/christbrt.html). There are many place names there as well relating to Christ and traditions of Christ showing the miners how to mine tin. Jesus wasn't interested in carrying on the "family business" and preferred to be involved in prayer and meditation. He eventually settled and built a home and church at Glastonbury. He did travel to Israel to visit relatives from time to time and to perform the traditional Jewish ceremonies of the day. Not until the age of 30 did he return to begin his ministry in Israel and get married.

After the crucifixion he returned to Britain from time to time and traveled all over the Mediterranean preaching the gospel. He was involved with Joseph of Arimathea in establishing disciples in Britain under Joseph as the bishop of Glastonbury. Evangelists trained by Joseph of Arimathea went forth to establish churches, particularly in France, where Mary Magdalene established her church. Mary Magdalene's first son, Jesus II, was born in France in AD 37. Their second son Josephes was born in AD 44 on the Island of Iona, Scotland, in the Hebrides. France was too dangerous at the time and the Romans invaded Britain in AD 43. The Roman incursion closed the church of Joseph of Arimathea for a time and scattered his followers. The Hebrides were the perfect safe place to "hide out" as even today anyone wanting to disappear into the remote islands and mountains could do so for years and never be found. At the time it was literally the end of the world. St. Columba founded his monastery at Iona and for a time (35 years) hid the Holy Grail there. His mission was to prepare for the second coming of Christ at the appointed time. St. Columba felt that Christ would return to be born on Iona. William Sharp's treatise on "Iona, the Isle of Dreams" (1900) refers to the ancient prophecy that **"Christ shall come again upon Iona." It is said that Christ personally blessed and attuned the island of Iona. It presently calibrates at 999 or a perfect Christ calibration.** The island contains seven chakra vortexes and the crown chakra vortex is believed to connect the initiate directly to the Holy Spirit as symbolized by the dove. St. Columba was traditionally referred to as "the dove." Even the dirt of Iona was considered holy and Scottish, French, Irish, Pictish and even Norse (Viking) kings were interred on the island. See the following link: (http://www.sacredconnection.ndo.co.uk/holyland/iona.htm). Author Richard Leviton's **The Galaxy**

on Earth (7) explains the spiritual significance of Iona and 56 other world sites. This volume is an excellent introduction to the greater mysteries and how to connect yourself to the cosmic energy. It also sheds some light on the role of Christ as a healer of the Earth as well as a healer of mankind. This premise would also account for the great deal of traveling Christ did around the Mediterranean to "repair" the Earth and attune and connect dozens of sacred sites for a higher consciousness and higher spiritual vibration.

THE KOLBRIN BIBLE

Proving that Christ was in Britain and Scotland is another matter. Fortunately, the Celtic priests of Britain were inspired to write what is known as **The Kolbrin Bible,** after meeting with Jesus. **This ancient text includes interviews with Jesus, who stopped to visit the Celtic priests while on a mining trip**. **It includes newly revealed first-person quotes from Jesus and a biographical sketch of him during this time period**. The Coelbook is a fusion of 3,600 year old Egyptian Mystery school documents, Druidism, Judaism and Celtic mysticism. It describes the flood of Noah, the plagues of Exodus, planet X or Nibiru and the coming destruction of the world. Nibiru was known as "the destroyer" by the ancients. This also relates to the Mayan prophecies of 2012. For additional information on Nibiru or planet X and the bible see: (www.planetxvideo.com). You may order Tim McHyde's ebook **Planet X in Bible Prophecy** from: (www.escapeallthesethings.com), which is also linked in the above website and the Kolbrin Bible. A selection of free video clips by authors in this field is also located on this site. You can also view the location of the **SOUTH POLE TELESCOPE, (SPT)** being built by NASA to view Nibiru, which was discovered in 1983 (http://yowusa.com/planetx/2006/planetx-2006-04a/1.shtml). The complete Planet X scenario can be downloaded by clicking on the PDF link. If the Planet X scenario is even partially correct "civilization" is going to take a hell of a beating! The massive NASA telescope will go online sometime in 2007, so check for more info when it does.

The 3,600 year old Egyptian Texts can be purchased separately as: **The Egyptian Texts of the Bronzebook**. The remaining five texts are entitled: **The Celtic Texts of the Coelbook: The Last Five books of The Kolbrin Bible** at: (http://yowbooks.com/html/coelbook.htl). The books are also available as a combined master edition knows as: **The Kolbrin Bible: The 21st. Century Master Edition.** A free audio report by Marshall Masters entitled, "Surviving the Next Global Catastrophe" is available online at: (www.kolbrin.com).

The Kolbrin Bible's biography of Jesus has a number of details about his life that clarify several age old questions. The Catholic Church created a mythology of Jesus that he disputes here in his own words. To those who wished he were the messiah he rebuked them **(BRT: 3:6).** (8) In **BRT: 3:49** it called the attempt to name Christ the Messiah a "manifest falsehood" (page 141). In **BRT: 3:50** it states that, "but were He born of a Holy Ghost and not **of Joseph**, then He did not fulfill the prophesy. Men step outside the bounds of truth in their beliefs." It also mentions his brothers Jacob, Joseph, Simon and James **BRT: 3:1.** Jesus is described as a brawny, strong, alert, and resourceful person, with a wit as quick as lightning. As a servant of God, he never ran from a fight.

However being a servant of God wasn't always an easy task for Jesus. His mother rebuked him for being a "tardy breadwinner," and clearly preferred a more practical and down to Earth son. She wasn't happy with a "dreamer and a preacher." Even worse in **BRT: 3:3** we read that "Jesus had spells of rapture, and his male kinsfolk declared he was out of his mind, so they sought to have him put under restraint." As Joseph, his father, died when he was 16, Jesus had a difficult time of it. So, he went into the wilderness beside the Jordan River **BRT: 3:5.** He joined the Society of Saints, which was beside the Sea of Heavy Salt. (The Essenes at the Dead Sea). When he came back to the Jordan, he was of direct and forceful speech, and was decisive and commanding. It reveals that Jesus was hung on the cross in his 27th year **BRT: 2:7.**

Discovering the whereabouts of Jesus for approximately fourteen years of his so-called lost years is a great addition to the historical record. The biography corrects many errors in our perceptions about Christ. However of even greater importance to us today is his description of the End Times. In **BRT: 3: 55 Jesus said we would know it by "the spirit of the times."** He goes on to describe a time of hate, crime, perversion, rape, incest and adultery when it is unsafe to walk the streets at night. A time when "Women will be as men and men as women." It appears he speaks of abortion when he says that "babies will be slain in the womb." Lastly he cites a time of "strange sicknesses that smite the people" (I believe he is referring to the AIDS epidemic). This is the time when "floods, famines, droughts and earthquakes will cause death and destruction." Continuing in **BRT: 3: 56,** Jesus talks about this time as when priests will defile their altars with their impurity." He comments that "**It is not God who marks the end days, but man who lives as though setting a pitfall for himself**." I believe that the period Jesus is talking about is NOW. The description of current events is too exact to ignore.

The final question about Jesus is, "If he didn't die on the cross, then where did he go and what did he do?" I've already covered some of these events about Jesus resuming his missionary work in France, Britain, Malta and, possibly, Greece and Turkey. David Childress in his book, <u>**Lost Cities of China, Central Asia, and India,**</u> states that Jesus is known in Hindu and Moslem traditions as "the Great Traveler" and "the Chief of Travelers."

According to Bishop Ignatius the Patriarch of Antioch, Jesus was alive "in the flesh" for at least 20 years after the crucifixion and lived to a great age. This statement was conveyed in his "letter to the Smyrneans" (Izmir, Turkey, today) before his death in the Roman arena by lions. He was believed to have been a disciple of both Peter and John. There are fragments of information across the ancient Silk Road indicating that Jesus traveled across Syria, Iraq, Iran and Pakistan to his final destination in Kashmir.

The Quran, Suratul Muminum , verse 50, states that:

"And we made the Son of Mary and his mother a sign, and gave them refuge on an elevated land of green valleys and springs of running water."

Where did Jesus go? This has been a nagging question for centuries. One popular location is believed to be the area of Srinagar,

Kashmir, where the crucified prophet Isa or Yuz Asaf is buried. The word "asaph" is associated with "healthy persons" or we would say a "healer" as Jesus is reputed to have healed lepers in Iran and they returned to become healthy persons. While Gardener and others don't believe in the theory of Jesus living to a great age and being buried in Kashmir, there are many who do. Locally the tomb in Srinagar is called "the Tomb of Jesus" (www.tombofjesus.com). You can read all the surviving documents and books here and view the sarcophagus of Yuz Asaf yourself (in the photo gallery) and make up your own mind. I DON'T believe this is the final resting place of Jesus. This question is the only one in this entire book that I had a great deal of difficulty solving. One must basically know the correct answer before testing it. I believe the identity of Yuz Asaf is that of the great Greek healer of antiquity known as Apollonius of Tyana. His exploits and healing ability were of such note that it has been suggested that he was a reincarnation of Jesus. I believe they were separate souls of a very close frequency and hence the confusion.

This was a difficult puzzle to solve and I struggled with it for weeks until I found a way to dissect the problem. The root cause of the problem is understanding the nature of the role of an avatar. Avatars are "Masters of the Wisdom" or "Masters of the Seven Rays." They are ascended masters who have "come down" from heaven to assist humanity spiritually unfold. Each ray is a frequency or an initiation that a master must pass in order to get to the next level of experience. This is the hierarchy of heaven. As all of the ascended masters are of such a high spiritual vibration, it is difficult to differentiate between them sometimes. I had to wait for the key to the problem and then ask a lot of questions to sort it all out. Eventually the key was given. I woke up one morning and the answers to several unresolved questions I had were simply given. The key was a geometric pattern overlaid over the landscape of Rennes-le-Chateau, France. I am not at liberty to divulge this pattern, but suffice it to say that I believe the mortal remains of Jesus are to be found in the Rennes-le-Chateau area as described in the book **The Tomb of God**. The late Graham Simmans (1919-2005) lived in Rennes-le-Chateau for 15 years to solve this very mystery. Simmans' **Jesus After the Crucifixion: From**

Jerusalem to Rennes-le-Chateau has invaluable information about the Egyptian roots of gnosticism and the lost years of the Grail family in Egypt. Ancient Coptic maps showing the route the Grail family took may prove to solve a large part of the Jesus mystery. I calibrate this book at **843** and thoroughly enjoyed it (www.InnerTraditions.com). Unfortunately hard evidence about the secret demise of Jesus in Rennes-le-Chateau has still eluded researchers. Only the Akashic records have shed some light upon the mystery.

The Other Side of History

Little-known Australian author Tony Bushby has added some great white shark sized teeth to the allegations posed by Dan Brown in The Da Vinci Code. His series of books rank as perhaps the greatest exposes of the Catholic Church and their cover-up written to date. Is this the beginning of the end for the embattled church of Rome or is the battle just heating up? If you consider yourself a Christian fundamentalist, you may want some resuscitation equipment standing by your armchair before you attempt to read The Twin Deception, The Bible Fraud, or The Secret in the Bible. (www.JoshuaBooks.com) Perhaps for the first time you'll get a glimpse of the "heresies" the church has been consigning to the flames for the last two thousand years. Once the lid is blown off even more secret material will appear. The popular movement started by Dan Brown can only intensify.

Tony Bushby's version of events begins with the fifteen year old virgin Mary possibly serving as a temple virgin at the palace of Emperor Augustus in Rome. As emperors can do as they please, the betrothed Mary was raped by Tiberius Julius Claudius Nero, ceremoniously named "The Panther." Mary leaves Rome in shame and returns to Jerusalem where she is taken in by the Essenes. Mary delivers a set of identical twins named Yeshu'a and Judas Thomas. Every time Mary gets remarried, the royal twins get a new name. The Essenes consider the twins the fulfillment of an Old Testament prophecy and they both are considered Messiahs. As Judas Thomas Ben Panther is the oldest he becomes the priest/king of the Essenes

225

and leader of the Zealots, the military arm of the Essenes. The more scholarly Yeshu'a (Jesus) Ben Panther becomes a rabbi and preaches the gospel. Judas Thomas becomes known as the "wicked priest," or evil twin of the two. He is famous for whore-mongering, drunkenness, violence, poor hygiene, bad temperament, and just plan ruthlessness and slitting of throats. Judas Thomas was considered a left-wing terrorist and savage in the eyes of the Romans with whom he was in constant warfare with.

Jesus eventually settles down with his second wife and half sister, the Celtic Princess Mary Magdalene. (This is why Mary Magdalene is always depicted in art with red hair). Mary gives Rabbi Jesus three children, named Princes Cadwalladr, Prince Polydore, and Princess Anna. Counting the five children from his first wife, this brings the Jesus family up to a total of eight children. A complete alternative royal bloodline is contained in The Bible Fraud and adds a totally new dimension to our understanding of the historical events of Europe. Only time and additional research will flesh out the truth.

The other brother, Judas Thomas, becomes "the khrestus" or "krst." This is essentially a military title of one who wears "the khrestus" or multi-colored plumed hat into battle. The khrestus resembles the helmet worn by the ancient Greeks or Trojans. The title essentially means leader, king, general, specifically commander-in-chief as we know that term today.

As Judas Thomas traveled to Rome and planned to launch a massive Roman revolt against his father Tiberius. However, during the long journey Emperor Tiberius dies and the infamous Caligula becomes emperor. When Judas Thomas attempts to start the revolt, he is betrayed by Judas Iscariot who works as a spy for the Roman Imperial Secret Service. A Roman division and 1,500 city police are called out and a battle rages for days. Judas Thomas is arrested, tried for treason, and sentenced to be crucified in Rome. Due to the royal status of Judas Thomas, he exercised the ancient tradition of a substitute for his crimes. Simon the Cyrene was switched for Judas Thomas, removed from his cross after only three hours, placed in the tomb of Joseph of Arimathea and then his corpse was secretly moved during the night. Judas Thomas vacated his titles and conferred them upon Jesus. Then he was sold into slavery by Jesus to an Indian merchant.

It being unhealthy for a Jew to be in Rome, especially those connected with the plot to overthrow Caligula, Mary Magdalene, Joseph of Arimathea, and the household of Joseph (called the Bethany Group) sailed to France and landed near Marseille, Provence. Joseph of Arimathea continued on to the British Isles.

Judas (Thomas) Khrestus's sons, Jacob and Simeon were crucified for leading an uprising in 46 AD. His grandson Eleazar was also crucified in 70 AD. Rebellions, uprising, and revolts continued for centuries against the power of Rome.

In this version of history, the only person who wasn't crucified was Jesus. His suffering, as portrayed in the Bible, was due to an initiation rite into the Egyptian Mysteries at the age of 33. The initiation rite performed by Jesus had all the same elements as the alleged passion of Christ, but wasn't fatal. The initiate carries his cross, is jeered by a crowd, beaten, curses, and tied to a cross with ropes. The iniate is given a soporific drink to embrace a near death experience. After being ceremoniously hit on the head three times, the initiate is wrapped in a linen like a mummy and placed in a coffin for three days. This ritual teaches the initiate the secret of the dead and he is reborn like Osisis. He is then resurrected! As scribes of later centuries weren't initiates themselves, the were unaware that his allegory was just a "ritual crucifixion" and not the real thing. The crucifixion story was embellished over the centuries until its origin in the Egyptian Mystery Schools was obscured. A description of the entire initiation ceremony is contained in the final chapters of The Secret in the Bible. Once you read it you'll comprehend how this secret wisdom is preserved in the Tarot cards and in the allegory of the passion of Christ.

Jesus is said to have lived to the age of sixty-three in this account. He was accused of revealing the great mysteries of the Torah to the common people. Specifically, he was accused of "burning his food in public." I believe this rather cryptic statement refers to the food "of the Gods" and to the preparation of white powdered gold. Therefore, Jesus was accused to teaching the secrets of alchemy to the common uninitiated man. He was tried by the Sanhedrin and found guilty. Consequently he was publicly stoned, hanged, and then put upon a vertical stake. This execution took place in the town of Lud or London as it is now known near Ludgate. There was no resurrection in this account, which can be found in Chapter 15 of The Twin Deception. At Ludgate now stands St. Paul's Cathedral on the probable site of the stoning of Jesus. Mary Magdalene's father Tenvantius built walls and towers around the city. Her grandfather was King Lud. Therefore family ties were the connection that brought Jesus to Lud or London and ultimately to his death by stoning. The disposition of the body of Jesus was not related in this account. I personally favor the burial of Jesus in France at Rennes Le Chateau, however this can not be proven at this time. I feel this mystery will be solved within the next 40 years at the latest.

According to Bushby, there are no supernatural manifestations, virgin births, crucifixions, or resurrection in any of the originals stories of Jesus. All of these elements are later additions. The story of the crucifixion itself appears to be a merging of the lives of both brothers with ample amounts of religious fanaticism added after the fact. Stories were merged, white washed, deleted, borrowed from ancient mythology, or simply created out of thin air when the situation called for filling the collection plates. The Jesus mythology as we know it today most closely resembles the elements of the mythology of Lord Krishna. Thousands of early books, manuscripts, and letters that proved to be an embarrassment to the later Catholic Church were burned. Those who refused to hand over original books and gospels to the Catholic Church were burned in addition to the confiscated books. Many copies of "heretical" works still exist in the secret Vatican Library and in private collections.

How all of this insanity began is of course one of the central themes of The Da Vinci Code. No argument about the origins of Christianity would be complete without a discussion of Roman Emperor Constantine and the Council of Nicea. Once again Bushby offers a very plausible and logical explanation as to why Constantine granted Christianity the official status of a state religion and confirmed the divinity of Jesus.

The future Constantine was born in York, (in the South of England) to Emperor Constantius "the Pale" and Helena, a British princess. York was a seaside resort and several Roman emperors chose to rule from there and are buried there. Upon the death of his father, Constantine became king of Britain, Gaul, and Spain. He raised an army of Britons, sailed to what is now Germany, and defeated the co-emperor Maxentius at Milvian Bridge in October of 312. Constantine and his army were welcomed to Rome and he was officially endorsed as the new Roman Emperor by the senate. Constantine consolidated his control as emperor in a series of smaller battles and emerged in full control of the entire Roman Empire in addition to Britain, Spain and Gaul which he inherited and already ruled.

Religious disorder had plagued Rome for centuries. Constantine felt that a common universal state religion would put an end to the revolts, riots, and continual religious battles. First an edict of religious tolerance was granted. In 324 Constantine sent his religious advisor, Osius of Cordoba to Alexandria with letters urging the bishops to settle their differences and make peace. The emperors' advice was ignored, so he summoned all presbyters to gather in Nicea near Constantinople. The presbyters brought with them 2,231 scrolls of their various gods and assembled on June 21st 325 in Osius" palace. The 2,048 attendees at this council were mostly illiterate and simple men. Most of them had to be thrown out by the army to keep the peace, until only 318 remained.

Constantine wanted them to choose one god from the fifty three gods represented and make a henceforth "universal" religion for the empire. The long list of gods was shortened to Caesar himself, Krishna, Mithra, Horus and Zeus. No Christian gods made the cut. However after one year and five months a decision about a universal god couldn't be reached. The council was deadlocked in fighting over their various gods. So Constantine made the decision for them! He chose Jesus Khrestus.

Historians have been seeking an answer as to why Constantine would support Jesus Christ as a "Son of God" and deify him. The answer lies in the rather complex royal bloodline of the Holy family and their unexpected intermarriages and alliances. The bloodline ascends to Constantine himself and Jesus' son King Caradoc married two daughters of Emperor Cludius. Therefore by deifying Jesus and cleaning up all the messy details, he deified himself as a Christ descendant and a "Son of God." This complex genealogy is contained in the preface of The Bible Fraud. This volume may be the greatest expose since the original Holy Blood, Holy Grail.

Constantine had a brilliant plan for the Catholic or universal church with him as its head. He gave white togas and twenty pieces of gold to those who joined the new church that he had built. He also exiled or put to death those who refused to join. Within the first year of Christianity as a state religion 12,000 members were recruited in Rome. The new testament he had ordered written unified all the churches with concession to myths from all the major pagan religions included. All political and religious power was thereby concentrated into the hands of the emperor.

One of the most significant roadblocks to unraveling this tangled web of history was the linguistic practices of the time. The first and last names of an individual weren't set in stone as they are today. Every time a person moved, married, changed professions. Or initiated into a religious school, he could gain a new name. Then there are all the codes, titles, and nicknames. Like Osiris, Jesus easily had two hundred names and titles and so did many of his companions. Once we make it through the genealogy and the titles of Jesus and his family we begin to get a picture of what may have happened.

Once we scrape away the varnish and embellishments of the Jesus myth, we might begin to see Jesus again for what he truly was. Embellishing the truth with countless pagan myths only makes Jesus and his message more distant from the outcast and downtrodden who really need him. The truth about Jesus is all we've ever needed. He was an ascended master who taught "the way" (the Tao) to the Christ within and gave his life for humanity. All the rest is just details.

There has been so much chaos and confusion over the last two thousand years most of us are lost in the wilderness. I recommend getting back to the spiritual basic skills and seeking enlightenment. When you're lost, you need a guide to get out. I would recommend taking a tour to India with Sondra Ray ((www.SondaRay.com) and finding answers for yourself.

Jesus was an Egyptian initiate of the Great Mysteries. He also appears to have been an Essene, Druid, and Tibetan master as well. In order to understand Jesus and his contemporaries and world history, you must first get a grasp of what the great mysteries of the Egyptian initiates were all about. The Torah (Old Testament) and New Testament can only be understood by an initiate into the mysteries.

There are four (4) levels or depths of understanding to the Torah. The words are actually irrelevant, it is the STAR language or Language of Light of the letters themselves that ARE the message. A full understanding of the mysteries makes the successful initiate a "master of Light" who can move freely between worlds and between life and death. A "master of light" can create light by attaining a specific wavelength. A fully trained initiate is a fully realized Christ or Krst (1420). Unsuccessful initiation candidates usually died from the experience or returned from their "little death" or near death experience completely insane. Those who quit before completing the twenty-two stages of initiation were sent to prison and shunned. Bushby does a remarkable and eloquent job of explaining the greater mysteries and the science behind them in The Secret in the Bible. Unlike other authors who endlessly speculate Bushby delivers the goods. No DVC library is complete without all the works of Tony Bushby. If you understand the principles outlined in this book, it will assist you in becoming "a Christ." Only by becoming "a Christ" can you fully understand what Rabbi Jesus was all about. All fictions will fall away in the light of truth. Only the pure gold will remain.

The Bible has always been the greatest seller of all time. No other book has received such a wide universal circulation. Both the Old and New Testaments contain the hidden mysteries and knowledge of all human history. Its texts have been continuously manipulated during every edition to convey additional secret information layer upon layer. It has been estimated that the Bible has been edited over 25,000 times. There may be as many as 100,000 different versions of the Bible.

231

The most well-known and well circulated version of the Bible in English is the Authorized King James edition which was first edited in 1610. The editor of this edition was Sir Francis Bacon (1561-1626). Francis Bacon was the most accomplished man of his age. He was an initiate into the mysteries and established several secret societies. He was intimately connected with the secret knowledge of the Knights Templar, Masons, and the Rosicrucian Order. He is frequently cited as a grand master of these organizations.

Francis Bacon was also the author of Shakespeare's plays and other writings. The "Spear-Shaker" is a well-known ancient Masonic personality that symbolized Athena, the Goddess of Wisdom. Bacon used both Francis Bacon and William Shakespeare as the letter key to his secret encryptions. Both names equal 33 in the progressive letter code and represent the 33rd degree in masonry. Bacon's plays, writings and Bibles containing secret ciphers were marked on the title page with AA hidden in the design to represent Athena.

Francis Bacon encrypted secret Templar and Masonic knowledge about Jesus, Mary Magdalene and the origins of Christianity into the King James Bible and the various writing of Shakespeare. Many of these ciphers remain to be decoded. One of the most significant messages to our story however is : Jesus Christ, Initiation, Great Pyramid." These passages can be found on page 120 of The Secret in the Bible. The alleged passion of Christ is an allegorical representation of the stages of initiation of Jesus into the Egyptian Mysteries in the Great Pyramid. They are identical. Understanding the connections Jesus had with all the mystery schools and other royal kings who were similarly initiated like him helps explain a great deal of the lost history of Jesus and his family. As the Bible says in Luke 8:17, "There is nothing hidden that will not be revealed, and there is nothing secret that will not become known and come to light."

THE QADOSH FATHERS:
THE KEEPERS OF THE SECRETS

It is said that we live in an "information age." Information seemingly grows by the ton everyday. Nearly 200,000 new books are published in English every year and the rate is climbing. The total world stock of books is estimated at 65 million. Society itself is becoming more and more divided into two groups: 1) Those who have access to information, and 2) All the rest who do not. The elite may rule solely due to their monopoly on the best information. Information delivered in time can save your life. Information that is late or never arrives can take it. In short, the entire "quality" of life is governed by the type of information you receive and digest. Only the truth can set you free.

The withholding of "secret" information began with Adam himself. He had wisdom received from his lord that he kept to himself and then passed on to his line. The luminaries of the Bible whom we all recognize were in fact a succession of "Wise Masters of the Secret Traditions." Wise men such as Noah, Isaac, Moses, Aaron, Joshua, King David, King Solomon and Hiram Abiff all possessed secrets the common man didn't have. John the Baptist, Jesus, Mary Magdalene all were keepers of the secrets. To be a keeper of the secrets, one had to attend a "mystery school" and learn to master them. And most importantly, these secrets weren't to be revealed to the "profane," usually upon pain of death. Secrets, secrets, secrets everywhere, from this civilization and from the previous ones.

Jesus and Mary Magdalene are reputed to have been involved with the Egyptian Mystery School of Isis. Jesus is also said to have traveled to Tibet and India and studied at the Mystery School of Shiva. In the Kolbrin Bible we see that Jesus was well known to the Druid priests of that day in Glastonbury, England. While in Israel, Jesus is associated with both John the Baptist and the Essene community on the Dead Sea. Jesus also visited Greece and Turkey. That is why he was called "the great traveler." He really got around. When we take a look at all the travels of Jesus and some of the apostles, we can see the roots of the knowledge he possessed. In practice however there were two vastly different sets of knowledge: one set for those who were initiated into the mysteries and another for those who were profane. Above all else, secret information had to be kept from those who would abuse it to enslave or rule others. **Jesus entrusted his secrets to a grand master chosen from his apostles**. I believe John, "the beloved of Jesus," was chosen as his successor and first grand master. As Christianity made many important converts, such as Ormus of Alexandria (converted by John Mark), the stream of knowledge grew. Also, as Israel was under siege and in chaos, surviving members of the Essenes and Therapeutae also joined the Christian community and merged with it. These grand masters were known as **the Qadosh Fathers** (also spelled Kadosh) and they were underground keepers of the secrets until they surfaced before the crusades as the Knights Templar of Jerusalem. For a time the entire list of grand masters from Christ to Hugh de Payens, called **the "Levitikon List"** was published on the internet at: (www.antiquillum.com). Unfortunately this website is currently down. Jonathan Sellers was the author of this website, beginning with "The Brethren of the Rose + Croix of Gold and the Disciples of Memphis." I had located it while searching for "Ormus and the Grail Chalice." If anyone has a surviving copy, please send it to me.

THE KNIGHTS TEMPLAR

The history of the Knights Templar has been shrouded in mystery to obscure its true origins and history from the profane. The real story goes back over 2,000 years. Around 1600 B.C. the prophet Moses put several stones with symbols into the Ark of the Covenant, along with a pyramid crystal capstone, a large quantity of Ormus powder, and a number of parchments. The Ark was placed in the Temple of Solomon and remained there for nearly a thousand years. However due to the conquest of Israel by the King of Babylon, the Ark was hidden under the temple mount in the maze of underground tunnels there. After burying the Ark, in 583 B.C. the daughter of King Zedekiah, Tamar "Teia" Tephi, and the prophet

Jeremiah brought one of the stones to Ireland. This stone was called "The Stone of Destiny," "Lia Fail," and Jacob's Pillow" (http://jahtruth. net/stone.htm). It was the stone used by the prophet Jacob as a pillow when he saw a vision of God. Since its arrival in Ireland it was used as a coronation stone for all the kings of Ireland and then was lent to Scotland. The stone had a succession of guardians, including St. Columba of Iona. Upon this stone my ancestor Kenneth MacAlpin was crowned king of Scotland.

The Highland Scots are believed to be descendants of the House of Judah and a different race altogether from the lowland Scots. John D. Keyser's recent article entitled **"Children of the Mist: The Story of the Scottish Highlanders!"** explains that the highland clans "abhorred pork and exhibited many traits of the Israelites of old" (http://www.hope-of-israel.org/i000066a.htm). There were seven clans that claim descent from Kenneth MacAlpin and they formed an alliance called **the "Siol Alpin." These seven royal Scottish clans are: the MacNabs, the MacGregors, the MacKinnons, the MacQuarries, the Grants, the MacAulays and the MacFies. The MacKinnons were the hereditary abbots of the Isle of Iona. My ancestors, the MacQuarries, were the lords of the adjacent island of Ulva and parts of Mull**. Each of these clans produced men of great renown including U.S. presidents (U.S. Grant) and Prime Ministers (Canada). The MacQuarries produced General Lachlan MacQuarrie, the "Father of Australia" (www.ulva.mull.com/). This site contains both maps of the area and a family history. So what is so special about these Highland clans? The MacQuarries claim descent also from St. Columba and hence the ancient Irish kings. This trail also leads back to ancient Israel. If we take a look at the coat of arms of the clans, such as the MacQuarries, (and the MacKinnons) an incredible pattern begins to unfold. Clan MacQuarrie's coat of arms has several very distinctive features. Starting at the top we see a bent arm with a dagger inside a crown. This signifies royal descent and the hand in armor stands for leadership in battle. However the royal descent may run much deeper than just Irish and Scottish royalty. The coat of arms also contains 3 castles, 3 crosses, 2 fish, and a ship without sails. These are duplicated on each side of the battle shield with background colors of green and red. Green and red are Templar colors relating to health, wealth and prosperity. Castles are related to safety and to Mary Magdalene. She was known as "the tower of the flock." The fish is an early Christian symbol of Christ. Mary Magdalene was also called the "Magdal Eder" or "Fish Tower." The tower refers to a lofty spiritual calibration and the fish swims in the celestial sea (the center of the galaxy where the healing creative God force originates.) A ship without sails refers to long sea voyages and can relate to the voyage of Mary Magdalene to France with the grail children. The number three can mean trinity or in this case the three grail children. I believe the message encoded on the family crest is that the seven royal clans were in fact grail descendants. The duplication of the symbols on both sides of the battle shied probably signifies the marriage of two ancient grail families therefore producing the clan known as the MacQuarries of Ulva. This hidden history of the Scottish Highlands may explain why the Scots fought so ferociously to maintain their independence. It also would explain why they rallied behind Templars such as Sir William Wallace and Robert the Bruce. These knights are also my ancestors. And the Templars did NOT originate in France. They originated in Scotland in the ancient royal houses there.

A Scottish noble family, as Qadosh fathers, became the guardians of the Stone of Destiny (I believe this family was that of the Saint Claires or Sinclairs of Roslyn, who were Christ descendants). The young son of the nobleman (Henri St. Claire?) went to the stone's hiding place in secret and held it. He was able to withstand the energy of the stone. This activated his Christ DNA memories, his hair flared out, and he was able to see the symbols on it and to decode them. The symbols held the clues as to the location of the Ark of the Covenant under the Temple Mount (www.thetruejesus.org). This was the secret beginning of the Inner Circle of the Knights Templar. (Go to Knights Templar Recover Jesus' Truth).

Previously no one had ever heard of Knights Templar or Qadosh Fathers. The guardians of the truth of Jesus had been kept underground for over 1,000 years, but around 1114 the Bishop of Chartres, France, became aware of them and wrote to friends about them. The Templars had no public organization until 1118. As the Holy Land was in the possession of Muslims, it would be impossible for the Templars to recover the Ark. Therefore, it was decided to form a military order under the guise of protecting pilgrims to Jerusalem. This is the point where the Templars enter the conventional history books and the 9 original Templars camped on the temple mount. By 1128 the Templars recovered the Ark of the Covenant and a number of parchments and artifacts and took them back to France.

A special Cistercian monastery was built by the cousin of the nobleman, St. Bernard of Clairvaux. The land for the monastery had been donated by Hughes de Payens in 1115. The Ark was placed there and the stone as well as the parchments were studied. Hugues de Payens was made the first Grand Master of the Knights Templar. The inner circle of the Templars was derived from Scottish, Flemish and French noblemen. Once the secrets of the Ark and the parchments had been decoded they were taught to senior Templars. **Most notable of these secrets were the healing codes used by Jesus and John the Baptist and the formulas for preparing white gold powders for spiritual activations (Ormus powders).**

The Templars had some military successes in the Holy Land. They were the special forces of their day and age due to the secrets they possessed. They also learned the benefits of the Arab system of banking and conveyed this system to Europe. As they were aware of the healing properties of Ormus materials, they developed healing centers for knights returning from the crusades. The area of Bejus, France was found to have abundant (Ormus) healing soils and free gold. The Templars set up shop there mining gold and making alchemical gold powders for healing and enlightenment. Bejus is a few miles from the infamous Rennes-Le-Chateau and a number of treasures are believed to be hidden in the area.

The Templars became wildly popular and over 300 monasteries were built within 25 years of their return to France. Their Gothic style cathedrals were built using sacred geometry recovered from the Ark and their famous stained glass was from Ormus gold glass made in the Egyptian manner. Thousands of young nobles joined and their lands were given to support the Templar cause. Their lands were a source of income or feudal "rents" that increased the power base of the Templars. Their main area of operations in France was in the Languedoc region, an independent principality. This was the land of the Cathars or Pure Ones and a center of the Mary Magdalene cults. A number of the Cathar noble families were Christ descendants and prominent Templars.

The Templars created the system of international banking that we know today. They had an empire maintained by battle-hardened warrior monks, large land holdings in several countries, a string of banks; a fleet of ships; a few gold mines; castles; fortresses; monasteries; and the secrets of healing and alchemy. They became a very powerful force in Europe and began to equal or surpass kings and popes.

In 1209 Pope Innocent III initiated a crusade composed of 30,000 men to crush the Cathar heresy. The crusaders murdered 100,000 Cathar men, women and children over a 35 year period. By 1233 the concept of an Inquisition had spread to all those in opposition to the dogma of the Roman Church, and approximately 800,000 were murdered over the next several hundred years.

King Philip IV of France was living an extravagant lifestyle on money borrowed from the Templars. He decided to conspire against them and kill them to avoid repaying his debts. After murdering two popes, he was able to get his own man in as Pope Clement V. His puppet pope then conspired with him to wipe out the Templars and steal their money. French troops and papal mercenaries attacked the Templars on October 13, 1307 and a number were tortured and eventually put to death. The Templars were outlawed and a major smear campaign was waged against them using confessions extracted by torture.

A few dozen Templars, including the Grand Master, Jacques de Molay were burned at the stake in 1314. However, there were thousands of Templars, and the Scottish and Flemish branches weren't immediately affected by events in France. The various branches went underground, quite literally, and have survived to this day. Miles of tunnels believed once to have been used by the Templars in Hertford Castle, Hertfordshire UK, have only recently been discovered (www.castlepictures.com/knights-holy-grail.shtml). Some branches continued to operate under different names or hid within various Masonic and Rosicrucian organizations. The Scottish branches remained viable for at least 400 years and then branched out to Canada and America. My ancestors, Sir William Wallace and King Robert the Bruce are said to have been Templars. According to American branches of the inner circle of the Templars, the Ark of the Covenant was used at the battle of Bannockburn in 1314. The Scottish army of only 8,000 men defeated the opposing English force of 30,000 men. I believe the Templars still guard the Ark of the Covenant until it is needed again.

Prince Henry Saint Clair (Sinclair) is said to have sailed west from Scotland in 1392 and established a Templar colony in Nova Scotia. His goal was to establish a New Jerusalem free from the persecution of the old world. He took with him two Italian mapmakers, the Zeno brothers. Graves bearing the coat of arms of septs of the Saint Clair family have been found in the New World (The Gunn family). The round tower of Newport, Rhode Island is reputed to be a Templar baptismal chapel. The Caspar Vopell map of 1545 shows the figure of a Templar knight on a map of Nova Scotia. Templars are said to have laid out the city plans for the City of Montreal, Canada. Author William F. Mann claims to have found a number of Templar sites in Canada, which he believes are from the 1392 voyage.

The most famous site of Templar lore in the Americas is the Oak Island, Nova Scotia, Money Pit said to contain the lost treasure of the Templars. Before the Templars were attacked in France, their treasure was supposedly loaded onto galleys in New Rochelle and shipped away to Scotland, then to the New World to be hidden for centuries. I believe this treasure site is genuine and the treasure could easily be recovered with the correct equipment and techniques.

Those of the inner circle of the Templars were nearly all murdered in the mid 18th Century in both Europe and America. Joseph Smith, founder of the Mormon Church, was the most notable American member of the inner circle and he was murdered by Christian fundamentalists in 1844. However a number of descendants have survived to this day. Dozens of branches are still in existence and still transmit the healing knowledge of Jesus and John the Baptist.

CAN YOU KEEP A SECRET?

Secrets are powerful things. They can determine who controls nations, who lives, and who dies. Who controls the money and who is deprived of it? However the greatest secrets are the ones governing life and the afterlife. As it may take hundreds of lifetimes to accumulate knowledge, it is imperative that knowledge so painfully gained is preserved and passed on to the next generation. This is true on the spiritual level as well. If knowledge gained in one lifetime can be passed on to the same soul in the next lifetime, then a shortcut to enlightenment is built. All of our good karmic points are like cell phone rollover minutes. We've already paid for them and want to keep them to use later. Whatever level of spiritual calibration we've achieved in our last life, we'd certainly like to pick up in the next life right where we left off instead of having to start the process all over again. Why waste 100 lifetimes if you've already paid for them in pain and suffering? A million years is a lot of time to waste, especially when there is a simple solution. What we need to do is leave a message in a bottle addressed to ourselves in the future that only we (or our group of souls) can understand. We want to preserve the message for our side and at the same time deny the message to others who might be profane and use our valuable information to the detriment of society. Civilizations, languages, writing systems and political systems all come and go. There are from time to time great cataclysms, wars, natural disasters, and plagues. How do we preserve knowledge from destruction that was so painfully gained?

While written language is a common method of knowledge preservation, books have a tendency to decay and/or burn. Occasionally this problem is solved by putting the desired text on gold tablets as gold never rusts. It can however be melted down. The best way to preserve a gold object is to form it into a priceless work of art, so that it will be treasured and preserved. The same holds true for sculpture or other works of art such as paintings. We hope that if the art object is priceless or at least unique, it will be preserved and we'll be able to find it again in our next lifetime. The Holy Grail is such a priceless object encoded with esoteric information and the super-science of the Sun. Modern paintings have sold at incredible prices. A Van Gogh recently sold for $85.5 million, while the collective works of Pablo Picasso amassed approximately $1.2 billion. Lastly, the least permanent method of preservation is to encode the message into a building, such as a cathedral. A number of churches and cathedrals featured prominently in The Da Vinci Code. As a building is essentially a huge canvas, a massive amount of data can be built into it. Aside from the pyramids of Egypt, two of the most prominent European structures are Roslyn Cathedral in Scotland and the Chartres Cathedral in France. I am not going to decode these for you; however, I will assist you in arranging a private guided tour of both locations. Go to (www.thetruejesus.org), and scroll down to guided tours of Roslyn and Chartes respectively. I will leave the discovery up to you.

Once we've decided upon an artistic medium, the next task is to decide how to encode the information so that only our side can interpret it. The more valuable the information is, the more we want to deny it to our enemy. The two main methods of encoding are pictures or numbers or a combination of both. The use of symbolism is the only way to preserve the data across the centuries where language and civilizations may fail. Numbers remain rather constant, as we hope man will always have ten fingers and ten toes. There is both a certain genius and an economy to symbolism. Symbols speak directly to the brain and elicit emotions. A massive amount of data can be stored in a single picture. Hundreds of bits of information can be stored in an apparently simple work of art. All one needs to decode it is the key.

The Da Vinci Code was chock full of codes and code breakers. Both our hero and heroine were experts at it. We learn that Sophie was taught at an early age how to break codes as a childhood game. As one rises in spiritual calibration, more and more complex codes can be broken by the initiate in less and less time. Like following a trail of bread crumbs, the code breaker eventually arrives at the encoded answer. Enlightened masters have been leaving encoded messages for themselves and others for tens of thousands of years. Everyone does it.

The main literary device for the plot of <u>The Da Vinci Code</u> is Leonardo Da Vinci's famous painting of The Last Supper. A number of artists painted the exact same theme and even in similar fashion. However Leonardo's painting is different because it is full of encoded information. The most recent discoveries by Italian researcher Slavis Pesci apparently show images of the Virgin Mary, a Knight Templar, a baby and the Holy Grail. The images can only be observed by a series of mirror images or computer enhancement (<u>www.leonardodavinci. tv</u>). The question remains as to the source of Leonardo's information. Allegedly, this is because Leonardo was a "keeper of the secrets" and a member of the Priory of Sion. This is not as far fetched as it may appear as many great artists of the period were initiates in various secret organizations. Their initiation into secret societies was actually the vehicle from which they received their high spiritual calibration and hence their tremendous creativity. Whenever we encounter a person of immense talent and creativity, we should immediately inquire as to the source of that wisdom and creativity. Few geniuses are made at birth; most are created intentionally later in life. True genius has to be unlocked in order to express itself fully.

Was Leonardo Da Vinci a member of a secret society? Yes According to modern descendants of the Knights Templar, he was indeed a member of a secret society. He is said to have possessed both documents relating to the life of Jesus and **THE WEDDING CHALICE OF JESUS AND MARY MAGDALENE**. Therefore, as he possessed a number of secrets passed down from the time of Christ, he encoded them into his paintings. The purpose of the encoded information is to "wake up" the memories of the target audience. In Leonardo's famous fresco of The Last Supper, he accomplished this by forcing the observer to do a "double take" regarding the identity of the apostle John figure on Christ's right. He deliberately made John rather feminine looking, forcing the observer to wonder what his meaning was and what other information may be encoded into the painting. His use of colors represents the "royal colors" and the "royal blood" or sang real. It wasn't necessary to identify Mary Magdalene in a direct or obvious fashion, as the intention had already been fulfilled. Nor do I believe that the M shape created by the spaces over Jesus and John refer to Mary Magdalene either. I believe this M shape refers to another code called the **Ave Millennium, (9)** which was popular at the time. **It refers to a time when the PURIFIED Christian commonwealth will overcome the anti-Christ (i.e. THE END TIMES).** This was a mystical goal of various brothers of the Rosy Cross. The Da Vinci Code also misses the apostle on the left side of Christ holding up his right hand in what is referred to as **"the John gesture."** This is the encoded symbol for John the Baptist and the healing secrets of Christ and the Templars. Many statues of Christ show this gesture with one hand of Christ and a Buddhist blessing made with the other hand. **Consequently, what Leonardo is saying is that the current church is terribly corrupt (the work of Satan) and that the true knowledge, teachings, and bloodline will triumph in the next millennium (Meaning now). In short, it is a prophecy encoded into art. Only those with "eyes to see" can see it. And that was the point. The recent discoveries of TT researcher, Slavis Pesci, would appear to confirm this interpretation.**

The **"John gesture"** is frequently found in the artwork of Leonardo Da Vinci. One reason is that it is the key to the healing power of Jesus, John the Baptist, and the Templars. It is also symbolic of John the Baptist teaching these symbols TO Christ. It is a secret tradition that John was the guru of Christ in a former life as well. The Johnnitte Traditions of his teaching are still with us to this day, but aren't very well known to the public. Leonardo frequently encoded John the Baptist symbolism into his works of art as a metaphor to his past life identity as John the Baptist. He was encoding his identity to his followers, but not to the profane.

Also "missing" from Leonardo's Last Supper is any depiction of the Holy Grail. This was a common theme in other depictions of the Last Supper by other artists. By deliberately making the Holy Grail "lost," it also infers that the Holy Grail will be "found" in the next millennium, <u>which it has been</u>. It will be found and restored in the new millennium and will help to usher in the New Kingdom. I believe this prophecy has been fulfilled.

We've already covered the whereabouts of the Holy Grail, but not the disposition of the Wedding Chalice of Jesus and Mary. I believe it was in the possession of a Templar-affiliated order until WWII. At that time it was "captured" by the Nazis and the guardians were tortured and killed. As Hitler had a number of secret treaties and covenants with the Pope (10), I believe Hitler gave the chalice to the Pope and that it has remained in the Vatican ever since. Don't plan on seeing it any time soon. Nor is anyone likely to acknowledge that it even exists.

Leonardo used every inch of his artworks to hide and encode information. It appears that all of Da Vinci's artwork contain hidden messages and new discoveries are being made all the time. Italian musician Giovanni Maria Pala recently discovered a musical score in The Last Supper. Leonardo used the hand positions of the apostles to signify notes and composed a "Hymn to God" that lasts for about forty seconds. Mr. Pala documented his discovery in <u>La Musica Celata</u> or The Hidden Music. He has performed the piece in concert several times to the amazement of audiences.

Leonardo Da Vinci was an exceptionally brilliant man. He loved codes and was quite the prankster. He had what would be called today an "outrageous" personality. Eccentric just doesn't go far enough. He was always the life of the party so to speak. This got him into a great deal of trouble at times and even once condemned to death. Those who have studied Leonardo know that he was a homosexual. Unfortunately for him, he was "caught in the act," tried for the crime of sodomy, and sentenced to death. Fortunately for him, his lover was a Prince and sole heir. Therefore Leonardo was released instead of being burnt at the stake by the Inquisition. Leonardo's art was of the highest caliber and his inventions were hundreds of years ahead of his time. If he had been killed by the Inquisition, it would have been a terrible loss to Western civilization.

Past lives or incarnations is one of the most important hidden dimensions of human behavior. If one is aware of all the major past lives of an individual, then it is easier to unravel the various "layers" of their personality and actions. In short, the past lives of an individual are what make the person tick. Leonardo is no exception to this rule. He believed that he was the reincarnation of John the Baptist and therefore held a higher truth than the established religion of his day. That is what made him tick and to gravitate to the "underground stream" of "heretical beliefs" of an earlier Gnostic viewpoint. He enjoyed the role of brilliant outcast in those lifetimes, as he still does today in his present incarnation. Leonardo seems to have found a type of lifestyle and personality that he enjoys and has repeated several times. I can sum these characteristics up in three words: brilliant, outrageous and non-conformist. Today, as in his incarnation as Oscar Wilde, he is true to form. In this life, "Leonardo" has performed brilliantly as a foreign playwright and author of 28 plays and one book on the occult. He has been on TV, was a college professor, and is well known in certain circles. As he has few family members living, he was a frequent guest in my home, particularly at holidays. As always, he is highly entertaining and emotionally intense with a flair for the dramatic. He often reminds me of the cartoon character Squidword of Sponge Bob fame. He is the ultimate curmudgeon. A few years ago he moved from St. Augustine, FL. to "retire" to Los Angeles.

Leonardo Da Vinci is but one of the "goodly company" of 2,000 who have chosen to incarnate at this time. All of the apostles are back at this time except Judas. (In the most recent incarnation of Judas, he was the famous poet Kahlil Gibran (1883-1931). Mary Magdalene is back. St. Francis is back (Dr. Wayne Dyer). Joseph, the father of Jesus, Mary, the mother of Jesus, Moses, Joseph of Arimathea, the grail children, Joan of Arc, General George Patton, and many saints are here now to do their work. The 2,000 of the "goodly company", including the apostles, are ALWAYS present to prepare for the next incarnation of Christ. That is their job and they are always on duty, except for a few years of transition time between lives. By tracking my own past lives, it appears that the average transition time is about 5 years. I believe Jesus is here also, but not in the role of redeemer this time. That is supposed to happen AFTER the "Christian Commonwealth" is established and therefore ready for its true leader.

The role of "the destroyer," earthquakes, Earth Changes, floods, pole shifts and other life changing events, is to separate "the wheat from the chaff" and to purify humanity. The role of the "goodly company" is to prepare those with "eyes that see" for these upcoming events and to wake them up to their duty at this time. Only 635 of the 2,000 are "awake" or spiritually activated at this time. I am not at liberty to tell you their names, as this would interfere with the fulfillment of their work. It's particularly hard to work when you're dead also. So, I am not going to infringe upon anyone's privacy or mission. That's not my job. I will only give the name of one apostle currently in the flesh as he wrote a book about his past life experiences as the apostle Paul or Saul of Tarsus. The book is entitled: **The Messengers: a True Story of Angelic Presence and the Return to the Age of Miracles** by G. W. Hardin and Julia Ingram. It describes the seemingly miraculous events in the life of Oregon businessman Nick Bunick. I rate it at **855** on the spiritual calibration scale and highly recommend it. I'm not going to reveal my past life identity either, as that would only interfere with my work. I have a job to do and will do it the best I can. It is up to everyone whether they want to pitch in and help by serving others or remain on the fence and serve themselves. I'll leave it at that. That is why Leonardo and thousands of others have left us messages in a bottle that have successfully traveled over time to reach us now at the end times.

I realize this may all be hard to comprehend. I appreciate the difficulty as it took me a great deal of time also to see it. However once you can see, it is as if a whole new world has suddenly opened up. Once you can "see," the messages are everywhere to be found. Thousands and thousands of them. You've all seen them; you just didn't pay attention to them as you were focused on something else. I took two semesters of history of art at Fredonia State College, read the rather massive Janson's History of Art, and didn't see a damned thing. I didn't have a clue at the time. But the messages are there. Everywhere.

I currently reside in St. Augustine, Florida and worked at Flagler College, which was built as the Ponce De Leon Hotel by Henry Flagler in 1888 (www.flagler.edu/). Every day I walked around the campus and never noticed the symbols on the walls until I started this project. Then the symbolism began to jump out at me from every direction. There are Holy Grails in the lobby, peacocks everywhere (symbols of everlasting life) and "engrailed" Templar crosses hidden in the woodwork. The porch of the new library is made entirely of engrailed Templar crosses. The college logo is the rampant lion of Scotland and the college flag is the red rampant lion on a yellow field with fleur-de-lis. Traditionally, this is the same flag the Scots carried into battle. Now it is carried at soccer games. Flagler College is a veritable Rosslyn Chapel of the collegiate world. Having discovered all this right in my backyard, I purchased the frequently quoted book **The Lost Language of Symbolism** by Harold Bailey and decided to have at it.

Once the door of symbolism is opened there is no turning back. I find that cracking every symbol I see is an irresistible urge. The messages contained are nothing short of incredible. Gothic cathedrals, Renaissance paintings, and even seemingly rather ordinary objects are full of esoteric symbolism and ancient messages. As the subject is so vast and the aforementioned book contains over 1,400 symbols, let's take a look only at symbols relating most directly to the grail family.

I've noticed a trend among several of the authors attempting to debunk the Da Vinci Code. They claim they can't find any evidence of the Jesus and Mary connection. I would like to go on record as stating that quite the contrary it is everywhere to be found. First of all you have to look in the correct locations. You can't find bears on the streets of New York City. You've got to go where they live. The same principle goes in looking for the descendants of Jesus and Mary. You've got to go where THEY lived and find the symbolism there. Knowledge of early Christian and ancient Hebrew symbolism is essential in this regard.

The easiest symbol to find everywhere is that of the Davidic lion. It signifies the house of David, king of Israel. The lion rampant is seen on the coats of arms of kings and queens in England and Scotland and many noble families. You've all seen it. There are several variations, some of which expressly relate to the grail children. A lion rampant with two intertwined tails represents "the vine" or the grail family. There are two clusters of grapes on the tail. It is unmistakable. You've all seen it, but just didn't realize its significance. Most recently the symbol was worn on a T-shirt by Rob Schneider's character Gus in the movie Benchwarmers. You've probably walked right by it at Blockbuster. The other variants are a little harder to see. Either the rampant lion is shown with three vine looking shoots issuing from the tail, three tufts on the tail, or the most difficult to see, a pomegranate on the end of the tail (Symbolizing fertility). They all have the same meaning, but the vine is the easiest to spot as it stands out very clearly. The oddest one is that of a lion with a cluster of grapes as its beard, again meaning "the vine." The Scottish battle flag with its red lion rampant on a yellow field, surrounded by fleur-de-lis, was originally carried by William I, King of Scotland. Why would the Scots be carrying a battle flag with French fleurs-de-lis? The flag represents the Lion of Judah, the grail family, and the intermarriage of Christ descendants to the royal houses of France. Many noble families intermarried into this line and it can be seen everywhere in Scotland, England, France, Wales and Ireland.

My membership certificate from **The Somerset Chapter of the Magna Charta Barons** contains the coats of arms of all the barons. It took me all of ten seconds to find nine of the very common Davidic lions. I am sure my readers can find thousands more once the search begins. Look at a clan map of Scotland or Ireland and you'll see dozens of them. They also frequently are associated with a crown, signifying the royal house of David. Crowns are also very easy to spot and whenever you see one start digging to see where the royal trail leads. The bottom line is that if "the vine" was without issue from Jesus and Mary, then the symbols wouldn't be displayed on thousands of coats of arms. If the line were dead, it wouldn't be represented. However, it is alive and well.

A second universally recognized symbol the world over is that of the "Fleurs-de-Lis." The "flower of the lily" is an ancient symbol of Israel and the pillars of the temple of Solomon were engraved with lilies. It also pertains to the covenant of circumcision. It is most commonly associated with the royal houses of France. The Merovingian dynasty is frequently mentioned in The Da Vinci Code as the French royal descendants of Jesus and Mary. **The name Merovingian actually means of Mary (mer) [meaning sea] and the vine (vin)**. These symbols are frequently seen in conjunction with crowns as above or the Merovingian bee. The bee is an ancient Egyptian symbol for royalty, thereby further designating the roots going back to Egypt, the source of the House of Israel.

The heraldic device for the royal house of Britain is probably the third most recognized symbol in the world. It consists of a Davidic lion on the left and a unicorn on the right. The unicorn is a Christ symbol, particularly the "virility" of Christ encoded as the horn of the unicorn. There are a total of nine lions on the crest. The coats of arms for Scotland is even more enlightening. It has several rampant lions, the lyre of ancient Ireland (and Israel), a Merovingian bear and an X, the hermetic symbol of the grail heresy (http://en.wikipedia.org/wiki/Royal_Coat_of_Arms_of_the_United_Kingdom).

I find it amazing that the grail heresy was hidden in so many ingenious ways right in front of our eyes. The only real question is how deeply imbedded the information is hidden. I find more and more hidden clues almost everyday. The more deeply imbedded codes combine [elements such as] an obvious symbol such as a tower, and then wavy lines to designate a number. The tower is easy to identify as that of Mary Magdalene, but the wavy lines symbolize the sea, truth and the code that is in the number of the waves or lines. A common one is the use of five lines on a coat of arms representing the 5th sign of the zodiac or Leo, the lion. So again we have the Davidic Lion (Christ) and the tower of Mary Magdalene. This device is very common and once you recognize it you'll see it everywhere.

The guardians of the grail have gone to extreme lengths to hide their message in every conceivable art form and vehicle. It is in art, sculpture, buildings, glass, tapestries, books, tarot cards, and oral traditions such as fairy tales like Snow White and Sleeping Beauty. There are even stags and lions on bottles of beer, liquor and pool tables. Perhaps the intent was to leave no one out? The Cathars had a monopoly on paper making and made many early bibles. They hid their grail messages in water marks on every page. Rather clever I thought. Margaret Starbird does a wonderful job of explaining all these codes and symbols. She has a spiritual calibration of **923** and her work is right on target. Her most well known work, **The Woman with the Alabaster Jar: Mary Magdalene and the Holy Grail**, has sold over 100,000 copies and rightly so.

There is a tremendous economy to symbolism. Several hundred sets of data can be encoded in just one piece of art and it doesn't matter what languages may be in vogue. Symbolism is a set of knowledge that remains eternal as long as the piece of art survives. The Holy Grail itself is the supreme example of this principal. One of my favorites is the set of tapestries called the Unicorn Tapestries. These date from the 15th century and were probably made in Brussels. There are seven main tapestries, each telling a story about a unicorn (Christ symbol) and a maiden (Magdalene symbol). These tapestries have several unique features, as the encoded information is primarily based in the botany of the flowers, plants, and animals of the garden background. These elements help amplify the meanings of the main characters and the action of the scenes. The resulting information is so complex and involved that it takes over 250 pages of analysis to sort it all out. Simply incredible! Medieval scholar and horticulturist John Williamson was able to decipher it in his rare volume, **The Oak King, the Holly King, and the Unicorn: The Myths and Symbolism of the Unicorn Tapestries**. While the unicorn is a very ancient symbol, it was frequently used to symbolize Christ and his virility. The maiden symbolizes Mary Magdalene and the garden is that of sexual union and procreation. She is seen with two rabbits and a number of plants that symbolize marriage, fertility, and aphrodisiacs. The creator of the work, who remains unknown, even managed to sneak in the "activation code" of the secret of the Templars and Christ. He also managed to label the church as the poison stream, by placing a number of poisonous plants near the stream being purified by the horn of the Unicorn. Although the unicorn is killed by the hunters, he is resurrected to purify the stream by his offspring. The Unicorn in Captivity is on display at the Cloisters Museum to the north of Manhattan owned by the Metropolitan Museum of Art (www.metmuseum.org/). It is not ironic that the family that donated the tapestry is the one most responsible for placing Jesus in captivity. Symbols work on many levels if only one can read them.

The bottom line is that works of art containing the Grail Heresy of the Cathars are everywhere to be found. It is virtually impossible to enter any art museum of note and not find one. You just have to understand the many variants of symbolism and what they stand for. Although the Cloisters is a very small museum, I found a very exciting piece there that has never been mentioned before in any books on the Grail family. It is known as the Opus Anglicanum or the English Work. It is a late 15th Century priest's vestment embroidered with many fleurs-de-lis and several other motifs. What is unique about these fleurs-de-lis is that they are "sprouting vines" in every direction on each one. They signify "the vine" of the Grail children born of Mary Magdalene reaching and sprouting in every direction. You may view the Opus Anglicanum by entering the works of art collection (for the Cloisters Museum) and then advancing to #5. At (http://www.metmuseum.org/Works_of_Art/viewOne.asp?dep=7 &viewmode=0&item+1982.432). As long as you're there, view the Unicorn in Captivity at # 41, and see how many other encoded pieces you can find in the Cloisters collection. There are several.

GOD WORKS IN MYSTERIOUS WAYS

Perhaps ironically, The Da Vinci Code has spurred a new quest for the Holy Grail and spiritual truth. I am sure Dan Brown was taken totally by surprise by the movement that his novel has spawned (www.danbrown.com). A recent Google search for the Da Vinci

Code resulted in 38 million hits! There is even a Da Vinci Code research guide online (http://altreligion.about.com/library/bl_davincicode.htm). I began this exercise in the search for truth with no reservations or preconceived ideas. Just a bit annoyed perhaps and that is all. What I found and what I experienced shocked me and has changed my life. As some of the material and ideas I've used came to me during sleep, I can't claim them as my own. I am just the piano player, not the writer of the tune.

The nay sayers will tell you that none of this is possible. At least a few of them have some objectivity. Lynn Picknett and Clive Prince, authors of **The Sion Revelation** and **The Templar Revelation** have tried to present something of a balanced picture of events. They have stated the obvious in that if indeed Jesus and Mary had descendants, there would be millions of them. However the most recurring problem that I see is the camps are rather evenly divided into two groups: those who have information and those who try to interpret it. In many respects, the whole process seems reminiscent of a gaggle of virgins writing a sex manual. I suggest that the key to sorting out this maze of facts and alleged facts is by using spiritual calibration as a tool and becoming "A Christ." In the final analysis, we must look at whether or not the authors even tried to find the material they say doesn't exist or tried the procedures they say don't work. Personally, I haven't encountered any of these difficulties. I keep finding a wealth of material on Jesus and Mary Magdalene. I've tried a dozen Ormus formulas and found that not only did they work, but they greatly surpassed my expectations. The whole story just keeps unfolding at an ever-increasing pace. And oddly enough all the various storylines are interconnected revealing a greater theme. Perhaps that is what God had in mind?

It is my sincere hope that the movement Dan Brown started will bring forth more and more scientific research into the mysteries at hand. There is enough work to be done to employ thousands of researchers in the field. There are 800,000 or more surnames to be checked for clues and family histories to be traced back to their sources. A very quick way to pop up your coat of arms is at The House of Names (www.houseofnames.com). I purchased a lovely parchment of my Frigon family coat of arms for only $19.95. This is only a quick starting point as it will take real research to find the most ancient versions of your surname and original coat of arms. This is particularly true in Scotland where there are both ancient and modern coats of arms and tartans. To arrive at what we're looking for you'll need the ancient original versions.

I believe the evidence will ultimately shed light on a great multitude of Christ descendants via royal and noble lines long forgotten in the mists of time. And as in the play Romeo and Juliet, it is inevitable that some Davidic royal princes and princesses married for love below their stations in life against the wishes of their parents. Those of you who have seen the movie Braveheart will be aware that there was also a feudal right called "the first night" or prima nocte. The lord of the manor had the inherent right to sleep with any new bride he chose on her wedding night. I think you can figure out what this does to our descendant factor! Just think of these lusty old lords as Bill Clinton in chain mail and you'll get my point.

There are many archives in the world that remain untouched and halls of records that remain hidden. Every manor house had the right to hold its own court and each kept its own records. Many of these are still in existence today. See The Manorial Society of Great Britain at: (http://www.msgb.co.uk/). Lastly, it appears that Napoleon captured a great many documents from the Vatican and placed them in the Arsenal Library in Paris in 1810. I say, "Have at it!" Now that we know what we're looking for, perhaps we'll find it.

As for the subplot of white powdered gold and all of its properties, the procedure to prove them is quite straightforward. Try them! I am sure they will hold up to scientific scrutiny. I've listed over 140 different brands in An End to All Disease. Until then I can only repeat what we used to say in the 1960s, "Don't knock it until you've tried it!" I am of the opinion that only a dramatic increase in world spiritual calibration has any hope of saving the planet. The use of ormus materials is a viable method of doing just that. I've experienced spectacular results and I am just beginning.

Advances in DNA testing may eventually put the whole Jesus and Mary issue to rest. We know where the mortal remains of Mary Magdalene are. Those of the historical Jesus may yet be found.

Scientific inquiry should be able to prove or disprove our theories. I say go for it. Either we are or we aren't, so let's find out! Better to know than going around in circles until the end of the world. The issues at hand are too important to be left to chance and endless speculation. Let's get busy. Time is running out!!

SEEK AND YE SHALL FIND

The Christ "mystery" is certainly complex and requires a great deal of honest detective work even to begin to sort it out! As there is so much myth added to the mystery, the only logical approach is to throw out everything we think we know and take an entirely fresh approach. In essence we must start at the beginning and look for clues in a forensic manner. As in a murder mystery, a seemingly tiny clue, long overlooked, might unravel the whole case of the Jesus mystery. In addition to clues we must test new hypotheses and see if any evidence supports them. We have grown accustomed to believing a story line that has in effect become institutionalized. The obvious hazard is that the energy of the myth concentrates power into the institutions that have vested interest in keeping the myth alive. The power is then held by the few at the expense of the many. Religions have thus become middlemen in the quest for salvation with services going to the highest bidder. The truth is middlemen aren't required and anyone can find God within. Jesus and every avatar who ever lived came to remind us of just that. All the rest is just details. When we begin to look at the mystery from a higher perspective, many of the blanks start to fill in and a new picture begins to emerge. It may be hazy at first, but the details will be revealed.

First of all, Christianity is portrayed as something radically new and fresh. One could say revolutionary in human experience. On the other hand, if Christ's truth is in fact eternal, then it is more likely from older sources. The purpose of any mystery school is to preserve very ancient knowledge, teach its initiates, and basically withhold it from those who aren't members. No religion or institution WANTS to suggest that much of our culture has survived previous civilizations. To do so would ruin the myths of "a chosen people" or we are holier than someone else. If it were proven that we are all of one family, a lot of priests and rabbis would be out of a job. Ancient languages such as Hebrew and Sanskrit are **STAR LANGUAGES** and that is an extremely inconvenient truth. Government big shots loose a lot of sleep over that one. It is therefore more likely that Christianity is a revival of "the old religion" rather than something totally new. There is nothing new under the sun. To find the first clues, we must look for pre-Christian religions headed for a new birth of ancient traditions.

Hebraic colonies existed all around the Mediterranean Sea and into the British Isles. These colonies were established along the ancient Phoenician trade routes. Important ports prospered from international trade and became centers of learning and monastic culture. During the time of Christ the British Isles possessed the largest number of universities, totaling 60, with 60,000 students under instruction. These Druidic universities were popular with the wealthy Romans who sent their children there for studies in law, science and religion (11).

The elite of the Western world traveled to the British Isles and likewise religious scholars from Egypt, Spain, Palestine and Scotland all met to exchange ideas. Egyptian Essenes had a working relationship with British Druid Magi. Some Druids, such as those in Fortingall, Scotland had a sister school on Mt. Carmel, Palestine and were therefore linked spiritually and culturally. Even monks from Tibet visited the British Isles and vice versa. This is hard for landlubbers to believe, but travel by ship was rather routine, although hazardous. And trade routes all the way to the Far East by caravan were in operation since remote antiquity. The Phoenicians had colonies as far away as Nicaragua for trade with the Chinese (12). There are small Egyptian pyramids in America and as far afield as Australia. The oceans of the world are one big superhighway and the arms race of the ancients was shipbuilding.

It was precisely in this prosperous, well traveled, and learned environment that the pre-Christian movement was planned. Note I said PLANNED! It may have taken hundreds of years, if not thousands, to prepare for such a major evolutionary step for mankind. The Grail

Bloodline began thousands of years prior to the birth of Jesus. A millennium passed between the birth of King David and Jesus. It took approximately 1,000 years to raise the spiritual calibration of the bloodline from the **520** of King David to the initial **999** needed to become "A Christ." This didn't just happen overnight! Monastic orders such as the Egyptian priests, Druids, Essenes and Tibetan monks all kept the ancient knowledge alive and passed it to their initiates. Those in the Grail Bloodline were trained in various orders until maturity and then married an individual of equal genetic and spiritual qualifications.

Although the genealogy of Jesus the Christ DOES EXIST, very little scholarship has been done on it to trace the spiritual roots of Jesus and Christianity. According to **Barry Dunford** and his exhaustive research into antiquarian British history, a pedigree of Jesus and his relations back to Adam and Eve exist at the English College of Arms, The Heraldry Office (13). MS 20 at Jesus College clearly shows the grandmother of Jesus and her links to various kings of the British royal family. The Grail family at the time of Jesus continued this tradition and intermarried with British and other royals.

Researchers and theologians have always totally ASSUMED that the lineage of Jesus was Jewish and completely based in the Middle East. The genealogy of Christ however tells a totally different story and provides the first of several breakthrough clues to our Jesus mystery. The first shocking clue is that the great-grandparents of Jesus were born and lived in the area of Fortingall, Scotland, where one of the first "mother churches" is believed to have been located. His grandparents Joachim and Anna (Hannah) moved to Galilee, but the rest of the family remained in Scotland. Anna wasn't Jewish, but of both Celtic and Hebrew royal lineages. According to the Akashic records, Joseph, the husband of Mary had some Celtic lines as well. Joseph of Arimathea is reputed to have taken a Celtic second wife and his daughter Anna was married to King Beli (14).

The plot of The Da Vinci Code revolves around both the Grail Bloodline and the Rose Line. If we could pinpoint the meaning and the location of these terms, we might begin to unravel the Jesus mystery! **Where the Grail Bloodline and the Rose Line intersect** is the solution to several mysteries (**http://sacredconnections.co.uk/**).

<u>The Da Vinci Code</u> novel comes to its climatic end with the descendants of Jesus and Mary meeting at the famous Rosslyn Chapel of the Sinclair family near Edinburgh, Scotland. We are told that Rosslyn means Rose Line and that the Sinclairs or St. Claires are Christ descendants. **This is symbolically encoded by an engrailed cross stained glass window surrounded with fleurs-de-lis at the entrance to the chapel.** There are however many more levels of metaphysical symbolism here and they need to be explained in detail in order to unravel the Jesus mystery. Although the codes within Rosslyn Chapel have been broken by ex-Royal Air Force code-breaker Thomas Mitchell (**www.tjmitchell.com/stuart/rosslyn.html**) revealing musical scores, first we must deal with the basics.

The symbolism of the Rose is often found in ancient texts. Mary, the mother of Jesus and Mary Magdalene are frequently referred to as "the Rose." An opening flower, such as a rose, lily, or in the East a lotus blossom, symbolizes spiritual unfoldment or enlightenment. Therefore the title "the Rose" is a code word for an enlightened person. You may have heard also of the term compass rose for the markings on a magnetic compass. A compass points the way along magnetic lines of force and points to magnetic north/south poles. A rose line is a magnetic line of force that can be plotted on a map. In the West these are more commonly referred to as ley lines. Thousands of standing stones and monuments trace these lines all over Europe. In the East, ley lines are called "Dragon Lines" and the art and science of Feng Shui seeks to balance these energies in harmony with nature.

Therefore these magnetic lines of force are related to navigation (both celestial and terrestrial), health, spiritual growth and harmonious living. Grand Masters of mystery schools were frequently called "navigators," or "THE NAVIGATOR." The Grand Master knows how to map, mark, and use ley lines to navigate a harmonious enlightened life. Jesus is frequently referred to as "A Navigator" and Mary Magdalene "the Rose." Jesus is also referred to as "The Rose of Sharon."

Ley lines can extend for hundreds, even thousands of miles across entire continents. Monasteries or churches can indeed be thousands of miles away from each other, but be on opposite ends of terminals of the same energy field or grid system. Churches, monasteries, or monuments such as Stonehenge, are built upon these energy "portals" to make use of them for spiritual, psychic, and agricultural purposes. The holy sites that our story revolves around are ALL powerful ley line terminals or portals of expansive energy. Churches and monasteries all over the world are interconnected, like a spiritual internet. We can spiritually calibrate any place on Earth and instantly see that these holy places have a calibration near or above the wavelength of enlightenment or **700** on our scale. The prophets of every major religion have made use of such sacred mountains in their beliefs and practices. Much of this knowledge has been lost in the West, but it is considered a duty in the East to make a pilgrimage to a sacred mountain, such as Mt. Kalais, once in a lifetime.

One of the keys to our mystery is that Mt. Carmel, Palestine and Fortingall, Scotland are indeed linked upon opposite ends of a major ley line system. This ley line system has four major branches that interconnect the holy sites in our story and provide a map and a solution to several mysteries (15).

I began setting the stage for this story in the beginning by telling how I gradually raised my own spiritual calibration. I did this to repair all the damage to my body from several auto accidents. Every person born does this; the only variable is whether it is done in one or two lifetimes or over the period of a million years of natural gradual evolution. The Grail bloodline, a "star seed" line, was created as a suitable genetic vehicle to withstand the rigors of higher spiritual calibrations. This took a few hundred generations to culminate in individuals such as the grandparents of Jesus, Joseph and Mary, and Mary Magdalene. They were ALL great initiates and each generation paved the way for the next. Again, the purpose of the offspring of Jesus and Mary Magdalene was to help humanity evolve to a higher calibration and meet the challenges of the End Times. Each generation added to the "**Ancestral Light**" or light carrying capacity. This was God's Plan and Jesus and Mary fulfilled it. Understanding this process is the solution not only to the Jesus mystery, but to your own health as well. **THE BOTTOM LINE IS THAT ANYONE CAN BECOME "A CHRIST" IF YOU KNOW HOW AND THAT EVENTUALLY EVERYONE DOES**. All roads lead back to God. Its just a matter of time. Jesus didn't just happen by accident, but rather came to show you "the way." He was the first to do so (the Alpha) and will be the last to do so when this planet shuts down (the Omega). He was the first man and will be the last one also.

There are no accidents in the universe and becoming "A Christ" is not a matter of chance. It is a planned event. The first two essential ingredients are: 1) A bloodline capable of withstanding higher spiritual frequencies and 2) A source of Christ or "Christos" frequencies. Using our spiritual calibration chart, by definition, the Christ frequency begins at around **999** (**995** to be technical). In Fortingall, Scotland near the early pre-Christian mother church we have exactly the conditions necessary. We have the great-grandparents and grandparents of Jesus and we have a large sacred mountain called **Mount Schiehallion** with a spiritual calibration of **995. Six of the twelve Grail families who migrated to Palestine were from Scotland, five directly from the Fortingall area.** There was a direct connection among the Druids of Fortingall, the Essenes of Mt. Carmel and the Egyptian initiates (16). The Druids predicted a savior named Jeshua and helped facilitate his manifestation. Druid means "initiates of the inner circle" or as we would understand the word "prophet" or "wise man."

And lastly we have an adequate supply of raw materials, particularly gold, to make gold ormus powders to facilitate the spiritual transformation. There were ample supplies of metals and gold in Scotland and Egypt. The Essenes on the Dead Sea used the wet method of extraction, as previously discussed to concentrate gold from the salts. Most of "the great work" was done in monastic environments in very isolated, but very sacred settings. The out islands of the Hebrides, the Egyptian desert, the area surrounding the Dead Sea, and later small remote villages in the Pyrenees of France provided the setting needed. It is easier to understand why the roots of Christianity are located in such remote locations once we understand the physical and spiritual requirements needed to nurture a monastic community and the work involved. The monastic communities at the time before Christ shared a common vision and a common goal of facilitating the spiritual evolution and uplifting of humanity.

Historians have focused to a great extent on the area of Palestine and essentially ignored the pre-Christian movement in Scotland and elsewhere. This may have been a deliberate attempt to focus attention away from Scotland so the Grail Family could do their work in seclusion, free from persecution. The Christian church of Britain remained independent of Roman Church control for hundreds of years. There were always two churches of Christ, the outer one for the masses, and the inner secret one for the initiated pure ones. The initiates of the hidden Church of the Grail were the guardians of the secrets. Royal guards, called the Klegnann, were the "guardians of the Thorn Branch." This guard was founded by a member of the ancient royal grail family: The Steward Clan. The thorn branch was the royal grail seal (17).

The location of the Grail Family was perhaps the greatest secret. And they were continuously on the move to safeguard the bloodline. Even the highest initiates of the various mystery schools NEVER spoke the name of Jesus. He was referred to as **"THE DOVE," "the Rose of Sharon," "the word of God,"** or others among numerous code words (18).

The various names of Jesus, are in fact spiritual titles, all meaning roughly "light- bearer." To follow the Grail Family and to find their most direct descendants today we must first look at these names or titles in several languages. Jesus is **Jeshua** in Tibet, India, and Greece. **Christ** or **Christos** is Greek. In Tibet there is a **St. Issa,** in Gaelic its **Iosa.** In Aramaic it is **ISA**, in Cornwall and Wales it's spelled **Essa. And don't forget all the code words for Jesus!** Once we understand the various spellings and code words we can track down place names such as Eilean Isa or Jesus Island, now called Isay in the Hebrides. On the Isle of Mull we find Essa Hill. And most importantly to this story we find **THE ISLE OF IONA, THE ISLAND OF THE DOVE. In our code book this would also mean The Island of Jesus.**

The sacred Island of Iona lies on the Fortingall (Christos Frequency) and Montrose (Mount Rose) ley line axis. It calibrates at 999 or a perfect Christos Frequency. This is where the surviving Grail son was born to Jesus and Mary Magdalene. Sir Laurence Gardener names the son Josephes, while the Akashic Records name him JOHN MARTIN (18). To complicate the matter further, the first birth is attributed to natural conception and the later as a "light-conception" or an immaculate conception as we commonly understand the term. As it is quite possible that Jesus and Mary had numerous children, both may be correct. The exact number of children hasn't been resolved. I've seen accounts stating three, five, and all the way up to thirteen children. A large number of children wouldn't have been uncommon in the day. We'll talk more about this issue later, but for now lets see if there is a method that we may use eventually to solve the Grail genealogy.

In the earlier part of this book we used coats of arms to get a general idea of the later Grail descendants and how they were dispersed. Barry Dunford discovered a more direct way: by decoding or translating the surnames themselves (19). We can use the St. Claires or Sinclairs, the hereditary Grand Masters of the Knights Templar, of The Da Vinci Code as an example. Their lineage came from ancient kings of Norway, such as Harold GILLICHRIST. GILLICREST translates as "son of Christ." Following this clue, we find Giliosa or Gili-Osa, again meaning "Son of Issa or Jesus in Gaelic. As this is a Scottish name the Mc prefix is added becoming McGilosa or "the son of the son of Jesus." Continuing on we find Gihies, McLeish, McGilchrist, Gihisa, and others in Scotland and Ireland. I am sure there are many more to be found and numerous variations. A great deal of work needs to continue in this regard, now that we have found a strategy for tracing the Grail family back to its true point of origin.

The other breakthrough clue we have is also to be found on The Isle of Iona. Despite it's small size, the Isle of Iona has at least 60 kings buried in its sacred ground. These include 48 Scottish kings, 8 Norwegian, and 4 Irish kings. Others list 4 French kings as well. I'm not sure why the French are often excluded, but perhaps their inclusion would be too obvious a clue to the Grail mystery. Clearly there has to be a very good reason why so many monarchs would have their mortal remains shipped hundreds of miles to a small monastery graveyard in the middle of nowhere. Why not Jerusalem? Why did St. Columba build a monastery here in 563 in the first place and bring the Holy Grail? I believe the answer is twofold. First of all I believe these kings were all members of The Hidden Church of the Holy Grail and they were aware of the birth of Jesus' son on Iona. And more importantly they were all initiates of the Hidden Grail Church because they were Christ descendants. THAT IS WHY THEY ARE BURIED THERE. Very few of the monuments and headstones have survived from St. Oran's Cemetery. However of the few remaining stones we can see a ship and a Davidic lion on the shield of our very first king on display at the museum there (http://www.scotshistoryonline. co.uk/dukes.html).

The seven royal Scottish clans known as the "Soil Alpin" derived from these ancient kings are all undoubtedly Jesus' descendants. The Isle of Iona is our other Rosetta stone for tracing the Grail Family back to its source. It will take some time, but we can do it now that we have some starting points! Unfortunately, due to Viking raids and the hazards of war, the burial of the kings was discontinued. The monasteries on Iona were built and destroyed several times. The medieval Benedictine abbey has been restored by The Iona Community (http://iona.org.uk/community/main.htm) which maintains the abbey and provides lodging and Christian fellowship on the island. If you are prepared to receive it, you may experience the Christos frequency (999) on the ley lines of Iona. It is believed that Christ personally attuned the island to this perfect frequency for this purpose.

Now that we have broken through the veil of secrets hiding the Grail mystery we can apply the same cross-referencing techniques to other targets of interest. 1) We can first look for surnames or code names indicating a Grail descent. 2) Coats of arms often reveal descent in antiquity that we can follow back to its source. 3) The Grail Family was of royal descent and is therefore most frequently found intermarried with other royals. 4) To maintain their high spiritual calibrations, Grail Family members generally live in close proximity to a sacred mountain, ley line, or other source of the Christos energy. 5) Monasteries, religious orders, and secret societies are associated with these sacred portals of energy and Grail family members were the grand masters of them. 6) Raw materials to make gold ormus powders or mineral salts are readily available to aid with the spiritual transformations of the aspirants. Using this model we can apply it to Iona, Rosslyn, Glastonbury, Provence, Rennes le Chateau, Egypt, or to the Dead Sea, and all the pieces begin to come together about the "great work" being conducted at these locations. Both Edinburgh and old Jerusalem are "Cities of the Lion" and laid out in a Grail matrix (20). Historians have never been able to connect the dots concerning the significance of the various sacred sites as they had no suitable model of the "good work." Now we do!

The Rev. Maia Christianne Nartoomid and her husband Simeon have stated that the Earth is ready for a new birth. The cosmic seeds of a new world have already been planted during the "Amaru crystal seeding project" and will be born in 2012. High in the Andes, near Lake Titicaca (http://www.spiritmythos.org/earth/mer/crystals/amaru-crystal-seeding.htm). Inca shamans have set the process in motion by transforming the crystalline structure of the Earth to begin a new Earth star. These Atlantcan/Inca initiates have transmuted a small crystal portal to receive more energy. Initiates can use these sacred crystals to attain a higher spiritual calibration. This is the initiation of 500 years of peace in Inca prophecy and the next step in the evolution of man towards recalibrating the human form into a PURE GEM BODY. This is the pure diamond body of the saints that I referred to in part one of this book. This is exactly the same process that Christ performed in each of his lifetimes at various locations. The process anchors more celestial energy of a higher spiritual calibration to the Earth allowing the humans living on it to receive it. Now our story has come full circle from where we began in book one.

THE 13 MISSING DEAD SEA SCROOLS

The prophet Nostradamus predicted that the third anti-Christ would capture Italy and level Rome. He would seek to destroy Christianity by revealing its secrets, long hidden in the secret Vatican archives. Until recently no one had any idea of what these great secrets might be.

New discoveries of rare and ancient documents occur all the time. There is a large and well established black market for significant historical documents. Few of these ever see the light of day for the simple reason that to possess, trade, or otherwise remove archaeological treasures is illegal throughout the world. As early Christian or Jewish treasures found in currently Islamic countries are politically incorrect they risk being destroyed upon discovery. As critical documents are however worth millions of dollars on the black market, these documents conveniently disappear into the hands of experienced underground collectors. On at least one occasion, copies of one of the Dead Sea Scrolls ended up in a CIA diplomatic bag and subsequently disappeared.

The rather infamous Abbe Beranger Sauniere of Rennes Le Chateau may indeed have been one of the first to receive a secretative bonanza from the sale of hidden documents. This provincial parish priest, who had barely twenty francs a month to eat suddenly acquired a millionaire lifestyle. After renovating his church in the 1890s, the Abbe acquired funds to build roads, an exquisite residence, and a mini castle or tower as a library. (According to the Akashic records, a daughter of Jesus Christ and Mary Magdalene is interred beneath this tower). His alleged documents essentially started the entire Holy Blood, Holy Grail phenomenon that we know today. While we may never know which documents attributed to Abbe Sauniere are authentic, he left a number of symbolic clues for us to discover and decipher. These fascinating clues have a direct bearing on our story and are cleverly concealed in plain sight within the stations of the cross at his church. Station eight (http://www.cassiopaea.org/Rennes-le-Chaeau/rennesstat8.html) shows **"a woman with a child standing beside Jesus: the child is wearing a SCOTISH TARTAN**

ROBE." It is believed that the woman in question is Mary Magdalene and the child is therefore Tamar, "the Sarah." (If the tartan could be identified, this would help corroborate the Jesus story contained in this volume). Station fourteen (http://www.cassiopaea.org/Rennes-le-Chaeau/rennesstat14.html) shows the body of Christ being carried OUT OF THE TOMB, under cover of darkness, while traditionally this station shows Jesus being placed into the tomb. This was accomplished by substituting the moon in place of the sun. Evidence of not only a "rigged" crucifixion but an heir to Christ as well are certainly inconvenient and persistent hermetic traditions that the Roman Church would like to see disappear (21). Abbe Sauniere is also believed to have left behind a model of the area containing the key to the tomb of Jesus (http://www.renneslechateau.com/anglais/octonovo.htm). However as of yet the alleged tomb of Jesus has not been found. Recently researcher Ben Hammett cracked one of the codes left by Abbe Sauniere and located a hidden Templar tomb. The crypt contains at least one body draped in a Templar shroud and what appears to be part of the treasure of Jerusalem. The discovery can be viewed in the documentary film Bloodline at their website: (www.bloodline-themovie.com/). The contents have not yet been investigated archaeologically.

A Shroud of Turin exhibit toured the USA about twenty years ago (1983?). A father Thompson was in charge of the exhibit and he had access to the secret Vatican archives. One day he was speaking to a stranger at a bar and having a "wee drink." He told of incredible treasures hidden away in the Vatican archives. There were statues made by Michelangelo that no one has ever seen and other long lost treasures. The most significant artifacts he spoke of seeing were the missing thirteen Dead Sea Scrolls. These scrolls told of the marriage of Jesus and Mary Magdalene and their thirteen children. This breach of secrecy was brought to the attention of "the powers that be." Father Thompson was dead within three days. The official cause of death was an auto accident, but it was said that his fatal injury occurred on the back of his head prior to the event. A nun who had accompanied father Thompson on the Shroud of Turin Tour was also found dead in the same time frame. These details are all somewhat sketchy, but I received them from an individual who claims to have overheard the conversation at the aforementioned bar. If anyone has more details, I would love to hear them. If true, such secrets would certainly fulfill Nostradamus' prediction about a great secret that could destroy Christianity if it fell into the wrong hands. I believe that "the truth shall set you free."

Michael Baigent states in his book The Dead Sea Scrolls Deception (22) that 75% of the scrolls (translations) have been withheld from the public. The Dead Sea Scrolls paint a very different picture of early Christianity from that which is commonly held.

The Inquisition of old is still with us, my friends, it has merely changed it's name twice to sanitize itself (23). In 1908 the Inquisition changed it's name to the Sacred Congregation of the Holy Office. Then in 1965 it changed its name again to the Congregation for the Doctrine of the Faith. It is still in the same building and still has the same role: to maintain the dogma of the church. Grand Inquisitors are now called "Prefects." Cardinal Joseph Ratzinger held this title from 1981-2005 and was elected pope in April 2005. Ratzinger (Pope Benedict XVI) has stated that "Revelation terminated with Jesus Christ." Given this background it is not surprising that popes have tried to destroy documents, even those allegedly written by "the adopted son of God" himself, Jesus Christ (24). Any documents that don't tow the party line of Christ as a celibate messiah are consigned to the fire.

Fortunately revelation is constantly occurring and the ancient "mysteries" of the once elect initiates are being revealed. The word church in the Bible is EKKLESIA in Greek. It refers to a "calling out." It is when one becomes an initiate to the mysteries (25). Somehow the meaning of the word changed to be understood as the building where this took place, instead of the act of receiving initiation by an individual. That is NOT the truth. You are the church- not the building. Once you comprehend this you are ready to begin.

Therefore the withholding of the greatest secret should be no surprise to us. The time has come to rejoice in the truth that Jesus and Mary Magdalene gave us their light that we may be better prepared for the End Times and the birth of a new Earth. They gave us the capacity for increased spiritual growth by sharing their ancestral light with us. All we have to do is look within. The kingdom is within. You are all the living Holy Grail! Now is the time to remember what Jesus said:

"I AM THE VINE AND YE ARE THE BRANCHES" (John: 15:5).

POSTSCRIPT: A SURPRISE ENDING

The End Times warnings found in Da Vinci's Last Supper are quite fascinating on the one hand and rather unnerving on the other. I don't know how each of you would prefer to go into the great beyond, but I am pretty sure I'd like to die of old age at 140. It works for me. The remaining choices between goat herder and rocket scientist aren't very appealing to me either. Goats smell and I hate math. Quite frankly, all this End Times stuff is pretty depressing. However I have a rule about leaving an audience hanging without a solution. If I didn't have a solution, I would have kept my mouth shut and never written any of this. Any fool can complain.

Actually the solution is in two parts. The first part is to be worthy of having someone risk his life to save you. And by worthy I mean getting off your butt and raising your spiritual calibration as far as you can push it in the time you have left. Only when a massive number of individuals raise their calibrations can the average calibration of the whole world be affected in a positive way. If a sufficient number of people WAKE UP, then it is impossible for an Armageddon to occur. Traditionally this critical mass of people is believed to be the 144,000 mentioned in the Bible. It simply can't happen unless enough people give their permission for it to happen. On the other hand if you choose to remain at a spiritual calibration level of mere cannon fodder, that is what you will get. If like the prophet Abraham, you master the ancient knowledge, kings and queens will que up at your door seeking your counsel. So, choose wisely! There are two ways to burn off karma, the easy way and the hard way. I can assure you in no uncertain terms that you won't like the hard way.

The second part is also governed by karma of the same general sort, but more of the aspect of group karma. I would label it "national karma" for lack of a better word. If all your leaders have kissed Satan's ring and they lead you down the path of perdition, then it's your fault for being asleep at the helm of your collective lives. As many of you may be new to using behavioral kinesiology to sort out your past lives, let me give you some guidance. First of all you can check my proposal and see whether or not I am telling the truth. You can check every line of this book and see what you get. If you learn only this lesson from this book, you've come a long way towards discerning truth. The truth will indeed set you free.

When I first developed the long list of spiritual calibrations for all the famous individuals at the beginning of this book I stumbled upon some very startling conclusions. I can assure you I am a very reluctant prophet and the conclusions I reached startled no one more than me. I started to see connections between people in this life and in their past lives by matching their spiritual calibrations. This was a very exciting dividend from this work and it seemed to be a viable way to sort out who was who. As stated previously, I have always been able to see the past lives of individuals when I do reiki treatments. When I took the second course of sacred merkaba ascended master training I was able to see past lives with just one touch on occasion. The use of gold powder regimens opened up a flood of past life experiences. Hundreds of them. A few months later as I made more progress, I started to be "introduced" to people in the present time by their past life identity. This generally happened while I was asleep and I had to wake up in a rush and write it all down before I forgot it. For example, I was "introduced" to my soul mate in Canada by her past life as Eleanor of Aquitaine. I saw her tomb in France and mine next to hers. I quickly did twenty questions and located her current residence in Cape Breton Island, Nova Scotia; her name; and general information. It was very exciting as this had never happened to me before. I was on new ground entirely.

One year ago I wrote that the only solution to our world dilemma would be to follow the example of Mary Magdalene and to look "between the gnosis where the treasure lies." As no one else has come forward with any solutions, I am forced to fulfill my own prophecy.

I've been in the Libertarian Party for a number of years, but I've never had the honor of introducing a candidate before. It was a real shock to me, but there is one man who is uniquely qualified to lead the world out of the morass of the End Times. Quite frankly, we need a man EXACTLY like "Old Hickory": Andrew Jackson. A man to clean out the nest of vipers and traitors who currently inhabit the sacred halls of our government. We need someone with the honor and integrity of a knight of old to clear the field of unholy bankers.

We need a zealot who won't back down from tyranny! And finally we need someone with the courage and tenacity to fight a hundred battles and never falter.

Looking from my somewhat unique perspective, I "see" only one man who in a previous life WAS **Andrew Jackson** and is now "in the flesh" upon this green Earth. A man who was **Geoffri de St. Omer**, one of the original nine Knights Templar upon Solomon's Temple. A man who walked with Christ as **Simon the Zealot,** and withstood the tyranny and persecution of Rome. A man named **Joshua,** who stood at the right hand of Moses and defeated the enemies of Israel. A man who has commanded armies in over 30 other previous lives that have been lost to history, but not to the collective unconscious. Ladies and gentlemen, let me introduce to you the only man I see turning the tide of darkness and plotting a new course. That man is **DONALD J. TRUMP!**

What we need in government I call "**Operation Clean Slate**." We need a man of the people and by the people to get in there and say "you're fired, you're fired, you're fired" and get the job done. As many of you know, Mr. Trump has a great deal of experience in this regard. The only way to get a clean and righteous government is to fire them all and start over. A new government with new leadership and new ideas could keep us from falling headlong into the abyss of the Fourth Reich.

But don't take my word for it. Calibrate Mr. Trump and all the other potential candidates and see what you get. If you've been paying attention, the whole purpose of tapping into the collective unconscious is to gain access to the truth.

The word heretic means "to choose." So choose wisely or you'll be choosing another body to reincarnate into soon. Those who are alive will be either eating goats and bugs or nameless green stuff from a tube in a space ship in outer space for the next 1,000 years IF they're lucky. Then maybe the Earth will heal itself enough to be inhabitable again. We don't have any choice about Earth changes and asteroids the size of Cleveland, but we do have a choice whether we live in love or in fear. And if you're not part of the solution, then you're part of the problem. The choice is up to you.

The world has always been full of prophecies. In this book we've talked about the prophecies of the Egyptian priests, Celtic priests and the Biblical prophets; Jesus, Mother Shipton, Nostradamus and Edgar Cayce. However, I have left one out for last. The pharaoh Akhenaton, better known as Moses, built a temple at Abydos, Egypt. He filled this temple of prophecy with his predictions of the future from top to bottom, with the last ones at the top. According to Gary Smith, there are jet planes, battle tanks, attack helicopters, and symbols for the mother of all bombs (MOAB) inscribed on the walls of the temple. The End Times would begin when the Eagle (USA) landed in the land of oil (Iraq). The Eagle and oil barrels are clearly symbolized (www. thetruejesus.org). That time is now.

It would appear that the world is in for a rough time to say the least. According to Nostradamus only 10% of the Earth's surface will remain above water. He also predicted that only 250 million people would survive (Roughly 5%). Given such circumstances, I feel that some spiritual planning would be advisable. Would you rather be one of the "pure" elite of God or the "purified"? (i.e. meaning dead). Fighting over political control of land and oil that will soon be underwater doesn't seem to make much sense. Insuring that the world remains a viable human habitat, however diminished in size, should be a top priority. This goal can only be accomplished by peace. Peace begins when individuals raise their spiritual calibrations into the level of truth. It is falsehood and lies that bring destruction. Truth fosters freedom! That is the message of this book.

As for me, I have no political ambitions. I won't be crying over any lost claims to a throne somewhere or starting a harem of young maidens anytime soon. Not much point in that. My kingdom is in heaven. Instead I propose a more radical departure. I plan to grow a garden, make my own necessities of life, get a little "cave time" and sit this one out. The only way to defeat evil is to refuse to participate in it. As Mahatma Gandhi said, **"You must be the**

271

change you want to see in the world." "The future depends on what we do in the present." Like Mr. Gandhi, I will do my best to be of service to others, fearlessly tell the truth and teach as many as I can. That is all anyone can do. Then no matter what happens I will rest in peace. My tombstone will contain a final lesson: "I stepped out for just a minute: I'll be right back!"

Yours in liberty,

Lt. Lawrence F. Frego, USNR, (ret.) HKt.B

"The Lion of Judah"

END NOTES

1) **Maurice Cotterell,** *Jesus, King Arthur, and the Journey of the Grail: the secrets of the sun kings.* **(Rochester, VT: Bear & Company) 2006. Pages 139-180.**

2) **Margaret Starbird,** *Mary Magdalene, Bride in Exile.* **(Rochester, VT: Bear & Company) 2005. Quoted text on enclosed audio CD of lecture, "Mary Magdalene, Bride and Beloved."**

3) **Laurence Gardner,** *The Magdalene Legacy: The Jesus and Mary bloodline conspiracy.* **(London: Element, 2005) Page 148.**

4) **Laurence Gardener, Ibid. Pages 13-14.**

5) **T. Lobsang Rampa,** *The Third Eye: the autobiography of a Tibetan lama.* **(New York: Ballantine Books) 1964. Pages 201-206.**

6) **Maurice Cotterell, Ibid. Page 18.**

7) **Richard Levittown,** *The Galaxy on Earth: a traveler's guide to the planet's geography.* **(Charlottesville, VA: Hampton Roads Publishing Co., Inc.) 2002. Pages 308-314.**

8) **Janice Manning,** *Celtic Texts of the Coelbook: the last five books of the Kolbrin Bible.* **(Silver Springs, NV: Your Own World Books) 2005. Pages 135-144.**

9) Margaret Starbird, *The Woman with the Alabaster Jar: Mary Magdalen and the Holy Grail.* **(Rochester, VT: Bear & Company) 1993. Pages 96-97.**

10) Peter Godman, *Hitler and the Vatican: inside the secret archives that reveal the new story of the Nazis and the church.* **(New York, NY: Free Press) 2004.**

11) Barry Dunford, *The Holy Land of Scotland, Jesus in Scotland & the Gospel of the Grail.* **(Glenlyon, Perthshire, Scotland: Sacred Connections) 2002. Page 7.**

12) David Hatcher Childress, *Lost Cities and Ancient Mysteries of North and Central America.* **(Stelle, Ill: Adventures Unlimited Press) 1992. Pages 24-25.**

13) Barry Dunford, Ibid. Page 8.

14) Barry Dunford, Ibid. Page 9.

15) Barry Dunford, Ibid. Page 140.

16) Barry Dunford, Ibid. Page 60.

17) Barry Dunford, Ibid. Page 86.

18) Barry Dunford, Ibid. Page 22.

19) Barry Dunford, Ibid. Page 22.

20) Barry Dunford, Ibid. Page 73.

21) Michael Baigent, *The Jesus Papers: Exposing the greatest cover-up in history.* **(New York: HarperCollins Publishers) 2006. Pages 17-19.**

22) Michael Baigent & Richard Leigh. *The Dead Sea Scrolls Deception.* (New York: Summit Books) 1991.

23) Michael Baigent, Ibid. Pages 100-101.

24) Michael Baigent, Ibid. Pages 268-271.

25) John V. Panella, *The Gnostic Papers: The undiscovered mysteries of Christ.* (Huntsville, Ar: Ozark Mountain Publishing) 2002. Page 41.

BIBLIOGRAPHY

Addison, Charles G. & Childress, David H. (introduction). 1997. *The History of the Knights Templars.* **Kempton, Ill: Adventures Unlimited Press.**

Anderson, L. Shannon. 2006. *The Magdalene Awakening: Symbols & synchronicity heralding the re-emergence of the divine feminine.* **St. Augustine, FL: The Pelican Press.**

Andrews, Richard & Schellenberger, Paul. 1996. *The Tomb of God: the body of Jesus and the solution to a 2,000-year-old mystery.* **New York, NY: Little Brown & Co.**

Baigent, Michael. 2006. *The Jesus Papers: exposing the greatest cover-up in history.* **New York: HarperCollins Publishers.**

Bayley, Harold. 2006. *The Lost Language of Symbolism.* **Mineola, NY: Dover Publications, Inc.**

Bock, Darrell L. 2004. *Breaking the Da Vinci Code: answers to questions everyone's asking.* **Nashville, TN: Thomas Nelson, Inc.**

Brown, Dan. 2003. *The Da Vinci Code.* **New York, NY: Doubleday.**

Burnstein, Dan. 2004. *Secrets of the Code: the unauthorized guide to the mysteries behind The Da Vinci Code.* **New York, NY: CDS.**

Bushby, Tony. 2004. The Crucifixion of Truth. Maroochydore, Queensland, AU: Joshua Books.

Bushby, Tony. 2003. **The Secret in the Bible.** Maroochydore, Queensland, AU: Joshua Books & Stanford Publishing Group.

Bushby, Tony. 2005. **The Twin Deception.** Maroochydore, Queensland, AU: Joshua Books.

Cayce, Edgar & Furst, Jeffrey (editor). 1968. *Edgar Cayce's Story of Jesus.* New York, NY: Berkley.

Childress, David H. 1987. *Lost Cities of China, Central Asia, & India (the lost cities series).* Kempton, Ill: Adventures Unlimited Press.
Cotterell, Maurice. 2006. *Jesus, King Arthur, and the Journey of the Grail: The secrets of the sun kings.* Rochester, VT: Bear & Company.

Diamond, Jared. 2005. *Collapse: how societies choose to fail or succeed.* New York, NY: Viking.

Dobson, C. C. 1936. *Did Our Lord Visit Britain as they say in Cornwall and Somerset?* Glastonbury, UK: The Avalon Press.

Dunford, Barry. 2002. *The Holy Land of Scotland: Jesus in Scotland & the Gospel of the Grail.* Perthshire, Scotland: Sacred Connections. (http://www.sacredconnections.co.uk/)

Dunford, Barry. 2008. *Vision of Albion: the key to the Holy Grail-Jesus, Mary Magdalene and the Christ family in the Holy Land of Britain.* Perthshire, Scotland: Sacred Connections.

Gardener, Laurence. 1996. *Bloodline of the Holy Grail: the hidden lineage of Jesus revealed.* Rockport, MA: Element

Gardener, Laurence. 1999. *Genesis of the Grail Kings: the Pendragon legacy of Adam and Eve.* London: Transworld Publishers Ltd.

Gardener, Laurence. 2003. *Lost Secrets of the Sacred Ark: amazing revelations of the incredible power of gold.* London: Element.

Gardener, Laurence. 2005. *The Magdalene Legacy: The Jesus and Mary bloodline conspiracy.* London: Element.

Gardiner, Philip. 2006. *Gnosis: The secret of Solomon's temple revealed.* Franklin Lakes, NJ: The Career Press, Inc.

Gardiner, Philip & Osborn, Gary. 2005. *The Serpent Grail: the truth behind the Holy Grail, the philosopher's stone, and the elixir of life.* London: Watkins Publishing.

Garlow, James L. & Jones, Peter. 2004. *Cracking Da Vinci's Code.* Colorado Springs, CO: Cook Communications Ministries.

Godman, Peter. 2004. *Hitler and the Vatican: inside the secret archives that reveal the new story of the Nazis and the church.* New York, NY: Free Press.

Hagee, John. 2006. *Jerusalem Countdown: a warning to the world.* Lake Mary, FL: FrontLine.

Hardin, G. W. & Ingram, Julia. 1996. *The Messengers: a true story of angelic presence and the return to the age of miracles.* Lake Oswego, OR: Skywin.

Harper, John Jay. 2006. *Tranceformers: Shamans of the 21st century.* Foresthill, CA: Reality Press.

Hawkins, David R. 2002. *Power Vs Force: the hidden determinates of human behavior.* Carlsbad, CA: Hay House.

Hawkins, David, R. 2005. *Truth Vs Falsehood: How to tell the difference.* Toronto: Axial Publishing Co.

Henry, William. 2006. *Mary Magdalene- The Illuminator: The woman who enlightened The Christ.* Kempton, IL: Adventures Unlimited Press.

Hidell, Al & d'Arc, Joan. 2004. *The New Conspiracy Reader: from planet X to the war on terrorism- what you really don't know.* New York, NY: Citadel Press.

Jasmuheen 2005. *The Law of Love & its Fabulous Frequency of Freedom.* **Noosa Heads, QLD, Australia: Self Empowerment Academy.**

Leloup, Jean-Yves. 2003. *The Gospel of Philip: Jesus, Mary Magdalene, and the gnosis of sacred union.* **Rochester, VT: Inner Traditions, Bear & Company**

Leviton, Richard. 2002. *The Galaxy on Earth: a traveler's guide to the planet's geography.* **Charlottesville, VA: Hampton Roads Publishing Co., Inc.**

Lewis, Lionel Smithett. 1953. *St. Joseph of Arimathea at Glastonbury or the Apostolic Church of Britain.* **London: James Clarke & Co. Ltd.**

Lipton, Bruce H. 2005. *The Biology of Belief: unleashing the power of consciousness, matter and miracles.* **Santa Rosa, CA: Mountain of Love/Elite Books.**

Mann, William F. 1999. *The Labyrinth of the Grail.* **Grand Bay, AL: Laughing Owl Publishing, Inc.**

Manning, Janice. 2005. *Celtic Texts of the Coelbook: the last five books of the Kolbrin Bible.* **Silver Springs, NV: Your Own World Books**.

Manning, Janice. 2006. *Egyptian Texts of the Bronzebook: the first six books of the Kolbrin Bible.* **Silver Springs, NV: Your Own World Books.**

Meyer, Marvin. 2004. *The Gospels of Mary: The secret tradition of Mary Magdalene the companion of Jesus.* ***New York, NY, HarperCollins Publishers.***

Nahmad, Claire & Bailey, Margaret. 2006. *The Secret Teachings of Mary Magdalene: including the lost verses of The Gospel of Mary, revealed and published for the first time.* **London: Watkins Publishing**.

Notovitch, Nicolas. 1894. *The Unknown Life of Jesus Christ.* Joshua Tree, CA: Tree of Life Publications.

Olsen, Oddvar. 2006. The Templar Papers: *Ancient mysteries, secret societies, and the Holy Grail.* Franklin Lakes, NJ: New Page Books.

Panella, John V., 2002. *The Gnostic Papers: The undiscovered mysteries of Christ.* Huntsville, AR: Ozark Mountain Publishing.

Pelikan, Jaroslav. 2005. *Whose Bible is it? a history of the scriptures through the ages.* New York: Viking.

Pelikan, Jaroslav. 2005. *Jesus through the Centuries, Mary through the Centuries.* New York: History Book Club.

Picknett, Lynn & Prince, Clive. 2006. *The Sion Revelation: the truth about the guardians of Christ's sacred bloodline.* New York: Touchstone.

Picknett, Lynn & Prince, Clive. 1998. *The Templar Revelation: secret guardians of the true identity of Christ.* New York: Touchstone.

Phillips, Graham. 1995. *The Search for the Grail.* London: BCA.

Rampa, T. Lobsang. 1963. *The Cave of the Ancients.* New York: Ballantine Books.

Rampa, T. Lobsang. 1964. *The Third Eye: the autobiography of a Tibetan lama.* New York: Ballantine Books.

Rathford, Michael. 2005. *The Nostradamus Code: world war III 2006-2012.* Massapequa Park, NY: Truth Revealed Publishing.

Rogak, Lisa. 2005. *The Man behind the Da Vinci Code: An unauthorized biography of Dan Brown.* Kansas City, MO: Andrews McMell Publishing.

Savoy, Gene. 1983. *The Essaei Document: Secrets of an eternal race.* Reno, NV: The International Community of Christ.

Savoy, Gene. 2008. *Jamil: Child of light & messenger of God.* Reno, NV: The International Community of Christ.

Savoy, Gene. 1984. *The Lost Gospel of Jesus: The hidden teachings of Christ.* Reno, NV: The International Community of Christ.

Savoy, Gene. 1983. *The Millennium Edition of the Decoded New Testament: Origins and history of the paradosis or secret tradition of the oral law called the gospel, with commentary on the canonical new testament, apocrypha, pseudepigrapha, Old Testament, Dead Sea scrolls, ancient fragments, and other religious texts.* Reno, NV: The International Community of Christ.

Schonfield, Hugh J. 1965. The Passover Plot. New York: The Disinformation Company, Ltd.

Simmans, Graham. 2007. Jesus *After the Crucifixion: From Jerusalem to Rennes-le-Chateau.* Rochester, VT: Bear & Co.

Sitchin, Zecharia. 2004. *The Earth Chronicles Expeditions: Journeys to the mythical past.* Rochester, VT: Bear & Co.

Sitchin, Zecharia. 2007. *The End of Days: Armageddon and prophecies of the return.* New York: HarperCollins Publishers.
Sora, Steven. 1999. *The Lost Treasure of the Knights Templar: Solving the Oak Island mystery.* Rochester, VT: Destiny Books.

Starbird, Margaret. 2003. *Magdalene's Lost Legacy: symbolic numbers and the sacred union in Christianity.* Rochester VT: Bear & Company.

Starbird, Margaret. 2005. *Mary Magdalene, Bride in exile.* Rochester, VT: Bear & Company.

Starbird, Margaret. 1993. *The Woman with the Alabaster Jar.* Rochester, VT: Bear & Company.

Ward, Paul Von. 2004. *Gods, Genes, and Consciousness: nonhuman intervention in human history.* Charlottesville, VA: Hampton Roads Publishing Co.

Weidner, Jay & Bridges, Vincent. 2003. *The Mysteries of the Great Cross of Hendaye: alchemy and the end of time.* Rochester, VT: Destiny Books.

Williams, J. E. 2005. *The Andean Codex: adventures and initiations among the Peruvian shamans.* Charlottesville, VA: Hampton Roads Publishing Co. Inc.

Williamson, John. 1986. *The Oak King, The Holly King, and The Unicorn: the myths and symbolism of the unicorn tapestries.* New York: Harper & Row.

Made in the USA
San Bernardino, CA
10 September 2013